Clinical Chemistry

Clinical Chemistry

Donald T. Forman, EDITOR

Evanston Hospital and Northwestern University School of Medicine

Richard W. Mattoon, EDITOR

Abbott Laboratories

Based on the

Annual Lecture Series

co-sponsored by the

Chicago Sections of the

American Chemical Society

and of the American Association

of Clinical Chemists,

Chicago, Ill.,

February 13–April 3, 1975

ACS SYMPOSIUM SERIES **36**

AMERICAN CHEMICAL SOCIETY

WASHINGTON, D. C.   1976

CHEM

Library of Congress CIP Data

Clinical chemistry.
(ACS symposium series; 36 ISSN 0097-6156)

Includes bibliographies and index.

1. Chemistry, Clinical—Addresses, essays, lectures.
I. Forman, Donald T., 1932-   . II. Mattoon, Rich-
ard Wilbur, 1912-   . III. American Chemical Society.
Chicago Section. IV. American Association of Clinical
Chemists. Chicago Section. V. Series: American Chemi-
cal Society. ACS symposium series; 36.
   [DNLM: 1. Chemistry, Clinical—Congresses. QY90
C641 1975]

RB40.C57   616.07'56   76-49983
ISBN 0-8412-0345-8   ACSMC8 36 1-293

ACS Symposium Series

Robert F. Gould, *Editor*

FOREWORD

The ACS SYMPOSIUM SERIES was founded in 1974 to provide a medium for publishing symposia quickly in book form. The format of the SERIES parallels that of the continuing ADVANCES IN CHEMISTRY SERIES except that in order to save time the papers are not typeset but are reproduced as they are submitted by the authors in camera-ready form. As a further means of saving time, the papers are not edited or reviewed except by the symposium chairman, who becomes editor of the book. Papers published in the ACS SYMPOSIUM SERIES are original contributions not published elsewhere in whole or major part and include reports of research as well as reviews since symposia may embrace both types of presentation.

CONTENTS

PREFACE

This book is the result of the eigth annual series of lectures for continuing education sponsored by the Chicago Section of the American Chemical Society. It is also the first volume in the ACS Symposium Series to be sponsored by a local section of the ACS. The purpose of the lecture series and this volume is to present topics that have a clinical chemical basis but are also of interest to specialists in other clinical areas. Indeed, several contributors to this volume represent the disciplines of pediatrics, endocrinology, and hematology. The material included is appropriate to both the clinical aspects of the subject and to analytical and technological advances. Chapters in this book are concerned with etiology of disease and diagnosis as well as technical advances which can be applied more practically in the very near future. We believe the chapters are excellent examples of the integral part that the clinical chemist plays in modern medicine. The chapters on competitive protein binding assays and drug interference in laboratory testing were not originally presented as lectures but were added because of the current interest in these subjects.

The editors hope that this book will be as enlightening and useful to the reader as the lecture series was to the participating audience. It is a great pleasure to thank our contributors and publisher for their excellent cooperation, without which this volume would not have been possible. A special note of grateful acknowledgment goes to Florence Forman and Debra H. Forman for their meticulous editorial assistance.

Evanston Hospital and Northwestern University
   School of Medicine
Chicago, Ill.   DONALD T. FORMAN
Abbott Laboratories
North Chicago, Ill.   RICHARD W. MATTOON
September 20, 1976

Separation and Characterization of Hemoglobins

TITUS H. J. HUISMAN

Departments of Cell & Molecular Biology and Medicine, Laboratory of Protein Chemistry, Comprehensive Sickle Cell Center, Medical College of Georgia, and Veterans Administration Hospital, Augusta, Ga. 30902

Human red cells are ideally suited for studies of genetic disorders mainly because they can easily and at any degree of frequency be obtained in relatively large quantities. It is, therefore, not surprising that in the course of time many genetic disorders involving this cell have been detected. It is interesting that some of these result in a severe hemolytic anemia, while other genetically imposed changes might not affect the life nor the function of the cell. An excellent example is the hemoglobin molecule; in some variants the chemical change does not influence the properties of this protein, whereas in others the change occurs at a critical site affecting its stability and/or functional properties. Identification and characterization of these variants have become routine procedures in some laboratories. The results of these studies have led to extensive investigations of patients with unexplained hereditary hemolytic anemias, of structure-function relationships of normal hemoglobins and of variants found in patients with an unexplained alteration in their oxygen transport system, of the different types of genetic polymorphism, and of the incidence of selected variants in several populations. It therefore appears appropriate to summarize general aspects of the normal hemoglobins and of selected hemoglobin variants, to review methods used to identify and separate these proteins, and to discuss some procedures useful in the characterization of possible chemical changes in this molecule.

Normal and Abnormal Hemoglobins

Hemoglobin is a large complex protein molecule; the atomic model of oxyhemoglobin at 2.8 Å resolution has been reported in 1968 by Perutz and coworkers, and a similar model of deoxy-hemoglobin in 1970 (1,2). The molecule is a spheroid, approx-

imately 65 Å X 55 Å X 50 Å. It is composed of four polypeptide
chains each resembling quite closely the myoglobin chain. The
three dimensional structure of the subunits is held together by
weak noncovalent bonds. The polar amino acid side chains are
in contact with the solvent, and the nonpolar residues are
located in the interior of the molecule or in regions which
form the contacts between chains. The heme group is located
in a pocket in each chain; residues in contact with heme are
invariable (i.e. are the same in different mammalian hemoglobins) and the bonds between heme and chain are hydrophobic
interactions. Contacts between like chains (α-α; β-β) are
limited to salt bridges involving the terminal residues but
contacts between unlike chains (α-β) are many. The largest
number of contacts is between the α_1 and β_1 (34 residues with
110 atoms being within 4 Å). These are primarily contributed
by amino acid residues of the B, G, and H helices. The α_1-β_2
contact is formed by 19 residues (in helices C, F, and G) and
is of importance for the functional interactions between subunits. The effect of deoxygenation causes an alteration in
distance between iron atoms. The most pronounced change is in
the β_1-β_2 distance, which increases 6 to 7 Å. The α_1-β_1 contact
undergoes only slight change whereas drastic changes seem to
occur in the α_1-β_2 contact. Figures 1 and 2 (from reference 3)
give further details on the structures of the α-and β-chains of
Hb-A and list the residues that participate in the contacts
with heme, and between chains.

The major type of human adult hemoglobin (Hb-A$_0$) is composed of two pairs of identical chains, and its formula can be
written as $\alpha_2\beta_2$. The primary structure of the two chains has
been known for several years. The second adult hemoglobin is
Hb-A$_2$ and it constitutes 2.5 to 3.0 percent of the total hemoglobin. Hb-A$_2$ also consists of four polypeptide chains, two
of these are α-chains and the other two (the δ-chains) differ
from the β-chains of Hb-A$_0$ by amino acid substitutions in 10
positions. The formula of Hb-A$_2$ can be written as $\alpha_2\delta_2$. A
small amount (less than one percent) of fetal hemoglobin (Hb-F)
is also present in red cells of the human adult. The electrophoretically fast moving fraction Hb-A$_3$ (which separates as
Hb-A$_1$ by chromatography) is a mixture of at least four distinct
minor fractions. One of these fractions (Hb-A$_{Ic}$) is present in
adult red cell hemolysates for 3.5 to 4.5 percent and is composed of two normal α-chains and two β-chains each with the
NH$_2$ terminal group being blocked by a carbohydrate. A second
fraction (Hb-A$_{Ie}$) has been identified as a mixed disulfide of
one molecule of Hb-A$_0$ and two glutathione residues. Increased
quantities of Hb-A$_{Ie}$ are found in aged red cell hemolysates.

Fetal hemoglobin is the major hemoglobin of the red cells
of the fetus and the newborn. It has the characteristic
property of being resistant to denaturation by alkali. Hb-F is
composed of two α-chains (the same as in Hbs A and A$_2$) and two

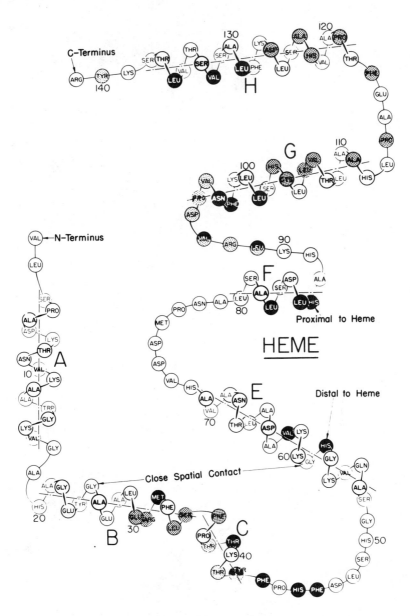

Figure 1. *Two-dimensional presentation of the α-chain of human hemoglobin.* ●, *residues in contact with the heme group;* ⊙, *residues that participate in the* α₁-β₁ *contact;* ⊙, *residues that participate in the* α₁-β₂ *contact* (3).

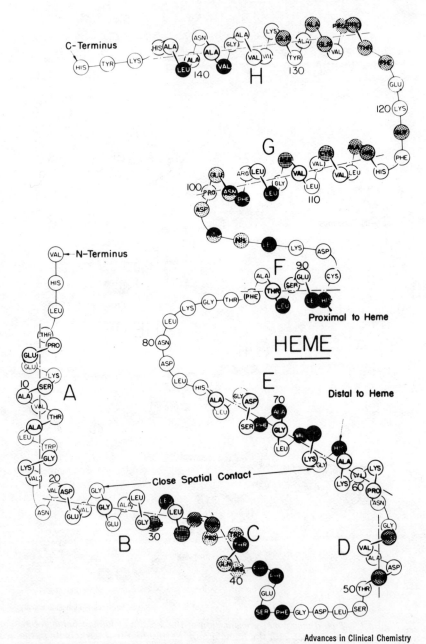

Figure 2. Two-dimensional presentation of the β-chain of human hemoglobin. See also legend of Figure 1 (3).

γ-chains which differ from the β-chains in 39 positions. The
formula of Hb-F can be written as $\alpha_2\gamma_2$. A minor hemoglobin
fraction, Hb-F1, which is present for about 7 to 10 percent in
a cord blood sample, has the structure of $\alpha_2\gamma_2$acetyl indicating that the NH_2 terminal glycyl residue of the γ-chain is
acetylated. Recently the existence of two structurally different γ-chains has been demonstrated; these two chains (the $^G\gamma$-
and $^A\gamma$-chains) differ at a minimum in one position, namely
position 136, which is occupied by a glycyl residue in the $^G\gamma$-
chain and by an alanyl residue in the $^A\gamma$-chain. The two chains
are present at birth in a ratio ($^G\gamma$ to $^A\gamma$) of 7 to 3 whereas
this ratio changes gradually after birth to the adult ratio of
2 to 3 (for references, see (3)).

Two additional hemoglobin chains exist which have been
termed the ε-and the ζ-chain. The ε-chain is found in two
hemoglobin components in young human (and animal) embryos.
One of these hemoglobins (Hb-Gower-2) has the probable structure
of $\alpha_2\epsilon_2$, whereas Hb-Gower-1 (ϵ_4) lacks α-chains. These hemoglobins are not present in a fetus 12 weeks and older, and are
apparently specifically synthesized during embryonic development.
A third embryonic hemoglobin (termed Hb-Portland-1) is composed
of a pair of ζ-chains and a pair of γ-chains (thus $\zeta_2\gamma_2$) and
has been found in very small amounts in normal newborn infants,
and in increased amounts in newborns with D1 trisomy. The ζ-
chain is likely an embryonic α-chain (4,5).

The occurrence of several hemoglobin polypeptide chains
(α, β, γ, δ, ε, ζ) makes it necessary to assume the presence of
at least six structural loci involved in the synthesis of the
different hemoglobins. This number is larger because the two
structurally different γ-chains ($^G\gamma$ and $^A\gamma$) are the product of
non-allelic γ-chain structural loci. There is also increasing
evidence that duplication of the α-chain structural locus may
have resulted in an α-chain gene multiplicity in some human
populations which is comparable to that found in several
mammalian species. It is obvious that the marked developmental
changes require additional mechanisms which regulate the rate
of synthesis of certain polypeptide chains during various stages
of development.

The demonstration of an abnormal form of hemoglobin (Hb-S)
in sickle cell anemia by Pauling *et al.* in 1949 (6) was followed
by the discovery of a large number of additional variants.
Many are distinguished from Hb-A by electrophoretic or chromatographic methods. The number and types of abnormal hemoglobins
that have been discovered thus far are indeed overwhelming. At
the latest count (December, 1974) at least 135 β-chain variants,
72 α-chain variants, 8 δ-chain variants, and 11 γ-chain
variants have been found. These include variants with single
amino acid substitutions (the majority), variants with two
substitutions (the β-chain variants, Hb-C-Harlem and Hb-Arling-
ton Park), variants with deletion of one or more residues

(nine variants of this type have been discovered), and even a
variant with an insertion (the α-chain variant Hb-Grady).
Moreover, there are 7 fusion hemoglobins, $i.e.$ hemoglobins with
either δβ-,βδ-or γβ-chains, and 5 hemoglobins with chains that
are extended at the COOH- terminal end. Several of these
variants have altered physical and/or functional properties
interfering with the life-span of the red cell or with the
normal oxygen delivery system. (For recent reviews see references 3, 7, 8; a list of variants is available upon request
from the Director of the International Hemoglobin Information
Center, Medical College of Georgia, Augusta, GA 30902, USA.)

The synthesis of an abnormal α-chain will result in the
presence of more than one abnormal hemoglobin since all normal
hemoglobin types are composed of the same pair of identical α-
chains and of different pairs of non-α-chains. An adult heterozygous for an α-chain abnormality produces several hemoglobin
types, namely $\alpha_2\beta_2$, $\alpha_2\delta_2$, $\alpha_2{}^G\gamma_2$, $\alpha_2{}^A\gamma_2$, and the abnormal
variants $\alpha_2{}^X\beta_2$, $\alpha_2{}^X\delta_2$, $\alpha_2{}^{XG}\gamma_2$, $\alpha_2{}^{XA}\gamma_2$. Four of these are
readily observed in the blood of the adult heterozygote, while
the γ-chain-containing components are usually identified
through analyses of blood of a heterozygous newborn. An adult
individual heterozygous for an α-chain variant and for a β-
chain variant will produce two additional hemoglobins since the
components $\alpha_2\beta_2{}^Y$ and $\alpha_2{}^X\beta_2{}^Y$ are the result of the presence of
a β-chain structural gene abnormality. The observation of two
different α-chain variants together with Hb-A in some members
of a family of Hungarian origin (9, 10) has been explained by
the presence of two non-allelic α-chain structural loci. The
absence of Hb-A in subjects with an apparent homozygosity for
the α-chain variant Hb-J-Tongariki (11,12) indicates that some
human populations have multiple α-chain structural genes while
others do not.

Abnormalities of structure may lead to changes in function
(for extensive reviews see references 3, 7, 8, 13, 14). A
hemoglobin will function normally if, (a) the hemes are present
and fixed in the appropriate position in each chain; (b) the
iron remains in ferrous form in deoxyhemoglobin; (c) the molecule
is able to change its configuration in the process of oxygena-
tion-deoxygenation through changes at the α_1-α_2, β_1-β_2, α_1-β_1, and
α_1-β_2 contacts. Hemoglobin abnormalities can be classified by
grouping the chemical replacements according to their positions
in the chains. Such an analysis leads to four major subgroups.
The $first$ concerns variants with replacements of residues which
are in contact with heme. This group includes several unstable
hemoglobins and also the four M hemoglobins in which either the
proximal or the distal histidyl residue is replaced by a tyrosyl
residue. The $second$ group consists of variants in which residues participating in the α_1-β_1 contact are replaced, and the
$third$ group that in which replacements of residues of the α_1-β_2
contact have occurred. Many of the structural changes occurring

in positions participating in the α_1-β_2 contact are associated with alterations in function. The *fourth* group concerns variants with replacements in external regions of the molecule which are usually without any direct effect on structure and function. There are notable exceptions such as some unstable hemoglobins and the notorious Hb-S which shows a decreased solubility in its deoxygenated form and will therefore be accompanied by pathological symptoms in homozygotes.

Some of the abnormal fetal hemoglobin variants are the product of an allele of the $^A\gamma$ structural locus and others of an allele of the $^G\gamma$ structural locus. The structural abnormality in all eight variants of Hb-A$_2$ has been determined.

Nine variants resulting from deletions have been described; all are β-chain variants. Deletions leading to shortening of the chain (from one to five residues) usually have severe functional consequences. It is likely that the genetic event causing the deletion of one or more of the corresponding nucleotide base triplets is the result of an unequal crossing over between homologous genes. Hb-Grady is a variant in which the α-chains are extended by three residues because of a tandem repetition of a short sequence (15). The underlying genetic alteration responsible for the α-Grady chain appears to be a tandem duplication of nine base pairs which might have arisen by a process of mismatched intragenic crossing over.

Another group of hemoglobins are the fusion hemoglobins of which seven have been reported. The three Lepore hemoglobins are composed of two normal α-chains and two chains that are part δ-chain (NH$_2$-terminal region) and part β-chain (COOH-terminal region). The $\delta\beta$-chain of Hb-Lepore is, like the β-chain and the δ-chain, 146 amino acid residues long. The genetic event leading to the formation of these hybrid chains involves a nonhomologous crossing-over between corresponding points of the δ and β structural genes. Three "anti-Lepore" hemoglobins, *it est* variants with a chain that is part β-chain (NH$_2$-terminal region) and part δ-chain (COOH-terminal region), have recently been described (Hbs-Miyada; P-Congo; P-Nilotic). This $\beta\delta$ hybrid chain apparently is the product of a gene which is the counterpart of that synthesizing the $\delta\beta$ hybrid chain of the Lepore hemoglobins. The discovery of the $\gamma\beta$-chain of Hb-Kenya (16, 17) is important because it has indicated for the first time that the γ, δ, and β structural genes are closely linked. The chain is a γ-β-chain in which the crossing-over has occurred between residues 80 and 87. The structure of this chain suggests that the nonhomologous crossing-over has removed parts of a γ and the β structural genes and the entire δ structural gene.

Hb-Constant Spring (18, 19) was the first variant discovered that has 31 additional residues at the COOH-terminus of the α-chain. Comparable hemoglobins are Hb-Icaria and Hb-Koya-Dora, and Hb-Tak which has 10 additional residues at the COOH-terminus

of the β-chain (20). It seems possible that these variant
chains have either arisen from a crossing-over with a gene for
a protein unrelated to hemoglobin or through a mutation of a
terminal codon thus permitting elongation of the protein.
Hb-Wayne, the fourth variant with an elongated α-chain, results
from the deletion of a single base in the DNA of the α-chain
causing a "frameshift" which results in a sequence of different
amino acids which are coded by the new succession of codons.

Different hemoglobins lacking α-chains have been described.
They consist solely of β-chains (β4 or Hb-H), γ-chains (γ4 or
Hb-Bart's), δ-chains (δ4), or ε-chains (ε4 or Gower-1). In
most instances these variants are present in patients with α-
thalassemia in which a decreased synthesis of α-chains will
lead to the formation of an excess of non-α-chains. The existence of different forms of α-thalassemia (heterozygous and
homozygous forms of α1-thalassemia and of α2-thalassemia, and
Hb-H disease) has been noted; these forms are best characterized
by the amount of γ4 present at time of birth (for references,
see (3)). Homozygosity for α1-thalassemia is incompatible with
life because the major hemoglobin in this condition at time of
birth, γ4, has a greatly increased affinity for molecular
oxygen and is unable to release it to the tissues. The heterogeneity of α-thalassemia is difficult to explain and the
genetics of the abnormality is complex; it is considered
possible that more than one α structural loci are involved.

In a second type of thalassemia the synthesis of specific
non-α-chains is impaired. The heterozygous form of β-thalassemia is characterized by a mild hypochromic microcytic anemia,
by an increased level of Hb-A_2 (4 to 7 percent), and, in the
majority of the cases, by an elevated Hb-F (1 to 15 percent).
In homozygotes, the synthesis of β-chains is greatly decreased
and as a result a severe anemia may develop after birth when
the γ-chain production ceases. β-Thalassemia, like α-thalassemia, is a heterogeneous condition which can be concluded
from the differences in suppression of β-chain synthesis. In
some cases β-chain production is completely absent (the $β^0$ type)
whereas, in others, a considerable β-chain synthesis can be
observed (the $β^+$ type). The severe anemia will lead, by a
mechanism which is still not completely understood, to an
increased production of γ-chains. Both types ($^Gγ$-and $^Aγ$-chains)
are present and are produced in heterozygotes in either one of
two distinct ratios, namely 7:3 as in the newborn or 2:3 as in
the normal adult (for a summary see 21).

Other types of thalassemia concern the suppression of both
δ-chain and β-chain production (δβ-thalassemia), and the existence of a δ-thalassemia and a γ-thalassemia.

Changes in the quantities of the various normal hemoglobin
components during developmental stages can be explained in terms
of ill-defined regulatory mechanisms which control the rate of
synthesis of the polypeptide chains. Such mechanisms have to

be responsible for the unequal suppression of the two types of γ-chains (^{G}γ and ^{A}γ) after birth and the simultaneous stimulation of the β-and δ-chain production. It is of great interest that a silent structural β-chain locus is present in Caprini species (goats, sheep) which is activated during (experimental) anemia and which is stimulated by erythropoietic factors of yet undefined nature. Apparently humoral factors may have important functions in the regulation of gene activities.

The condition known as the hereditary persistence of fetal hemoglobin (HPFH) is characterized by the presence of 5 to 35 percent Hb-F in the heterozygote and in 100 percent Hb-F in the homozygote. It has been postulated that this anomaly, which is clinically benign, is caused by deletion of specific structural loci. The condition is rather heterogeneous. For instance, only ^{A}γ-chains are found in the Hb-F from carriers of the Greek type of HPFH and only ^{G}γ-chains in the Hb-F from carriers of a certain type observed in India and among blacks, whereas both ^{A}γ-and ^{G}γ-chains are present in varying ratios in the Hb-F of the HPFH condition that is most frequently observed in blacks. In most forms of HPFH the production of β-and δ-chains is completely absent *in cis* of the HPFH determinant.

Only a few of the many hemoglobin variants occur in high frequencies in certain parts of the world. The Hb-S and Hb-C abnormalities are observed mainly in blacks, and occur in tropical Africa and in emigré populations. Hb-D-Los-Angeles is common in certain areas of India and Hb-E is rather exclusively found in the population of Southeast Asia. The various forms of β-thalassemia are known to occur mainly in the population of Mediterranean countries and in Asia, with a specific form being present in the Negro. The α-thalassemias are primarily found in the Far East and the Mediterranean area with again a specific form in the Negro race.

The complexity of the problem of hemoglobin heterogeneity has made it necessary to use rather advanced biochemical investigative procedures. Many analyses require advanced protein chemical techniques. The second part of this review describes some of these methods.

Identification And Characterization Of Hemoglobins

Hematological Methods. Hematological analyses can include the determination of the total hemoglobin concentration (in g%), the packed cell volume (PCV in %), the red blood cell count (in $10^6/mm^3$) and reticulocytes count (in %), calculation of the red cell indices, examination of a blood film, tests to demonstrate the presence of inclusion bodies and of sickle cells, tests to evaluate the distribution of fetal hemoglobin (Hb-F) inside the red cells, the red cell osmotic fragility, the concentration of serum iron (SI), total iron binding capacity (TIBC), and the survival time of the red cells. Details of all

methods will not be presented; they are available in appropriate
laboratory manuals (22-26).

A search for Heinz bodies is helpful in the detection of
an unstable hemoglobin, of α-thalassemia, homozygous β-thalassemia and related abnormalities, because hemoglobin often
precipitates in the red cells of patients with one of these
disorders. Inclusion bodies may consist of precipitated unstable hemoglobin, of β-chains (in α-thalassemia), or of α
chains (in β-thalassemia).

Anemia is a constant feature of the thalassemias, the
Lepore hemoglobinopathies and of many (unstable) hemoglobinopathies. Morphological changes of the red blood cells are not
always characteristic. Determination of red cell indices is
of help in the diagnosis of β-thalassemia, and the MCH and MCV
values are useful in distinguishing milder forms of β-thalassemia from other forms of hypochromic anemia. It is not always
possible to differentiate between iron deficiency anemia and
heterozygous β-thalassemia, and the determination of the serum
iron content, the total iron binding capacity, and the
level of $Hb-A_2$ is of decisive importance. The presence of
inclusion bodies supports the diagnosis of thalassemia. In
Hb-H disease the number of inclusion bodies depends on the
amount of Hb-H that is present, and in heterozygous α-thalassemia only a few cells will contain inclusion bodies. In
homozygous β-thalassemia and related disorders the number of
inclusion bodies is increased considerably after splenectomy.

Handling Of Blood Samples. A relatively small (5 to 10 ml)
sample is sufficient for nearly all hematological and biochemical studies; the material is collected by venipuncture with
heparin, oxalate, or EDTA as anticoagulant. When microtechniques are used a small sample can be collected in hepa-
rinized hematocrit tubes from a fingerstick or on filter paper
from which the hemoglobin can be eluted with a few drops of a
hemolyzing solution. Blood samples should be stored in the
refrigerator for a period not exceeding 4 weeks. Shipment
requires that the sample of blood or the saline washed red
cells be kept cold but not frozen. Addition of a small amount
of penicillin and/or streptomycin is useful in preserving the
samples that are shipped around the world. Hemoglobin solutions
are prepared by centrifugation of packed red cells which are
washed at least three times with 0.9 g% NaCl and are hemolyzed
by addition of one volume of distilled water and about 0.3
volume of carbon tetrachloride, chloroform, or toluene.
Hemoglobin solutions should be stored in the cold for not
longer than four weeks, but can be kept at $-50^\circ C$ unchanged
for a longer period of time.

Electrophoretic Methods. Abnormal hemoglobins are usually
detected by electrophoresis either at pH 8.5 - 9.0 or at

pH 6.0 - 7.0. Many types of supporting material are used, such as: paper, cellulose-acetate, starch-block, starch gel, agar gel, and acrylamide gel.

Starch gel electrophoresis at pH 8.8 - 9.0 is considered the most accurate and reliable method even in routine testing programs. Several commercial systems are available, but simple, inexpensive, horizontal models can be constructed in every laboratory. The starch that is used is partially hydrolyzed starch which has certain physical properties allowing superior separation of hemoglobin variants. The buffers which have been used most successfully for the preparation of the gels are tris-EDTA-borate buffers, pH 8.6 - 9.0. The buffer in the electrode vessels is usually 3 to 4 times more concentrated resulting in a discontinuous system that gives improved resolution mainly of slowly migrating minor hemoglobin components. A phosphate buffer system (pH 6.5 - 7.0) is useful for detecting small quantities of the hemoglobins H and Bart's; these variants will both move toward the anode while Hb-A remains at the origin. Figure 3 gives some examples of separations that can be obtained.

Cellulose acetate electrophoresis is a simple, fast, and sensitive method for preliminary testing of abnormal hemoglobins. Cellulose acetate media may differ in pore size, distribution, volume, length of cellulose chain, and degree of acetylation of the cellulose. Plates on which eight samples can be applied simultaneously are satisfactory for screening purposes. Electrophoresis is made in tris-EDTA-borate buffer, pH 9.0, at about 350 volts for 20 to 30 minutes, after which the plate is stained with 0.5% Ponceau S in 5% trichloroacetic acid, Figure 4. The method can be adapted for quantitative purposes.

Citrate agar electrophoresis has the advantage of distinguishing Hb-S from Hb-D and hemoglobins C, E, and O-Arab from each other. The method is also most useful for the demonstration of small amounts of Hb-A in samples from persons with Hb-S-β^+ thalassemia. There are many modifications of this method; however, the commercial kit marketed by Helena Laboratories gives excellent results. All methods use an 0.05 M citric acid-citrate buffer, pH 6.0. The agar slides can be stained with O-dimethylbenzidine until a blue color begins to appear whereafter they are washed with distilled water. Figure 5 gives examples of some separations that can be obtained.

Isoelectric focusing is a more recently developed method. Successful application of this method depends upon the difference in the isoelectric points of at least 0.02 pH units between the hemoglobins. Polyacrylamide gels are most popular as a supporting medium; they provide great stability, excellent resolution, and are easily prepared. Analysis in polyacrylamide gel can be carried out in slabs or in tubes, and the hemoglobins can best be separated with a pH gradient between pH 6 and 8 in 4% polyacrylamide gels, developed with carrier ampholyte. When introduced into such a system, each hemoglobin will migrate to the

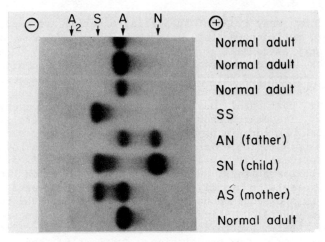

Figure 3. Starch gel electrophoresis of hemoglobins.
Tris-EDTA-boric acid buffer, pH 9.0. O-Dianisidine
stain.

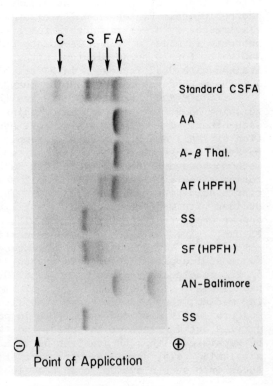

Figure 4. Cellulose acetate electrophoresis of hemoglobins. Variations in the quantities of Hb–A₂
are hardly detectable (compare the
samples 2 and 3 from top). Hb–N–
Baltimore is a β-chain variant in
which lysyl residue in position 95
is replaced by a glutamyl residue.

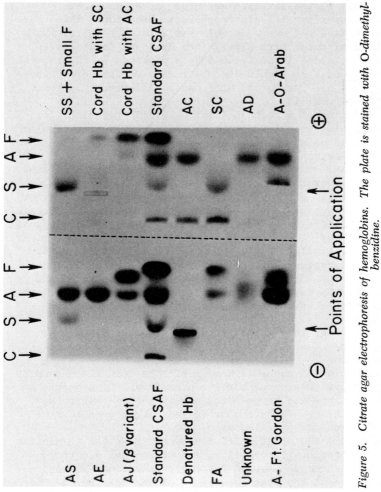

Figure 5. Citrate agar electrophoresis of hemoglobins. The plate is stained with O-dimethyl-benzidine.

Two sets of samples have been analyzed on one plate with a standard mixture of the hemoglobins C, S, A, and F occupying the fourth position from the top. The data show that the hemoglobins A, F, S, and C are readily separated; that the hemoglobins E and Dβ do not separate from Hb-A; and that some β-chain variants can readily be separated from Hb-F, Hb-A, Hb-S, or Hb-C (examples are the uniden-tified Hb-J, Hb-Fort Gordon (see also Figure 14), and Hb-O-Arab).

pH that is its isoelectric point, and will focus into a sharp
band. The separated hemoglobins can be quantitated either with
the use of a densitometer without staining or by elution of
each band.

The techniques mentioned here provide a basic approach to
the study of hemoglobinopathies since the identification of
many variants is dependent upon their net charge. However,
certain changes in the tertiary structure of a hemoglobin
variant may also alter its electrophoretic behavior. This
is well documented for many unstable variants such as for
Hb-Köln which migrates more slowly than Hb-A but in which the
neutral valyl residue in position $\beta98$ is replaced by the neutral
methionyl residue. It should also be mentioned that differences
in the level of heme oxidation will cause differences in the
electrophoretic mobility.

The selection of a certain electrophoretic technique for
the detection of abnormal hemoglobins in a large number of blood
samples is based on simplicity, convenience and economy; cellulose acetate electrophoresis is, therefore, most often the
method of choice. This technique allows the separation of many
commonly observed variants but differentiation of rarer hemoglobin variants and of the different forms of thalassemia–abnormal hemoglobin combinations is often difficult to make. Citrate
agar electrophoresis has a restricted application for large scale
screening purposes because many of the common hemoglobin variants
have a mobility similar to that of Hb-A. This technique, however, is most important for the differentiation of Hb-S from
Hb-D, of Hb-A from Hb-F, of Hb-O-Arab and Hb-E from Hb-C, and
of the AS, AC, SS, CC, and SC conditions in newborns. Isoelectric focusing separates the hemoglobins F and A, and also the
hemoglobins D and S. Minor hemoglobin components are more
readily detected by this method than by any other electrophoretic procedure. The technique has not yet been adapted to
routine screening.

The detection of abnormal hemoglobins in cord blood samples
is usually made with electrophoretic procedures. Four types of
hemoglobin variants can be present, namely γ–chain variants,
β–chain variants, and Hb-Bart's or γ_4 indicating some form of
α–chain deficiency or α–thalassemia.

All eleven γ–chain variants, discovered thus far, exhibit a
change in electrophoretic mobility, and starch gel electrophoresis is the recommended method for their detection. Quantitation of the variant can best be done by chromatography on
columns of either DEAE-Sephadex or CM-Cellulose. The quantities
of some variants in heterozygotes differ greatly. For instance,
the relative amount (expressed in $\%F_x/F_{Total}$) varies from 20-25%
(F-Malta-I) to 10-15% (most γ–chain variants) to 5-6%
(F-Malta-II). Hybridization studies or chain composition
analyses are often needed to identify the abnormality as a γ-
chain abnormal hemoglobin.

The α-chain variants are characterized by the presence of two abnormal components, an abnormal Hb-F ($\alpha_2{}^X\gamma_2$) and an abnormal Hb-A ($\alpha_2{}^X\beta_2$). Of these two, the $\alpha_2{}^X\gamma_2$ component dominates and the $\alpha_2{}^X\beta_2$ component is often difficult to detect. The methods of choice are starch gel electrophoresis and anion-exchange chromatography using DEAE-Sephadex or DE-52 Cellulose. Chain analyses of these isolated hemoglobin components will lead to a definitive identification.

The demonstration of β-chain variants in heterozygotes is complicated by the presence of the large amount of Hb-F. Another obstacle is the nearly identical electrophoretic mobilities of Hb-A and the minor Hb-F1 component. Despite these difficulties, abnormalities such as AS, SS, AC, CC, SC, and others can readily be detected using cellulose acetate electrophoresis, starch gel electrophoresis, acid agar electrophoresis, and by CM-Cellulose microchromatography to be described in a separate section.

Hb-Bart's or γ_4 can best be demonstrated by either cellulose acetate or starch gel electrophoresis. The amount of Hb-Bart's can differ from 1% to over 80% dependent on the abnormality involved. Quantitative determination is most accurately made by CM-Cellulose or CM-Sephadex chromatography.

<u>Macrochromatographic Methods</u>. These procedures use cation exchangers, such as Amberlite-IRC-50, carboxymethyl-Cellulose (CMC) and carboxymethyl-Sephadex (CMS), and the anion exchangers diethylaminoethyl-(DEAE)-Cellulose and DEAE-Sephadex.

Cation-exchange chromatography - The CMC-chromatographic method was developed in 1958; presently the best material available is the microgranular, pre-swollen CM-52 with a capacity of 1.0 mEq/g dry weight (Whatman). The cation-exchanger is stirred with distilled water for at least 12 hr and equilibrated with 0.01 M sodium phosphate buffer, pH 6.7, containing 100 mg KCN/1000 ml. Hemoglobin samples are dialyzed overnight against a similar buffer at 4°C, and 50 to 60 mg oxyhemoglobin in 1.0 to 2.0 ml volume is applied to a 1.8 X 35 cm column. The chromatogram is developed at room temperature with a pH gradient obtained by mixing 0.01 M sodium phosphate buffers of selected pH values (between 7.2 and 8.2) with the 0.01 M sodium phosphate buffer, pH 6.9, contained in a constant volume mixing flask. Absorbance readings of the effluent are made at 415 nm in 1 cm cuvettes using any suitable (semi-automated) spectrophotometer. Quantities of the various zones are calculated as percent of the total amount of hemoglobin recovered from the column. The procedure can easily be automated and several chromatograms can be developed simultaneously when a constant volume delivering pump is used.

The procedure is the method of choice for the separation of Hb-A$_2$ from slow-moving hemoglobins such as Hb-C, Hb-C-Harlem, Hb-O-Arab, Hb-I-Indonesia, and Hb-Agenogi. Many of these variants can also be distinguished from each other by this procedure. Exceptions are Hb-S and Hb-E, which are eluted together with

Hb-A$_2$, and chromatography on DEAE-Sephadex or DEAE-Cellulose is
required for the quantitation of Hb-A$_2$ in blood from Hb-S heterozygotes and homozygotes. Since some Hb-D variants elute at pH
values slightly different from that of Hb-S, it is possible to
obtain an (incomplete) separation of Hb-D and Hb-S and of Hb-D
and Hb-A$_2$. Minor hemoglobins, such as F$_1$, A$_1$, and C$_1$, emerge
first from the column and are followed by their respective major
hemoglobin component. Figure 6 gives some examples of resolutions
that can be obtained.

In certain instances the replacement of CMC by CM-Sephadex
(C-50) may have advantages. Excellent separation of various
major and minor hemoglobin components can be observed when 80 to
120 mg of hemoglobin are chromatographed on a 50 X 0.9 cm column
of CM-Sephadex with 0.05 M tris-maleic acid buffers (containing
100 mg KCN/1000 ml) of pH values between 6.5 and 7.5, as
developers. However, such a system is time-consuming and highly
sensitive to small variations in the pH values of the eluting
buffer system.

Amberlite IRC-50 chromatography is well suited for the
isolation and purification of major and minor hemoglobin fractions. The development of a chromatogram is greatly dependent on
the problem involved and an initial adaptation of the elution
system is required prior to routine application. The resin is
Amberlite IRC-50 of the appropriate mesh size (either 200-250 or
250-325 mesh/sq. inch) and the developers are sodium phosphate
buffers of different molarities and with a pH varying between
6.7 and 7.2. The chromatogram is developed at a slow flow rate
(5-6 ml/hr) at 6°C; separation of the various components requires
that this temperature be kept constant within 0.2°C. At the end
of the chromatogram the columns are warmed to 28°C while the
flow-rate is increased to approximately 10 ml/hr. The absorbance
of each fraction is measured in a 1 cm cuvette at 415 nm and
preferably also at 280 nm.

Anion-exchange chromatography - The use of DiEthylAminoEthyl-
anion exchangers for the separation of hemoglobin components was
introduced in 1962; analyses with DEAE-Sephadex are carried out
exclusively with DEAE-Sephadex A-50, capacity 3.5 ± 0.5 mEq/g
dry weight; particle size 40-120 μ (Pharmacia Fine Chemicals,
Inc.). The dry material is suspended and equilibrated in a
large volume of 0.05 M tris-HCl developer, pH 8.5, under occa-
sional stirring. The columns used for analytical purposes are
about 1.0 X 65 cm and the resin height is about 50 cm. Variable
amounts (30-80 mg) of oxyhemoglobin are chromatographed; the
hemolysate is dialyzed overnight against a selected tris-HCl
developer. The chromatograms are developed at room temperature
by applying a pH gradient to the column in the same manner as
described for the CMC-chromatographic procedure; the flow-rates
are kept at 14 to 16 ml per hr and the effluent is collected in
4 ml fractions. The gradient usually requires mixing of developers with pH values 7.9, 7.5, 7.1, 6.8, 6.5, with a developer

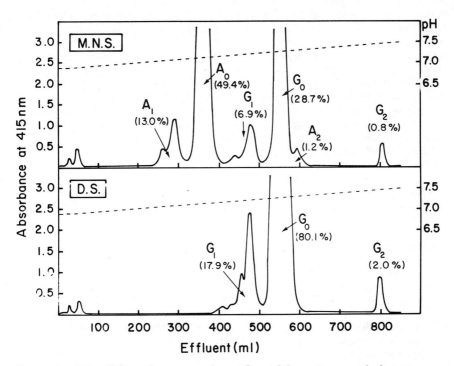

Figure 6. CM-cellulose chromatography of hemoglobin. Top panel: heterozygous Hb–G_α. Note the incomplete separation of Hb–G_α and Hb–A_2. Bottom panel: homozygous Hb–G_α. Note the complete absence of Hb–A. Hb–G_α was identified as Hb–G-Philadelphia or $\alpha_2{}^{68}Lys\beta_2$. The broken line represents pH values of the effluent.

pH 8.3, contained in a constant mixing flask. The effluent
fractions are analyzed for hemoglobin concentration by measuring
the absorbance at 415 nm. The use of an open two-vessel gradient system might facilitate the operation without considerable
loss in resolution of the hemoglobin components. The order in
which the more common hemoglobins are eluted from the column is
as follows: Hb-A2' or B2; Hb-A2 and Hb-C which elute together;
Hb-S; Hb-A0; Hb-A1 + Hb-F0. With exceptions such as Hb-A2 and
Hb-C, Hb-A0 and the minor variant Hb-S1, Hb-F0 and the minor
components Hb-A1, a complete separation of various hemoglobin
types can be obtained.

Chromatography of hemoglobins on columns of <u>DEAE-Cellulose</u>
(DE-52 microgranular, preswollen Whatman) often results in
excellent separations of many variants, because the hemoglobins
are eluted as sharp, narrow zones generally widely separated
from each other. The hemoglobin zones are eluted from the DE-52
columns at a distinctly higher pH value than from a similar
DEAE-Sephadex column.

<u>Microchromatographic Methods</u>. During the past two years
rapid, inexpensive, miniaturized column chromatographic methods
for the separation of hemoglobins have been developed. These
methods are designed for the qualitative detection and quantitative determination of hemoglobins in normal and abnormal conditions and cover the quantitation of Hb-A2; the detection of
Hb-S, Hb-C; other abnormal Hbs; differentiation of various conditions in adults; and the detection of hemoglobinopathies
especially sickle cell anemia at birth (<u>27, 28, 29, 30</u>).

Conventional chromatographic procedures for hemoglobins
have used columns about 1 to 10 cm in diameter and 20 to 100 cm
in length for analytical and preparative purposes. However,
microchromatographic procedures use small Pasteur pipets, 0.5 cm
in diameter and only 8 cm long. The general procedure is as
follows: after a plug of cotton has been lightly tapped into
the restricted part of a Pasteur pipet, a 0.5 X 6 cm column is
poured with the equilibrated ion exchanger. In special cases,
the column may be 0.5 X 15 or 20 cm. The sample which may be
whole blood or conventional hemolysate is diluted with water or
appropriate buffer, placed on the column, allowed to run in,
and then covered with the appropriate developer. The column is
next attached by rubber tubing to a supply of developer in a
funnel or manifold. Flow rates of developer are 20-40 ml per hr
and procedures are usually completed in 30-120 min.

Quantitative determination of Hemoglobin A2 *by microchromatography* – By means of this simple method (<u>29, 30</u>), Hb-A2 may
be rapidly and accurately determined in blood samples from
subjects with and without Hb-S or Hb-D. The procedure makes use
of DEAE-Cellulose, inexpensive laboratory glassware, and allows
one technician to determine the level of Hb-A2 in 50 samples a
day. Whole blood samples, red cell hemolysates, and blood

collected on filter paper can be analyzed with comparable accuracy. The anion exchanger, diethylaminoethylcellulose, is equilibrated by mixing with an equal volume of 0.05 M tris-HCl buffer, pH 8.5, which contains 100 mg KCN/1000 ml. After nearly all material has settled, the supernatant with the fines are removed, and the equilibration procedure is repeated three times. The DE-52 is stored as a slurry; the supernatant volume of buffer is about 0.7 of that of the settled anion exchanger. A 6 to 7 cm column is prepared by pipetting the DE-52 cellulose slurry with a Pasteur pipet. One drop of a 10 g% hemoglobin solution is diluted with 5 to 6 drops of distilled water and applied on the top of the column. Whole blood or blood spots collected on filter paper can also be used. The column is developed with 0.05 M tris-HCl developers, pH 8.3, containing 100 mg KCN/1. The Hb-A2 fraction is eluted as a sharp band in 6 to 8 ml and is collected in a tube graduated at 10 ml. The remaining hemoglobin is eluted with a second developer (0.05 M tris-HCl, pH 7.0, containing 100 mg KCN/1) and collected in a tube graduated at 25 ml. The volumes of the two fractions are adjusted to 10 and 25 ml, respectively, and the optical densities determined at 415 nm. The procedure is also suitable for the quantitation of Hb-A$_2$ in hemolysates containing Hb-S using a 0.5 X 15 cm column. This procedure requires that the Hb-A$_2$ zone is eluted with pH 8.35 developer, Hb-S with pH 8.20 developer, and the remaining hemoglobin with pH 7.0 developer.

A modification of the microchromatographic procedure for Hb-A$_2$ which utilizes DEAE-Cellulose allows the quantitation of Hb-A$_2$ without interference from any Hb-S in the sample. Elution of Hb-A$_2$ with a 0.2 M glycine-0.01% KCN developer is much less sensitive to minor changes in pH of the developer, but is greatly dependent on the pH of the ion exchanger. About 100 gm of DEAE-Cellulose is mixed with sufficient developer to give a total volume of 400 ml. This procedure is repeated twice whereafter the ion exchanger is resuspended in fresh developer. After stirring for 10 min, the pH of the stirred *suspension* is adjusted to 7.5 with about 12-15 mEq of HCl. After settling, some supernatant fluid is removed so that the volumes of settled ion exchanger and supernatant fluid are about equal. Next, a test chromatogram is made with a fresh sample from a Hb-S heterozygote. If Hb-A$_2$ does not emerge in the first 3-4 ml and Hb-S in the next 15 - 20 ml of the developer, the pH of the suspension is readjusted under stirring and another test is made. If necessary, further reduction of pH and testing is made until the "correct" pH is reached. Subsequent preparations of DE-52 should be adjusted to this pH. If the pH has decreased or has been adjusted to too low value it cannot satisfactorily be raised to the proper value.

More than 15,000 samples have now been studied by these methods, and application of these methods has been made in the Augusta area, in California, in Yugoslavia, and in Ghana. The total number of individuals participating in the study in

Georgia was more than 5,000. The majority participated in a testing program in a school district. Others were from subjects participating in testing programs in other areas in the USA or
abroad; included are 10 subjects from Holland with a heterozygosity for the Dutch type of β-thalassemia. Figure 7A presents some
of the Hb-A2 data. Differentiation of A-β-thalassemia from AA,
and of S-β-thalassemia from SS can readily be made and in only a
few known SS patients did the Hb-A2 levels fall within the S-β-
thalassemia range. The Hb-A2 level in the Dutch β-thalassemia
heterozygote is considerably higher than that of persons with the
same condition but from another ethnic origin. It is worth noting
that the Hb-A2 levels in persons with AS or SS are only slightly
higher than those in normal persons.

The studies in Sr. Macedonia, Yugoslavia, were only concerned
with the evaluation of the usefulness of the microchromatographic
procedure for the determination of Hb-A2 and thus for the detection of the β-thalassemia heterozygote. Nearly 6,000 persons participated in the study. All participants were school children
from five Macedonian cities who voluntarily participated in these
testing programs; parents and relatives of known patients with a
β-thalassemia homozygosity are also included in this review.
Figure 7B gives the Hb-A2 levels in all subjects; no overlap between the values of the normal persons and those of the β-thalassemia heterozygotes was apparent. The values are comparable to
those found in the survey in Georgia (Figure 7A). Figure 8 presents the relationship between the hemoglobin level and the Hb-A2
level in more than 5,000 normal adults and in 326 β-thalassemia
heterozygotes. Again no overlap is evident. The β-thalassemia
heterozygote could readily be identified by the elevated level of
the Hb-A2 alone, although a slightly decreased Hb level and a
considerable decrease in the MCH level were helpful observations.

Hb-A2 can also be quantitated by electrophoresis. The most
accurate procedures are starch block electrophoresis, cellulose
acetate electrophoresis, and isoelectric focusing.

*Microchromatographic Testing Methods for Sickle Cell Anemia
and Related Disorders in the Adult.* The procedures described in
the preceding Section are, in fact, applicable to the detection
of hemoglobinopathies in the adult, and any quantitative determination of Hb-A2 immediately becomes a qualitative test for abnormal Hb's. If, instead of the very small zone of Hb-A2, a promi-
nent zone moves in the same way, Hb-C (or Hb-E) is indicated.
Hb-S (or D), if present, is readily apparent as is Hb-A although
Hb-F in large percentages might be confused with Hb-A. The quantitative procedure for Hb-A2 has been used as a qualitative test
for Hb-S and Hb-C under suboptimal conditions in Ghana. Of the
2,350 samples that were studied there, 2,005 could be reevaluated
by starch gel electrophoresis. The same identification by both
methods was made in 98.9% of the cases. Misidentifications were
due to such technical problems as 1) changes in pH of buffer
because of the growth of mold; 2) high temperature (33°C)

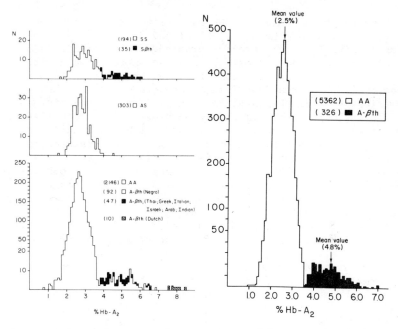

Figure 7. Microchromatography on DEAE–cellulose. A, The levels of Hb–A₂ in normal adults, in β thalassemia heterozygotes, in Hb–S traits, and in patients with sickle cell anemia and Hb–S–β-thalassemia (Georgia survey). B, The levels of Hb–A₂ in normal adults and in β-thalassemia heterozygotes (Macedonia survey).

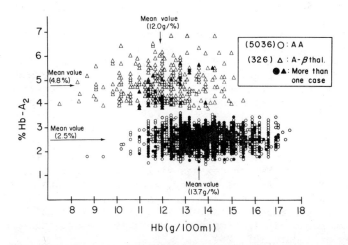

Figure 8. Microchromatography on DEAE–cellulose. The relationship between the total hemoglobin levels and the levels of Hb–A₂ (Macedonia survey).

and high relative humidity (80-90%) which sometimes caused
erratic behavior of the hemoglobins; and 3) lack of a pH meter
which required that the proper chromatographic conditions be
attained by repeated chromatograms of a control sample until
correct behavior was obtained. Despite these suboptimal conditions, only 1% of the identifications were in error. Table I
summarizes some of the data. At least 25% of the participants
had a hemoglobinopathy. The testing programs in the village
population and the school district did not uncover additional
sickle cell anemia patients or patients with SC disease; these
patients were already seen by the physician of the hospital.
The method has also been used in the Augusta area to quantitate
Hb-S in nearly 300 AS cases and Hb-C + A2 in 150 AC cases.
Percentages were comparable to those by more conventional chromatographic methods.

These microchromatographic procedures allow:

a. A rapid and accurate identification of the most common hemo-
    globin variants AS, AC, SS, SC, and CC.
b. A rapid and accurate quantitation of Hb-A2 in samples from
    normal persons or from β-thalassemia heterozygotes.
c. A slight modification will allow the quantitation of Hb-A2
    in Hb-S (or Hb-D) containing samples, and will aid in the
    differentiation between SS and S-β-thalassemia.
d. Samples to be studied can be analyzed as whole blood, red
    cell hemolysate, or as blood collected on filter paper.
    These samples should preferably be kept in the cold and in
    the dark, and should be studied within 20 to 30 days after
    collection.
e. The method can readily be adapted to testing under less
    optimal conditions when identification of variants by elec-
    trophoresis is not possible.
f. The microchromatographic procedure does not permit the
    identification of "fast-moving" variants nor does it separate
    the hemoglobins A and F. However, a combination of two
    methods, starch gel electrophoresis and microchromatography
    on columns of DEAE-Cellulose, will allow the identification
    of many different hemoglobin variants in various combinations.

*Cord Blood Testing for Sickle Cell Anemia and Related Dis-
orders by Microchromatographic Methods.* The CM-Sephadex procedure easily detects Hb-S and Hb-C at birth but the diffuse zone
of Hb-A has on occasion been difficult to see. Substitution of
CM-Cellulose for CM-Sephadex has yielded a superior microchromatographic method, and the compact, well-defined zones of the
CM-Cellulose column facilitate the interpretation of the results
even though the amount of sample is only 20% as great. The CM-
Cellulose method is as simple and rapid as the original CM-
Sephadex procedure (27, 28).

Developer A is 0.03 M tris-HCl; 0.025 M NaCl; 0.01% KCN at
pH 6.1 and Developer B is 0.03 M tris-HCl; 0.04 M NaCl; 0.01% KCN
at pH 6.3. CM-Cellulose (CM-52, microgranular and preswollen,

TABLE I

Data in Number of Cases Obtained by Microchromatography

During a Survey in Ghana

	AA (%)	AS (%)	AC (%)	SS	CC	SC	Others
Village (4)	378 (77.9)	71 (14.6)	34 (7.0)	0	2	0	0
School (1)	519 (72.4)	117 (16.3)	79 (11.0)	0	1	1	0
Hospital Clinics	828 (72.1)	173 (15.1)	107 (9.3)	15	4	21	0
Total (n=2350)	1725 (73.4)	361 (15.4)	220 (9.4)	15	7	22	0
By Starch Gel Electrophoresis:							
Total *(n=2005)	1433 (71.5)	317 (15.8)	175 (8.7)	8	7	23	42**

*   Microchromatographic analyses were made in Ghana, and starch
    gel electrophoresis in the USA. 112 samples lost in trans-
    port; 145 samples not mailed; 88 samples not identifiable.

** 32 cases with A-HPFH; 8 cases with Hb-A_2' heterozygosity;
    1 case with AN and 1 case with SN.

Reeve Angel and Co., Clifton, N.J. 07104) is equilibrated with
Developer A, and the pH of the stirred suspension is adjusted
to 6.1 with 6 N hydrochloric acid. Several settlings in Developer A should be made in order to remove fine particles.
Supernatant buffer and settled resin should be equal in volume
for the slurry that is used to pour the column. One column,
6 cm in length, requires about one gram of CM-52. A 0.02 ml
portion of blood, 0.3 ml of Developer A, and 0.2 ml of 0.004 M
maleic acid are mixed, and hemolysis is carried out for five
minutes at room temperature. This sample is carefully applied
without disturbing the top of the column and allowed to flow
in. The tube above the column is filled with Developer A, and
the column is attached with rubber tubing to a manifold. The
chromatogram is developed with 40-50 ml of Developer A with a
liquid head of about 50-60 cm to give a flow rate of approximately 20-25 ml per hour. If a strongly fixed hemoglobin is
present after this development, the solvent above the column is
replaced by Developer B and 6-8 ml are passed through the
column.

The appearance of chromatograms after the development with
Developer A is shown by the left chromatogram of each pair in
Figure 9 for cord bloods from AA, AS, SS, and AC children. The
Hb-F in the sample remains partly on the columns, but some is
in the effluent. Hb-A forms a zone with limits between about
10 and 25 mm from the top whereas Hb-S is in a 2-3 mm zone that
has barely moved from the top and Hb-C remains in the upper
0.5-1 mm. The hemoglobin zones are compact and well visible
against the white of the CM-Cellulose column. Hb-S and Hb-C
may be distinguished by the fact that Hb-C is very strongly
fixed whereas Hb-S moves slightly down the column. The conclusion is substantiated by change to Developer B with the result
seen in the right chromatogram of each pair in Figure 9.
Because tris has only meager buffering action at pH 6.1, fluctuations in the pH of ion exchanger and solutions may occur and
may result in abnormal chromatographic behavior. Buffered
conditions may be obtained by substituting bis-tris which has a
pK_a of about 6.5, and virtually identical behavior results if
Developer A is constituted with 0.03 M bis-tris-HCl; 0.03 M NaCl;
0.01% KCN at pH 6.2.

The validity of diagnosis by this technique has been
examined by comparing more than 2,000 samples by the CM-Cellulose procedure, the original CM-Sephadex procedure, and by
starch gel electrophoresis. It is interesting that occasionally
the AS condition at birth is not diagnosed by the electrophoretic technique.

The Determination of Fetal Hemoglobin (Hb-F). Specific
properties of Hb-F have given rise to various methods for its
detection and quantitation which are based on electrophoretic
and chromatographic mobilities of Hb-F, on its slow rate of

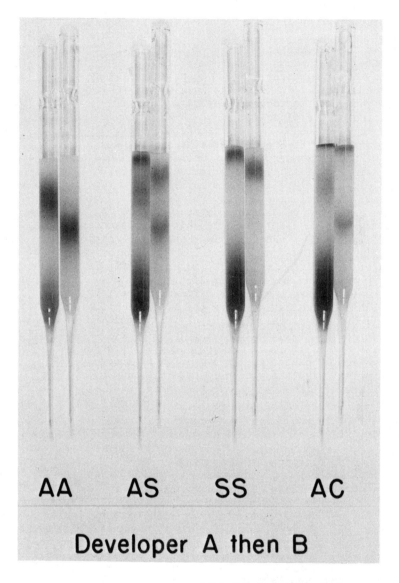

AA   AS   SS   AC

Developer A then B

Journal of Laboratory and Clinical Chemistry

Figure 9. Chromatograms of cord blood with the indicated conditions on 0.5 × 6 cm columns of CM–cellulose. The left-hand member of each pair shows the result after completion of chromatography with Developer A. The right-hand member shows the added movement that occurs with subsequent use of Developer B and thereby distinguishes Hb–S and Hb–C (28).

denaturation at pH 10.5-11, its specific ultraviolet spectral
absorption, and on its immunological specificity. The method
used for the demonstration of Hb-F in the red cells is based on
the difference in rate of dissociation into subunits that exists
between the hemoglobins A and F at pH values below 4.

The acid elution technique is a useful tool for the
demonstration of increased amounts of Hb-F as well as for the
evaluation of the distribution of Hb-F in red cells. The
method is described in detail in references 31, 32, and 33.
Cells containing Hb-F are densely stained with erythrosin and
cells with Hb-A appear as ghost cells; intermediate cells are
stained more or less pink. Reticulocytes with Hb-A sometimes
resemble intermediate cells and may also show some intracellular
granulation. Inclusion bodies are visible in eluted cells as
compact particles of differing sizes. Figure 10 gives some
examples. The method is ideally suited to demonstrate the
presence of newborn red cells in the maternal circulation. The
method is also widely used for the evaluation of the distribution of Hb-F within red cells, mainly to differentiate between
the HPFH condition and the β-or βδ-thalassemias. Evaluation of
F cell smears in such cases is difficult; the term "equal
distribution" usually indicates the presence of Hb-F in each
red cell but not necessarily in the same amount.

The laboratory quantitation of Hb-F by *alkali denaturation*
($\%F_{AD}$) is one of the more difficult routine procedures. Accurate and reproducible results are often achieved only in
laboratories where the procedures are in daily use. Three
methods are available which are discussed in detail in references
24 and 25. Comparative studies of these three procedures have
demonstrated that the method of Betke *et al* (34) is the most
reliable for the quantitation of low percentages of Hb-F (below
10 to 15%).

Hb-F can also be separated from Hb-A and many of its
variants by both *anion- and cation-chromatography*. However, in
most instances Hb-F elutes together with the minor adult hemoglobin Hb-A1 thus preventing its accurate quantitation.
Recently, a method has been devised (35) which is based on the
fact that the αγ dimer contains four isoleucyl residues, 35
leucyl and 15 phenylalanyl residues, whereas the αβ dimer contains no isoleucine, 36 leucyl and 15 phenylalanyl residues.
Thus, the determination of the content of isoleucine in relation
to leucine and phenylalanine can be used as a measure of the
relative amount of Hb-F in mixtures. The procedure involves
the chromatographic isolation of the Hb-F containing zone and
the determination of the isoleucyl, and phenylalanyl content in
a 72 hour acid hydrolysate of the hemoglobins in this zone.
This procedure is presently the most accurate method for the
quantitation of Hb-F. However, it has the great disadvantage
of being laborious and not easily applicable to clinical problems. The development of new microchromatographic procedures,

using either DE-52 columns or CM-Sephadex columns, might be important particularly when these techniques can be simplified and
used in routine analyses.

Detection of Sickling Hemoglobins. *Microscopic methods* will
aid in detecting Hb-S and related variants with the same structural abnormality such as Hb-C-Harlem because these hemoglobins
have greatly decreased solubility in the deoxygenated state which
causes a distortion of the cell membrane. The cells generally
take on an oak leaf or maple leaf shape and under prolonged deoxygenation the sickle shape appears. The procedure has been done
in many ways usually using fingertip blood. The blood is covered
with a cover glass, sealed with petroleum jelly, and examined for
sickling properties after 2 and 24 hr , or a reducing agent is
added (usually a freshly prepared 2% solution of sodium metabisul-
fite is mixed in excess with blood and allowed to stand for 5
min). The methods are simple and popular but are subject to a
number of errors. False results can be obtained when blood is
drawn within 4 months after transfusion, when it is old, exposed
to heat, contaminated with bacteria, or allowed to dry during
testing. Abnormally shaped erythrocytes can easily be confused
for sickling types. Hb-F when present in sufficient quantity and
in every cell will inhibit sickling. Plasma is essential to demonstrate sickling; prolonged washing of cells with 0.9 g% NaCl
will inhibit sickling.

The *solubility test*, which is specific for the demonstration
of Hb-S or Hb-C-Harlem, was originally developed by Itano in 1953
(36), and many modifications, both bad and good, have been published (for references see (25)). All are based on the original
principle that deoxy-Hb-S is less soluble in concentrated phosphate buffers than are all other hemoglobins. Many of the new
procedures have added saponin to the buffers so that whole blood
can be used. The most simple method uses these buffers: a potassium phosphate buffer, pH 6.5 and 2.50 M, and a phosphate
buffer, 1.00 M, which is prepared by the proper dilution of the
2.50 M phosphate buffer. About 1 ml each of the 2 buffers are
placed in separate test tubes. One or two drops of hemolysate
are pipetted in each tube, and, after mixing, 3-5 mg $Na_2S_2O_4$ are
added to deoxygenate the hemoglobin. When Hb-S is present the
content of the tube with the 2.50 M phosphate buffer will become
turbid while that of the tube with the 1.00 M phosphate buffer
remains clear. This method has not given false-positive or
false-negative results in over 50,000 samples tested and checked
by electrophoretic procedures. The use of whole blood shortens
the procedure considerably but it also introduces additional
errors due mainly to the presence of cellular debris, low hemoglobin concentrations in blood samples from patients with a
severe anemia, and high levels of plasma proteins in conditions
such as multiple myeloma and others. The use of hemolysate also
eliminates the false-positive readings seen in samples from

patients with an unstable hemoglobin variant when Heinz bodies are present in the erythrocytes.

The *mechanical instability of oxy-hemoglobin S* has been used as a new screening method for Hb-S. Such a test does not exclude unstable hemoglobins and other variants with even a slightly decreased stability and will likely not distinguish between heterozygotes and homozygotes.

Detection of Unstable Hemoglobins. The stability of the hemoglobin molecule depends to a great extent on bonds between the chains, between chains and the heme groups, and on bonds within the chains. Thus, when the replacement of an amino acid residue affects one of these many bonds, the stability of the molecule can be impaired. The hemoglobin readily precipitates in the red cell and *intraerythrocytic inclusion bodies* can appear leading to increased cell destruction with subsequent anemia. These bodies are more easily observed in a blood sample from patients with such an anomaly after the spleen has been removed; Figure 11 demonstrates Heinz bodies in the blood of such a patient.

Other tests useful for the detection of unstable hemoglobins are the heat stability test, the isopropanol precipitation test, and the PCMB or PMB precipitation test.

The *heat stability test* was first applied to blood from patients with Hb-H disease and later to patients with Heinz body anemias. In this test the heat stability of the hemoglobin variant in hemolysate is compared with that of a normal control. The hemolysates are incubated in a phosphate buffer at 60°C to 70°C, and hemoglobin precipitation evaluated either visually or spectrophotometrically. Precipitation of normal hemoglobin is minimal when incubated at 60°C for 30 minutes, but many unstable hemoglobins are almost completely denatured under these conditions. Figure 12 gives some examples.

The *Isopropanol precipitation test* is a simple screening test, recently described by Carrell and Kay (37). Hemolysate is mixed with an isopropanol-tris-buffer, pH 7.4, incubated at 37°C for various times and the hemoglobin precipitation evaluated either visually or spectrophotometrically. Technical details are also given in reference 25.

The *PCMB precipitation test* is a most useful test for the detection of an unstable hemoglobin and is based on reaction of hemoglobin with p-chloromercuribenzoate (PCMB). PCMB was first used by Bucci and Fronticelli (38) for the isolation of native hemoglobin chains. Modification of their method has broadened its applicability to hemoglobin variants that dissociate more readily. When normal hemoglobin reacts with PCMB the protein dissociates into subunits but no precipitation occurs. However, many unstable hemoglobins dissociate more readily when exposed to PCMB and often the abnormal chain precipitates. Electrophoretic examination of the PCMB treated hemolysate will,

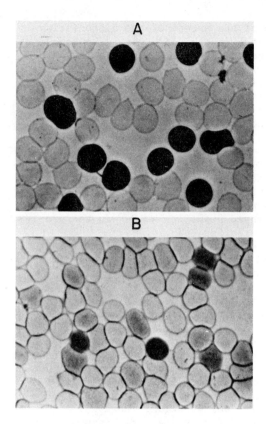

Figure 10.   Red cell smears after the application of the acid elution technique. A, artificial mixture of cells from newborn and adult. B, blood sample from a patient with Fanconi's anemia (Hb–F$_{AD}$: 14.6%).

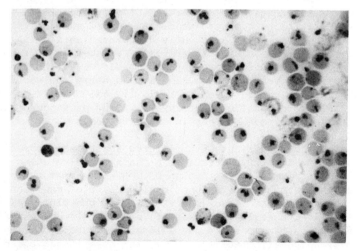

Figure 11.   The formation of Heinz bodies in a subject with an unstable hemoglobin (courtesy of Dr. E. Kleihauer, Ulm, Germany)

therefore, allow evaluation of the extent of the dissociation
and of the precipitation of the unstable subunit. The same
method can be used on a preparative scale for the isolation of
a large quantity of the abnormal chain.

Unstable hemoglobin variants are often found in persons
with unexplained hemolytic anemias. Below are some guidelines
for their detection.

1. Red cells of a freshly collected blood sample will form
Heinz bodies in the presence or absence of phenylhydrazine in a
greater number than red cells of a similar blood sample from a
normal control.

2. The stability of hemoglobin in a freshly prepared red cell
hemolysate at temperatures varying between 50° and 70° is distinctly less than that of a normal control. The unstable
variant will also show decreased stability at 37° in the presence of the isopropanol-tris buffer, pH 7.4.

3. An increased dissociation of the hemoglobin molecule to
monomers can be demonstrated after treatment with p-chloromercuribenzoate; often, the unstable subunit will precipitate
irreversibly.

4. Free α-and β-chains can be demonstrated in a freshly prepared hemolysate using starch gel electrophoresis at alkaline
pH.

5. Often unstable hemoglobins have a decreased number of heme
groups. This number can be calculated from the optical densities
of a solution of the cyanferri derivative of the isolated
variant at 540 and at 280 nm using normal Hb-A as control.

Unstable variants are often found in a single member of a
family, and are the result of a new mutation. However, occasionally many members in a large family are heterozygous for
such a variant; these persons are not easily identified unless
some specific techniques are used. A typical example is the
family with Hb-Atlanta, a recently discovered variant in which
leucyl residue in position 75 (E19) is replaced by a prolyl
residue (39). Figure 13 presents the pedigree of the family in
which twelve members in three generations carry the variant.
Hematological data are given in Table II; only a mild hemolytic
anemia is present in the heterozygotes. The presence of the
variant was confirmed by four instability tests.

Detection of Variants With Altered Functional Properties.
When substitutions in either α-or β-chains involve amino acid
residues that participate in the contact with heme or the contact
between chains, changes in functional properties can occur and
the determination of the oxygen affinity of the blood sample or
of an isolated hemoglobin variant is desirable. Oxygen affinity
is affected by temperature, pH, salt concentration, the level
of 2,3-diphosphoglycerate (2,3-DPG), and to a lesser extent by
the concentration of the hemoglobin. The concentration of
2,3-DPG in blood changes rather rapidly after collection and a

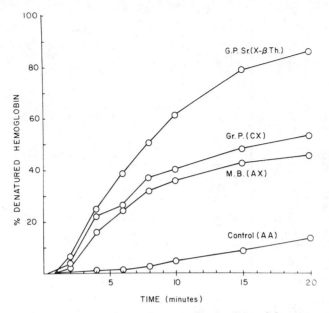

Figure 12. *Heat denaturation curves of hemoglobin from three members of a family with Hb–Leslie, a newly discovered unstable variant with a deletion of residue 131 of the β-chain. G.P.Sr. has Hb–Leslie–β-thalassemia; the %Hb–Leslie is 85% (DEAE–Sephadex chromatography); Gr.P. has Hb–Leslie– Hb–C; %Hb–Leslie is 28%; M.B. has Hb–Leslie trait; %Hb– Leslie is 28%.*

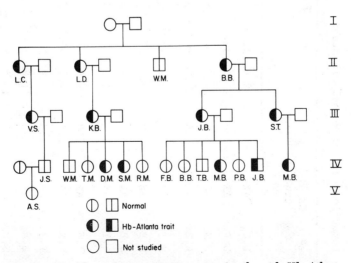

Figure 13. *The pedigree of a Caucasian family with Hb–Atlanta or $\alpha_2\beta_2{}^{75}Leu \rightarrow Pro(E19)$*

TABLE II

Hematological and Hemoglobin Stability Data on 22 Members of the Family with Hb-Atlanta

Case[a]	Condition[b]	WBC $10^3/mm^3$	Hb g%	PCV %	RBC $10^6/mm^3$	MCV μ^3	MCH $\mu\mu g$	MCHC %	Heat[c] Stability	Iso[c]-propanol	Free[c] α Chains	Heinz[c] Bodies
II. L.C.	AX	-	9.6	31	3.35	91	29	31	+	+	+	+
L.D.	AX	11.6	11.6	36.5	4.05	88	28.5	32	+	+	+	+
W.M.	AA	6.0	14.3	44	5.48	81	25.5	31.5	-	-	-	-
B.B.	AX	7.6	11.4	36	3.75	98	32	32.5	+	n.d.	+	+
III. V.S.	AX	6.1	10.6	33.5	3.65	89	29	32.5	+	+	+	+
K.B.	AX	7.2	12.4	37	4.06	92	31	33.5	+	+	+	+
J.B.	AX	6.8	11.9	38	4.35	88	29	32.5	+	n.d.	+	+
S.T.	AX	11.1	11.3	37.5	4.40	86	27	31	+	n.d.	+	+
IV. J.S.	AA	7.9	16.0	47.5	5.38	87	29.5	33.5	-	n.d.	-	-
W.M.	AA	7.1	14.1	43.5	5.19	83	27.5	32.5	-	n.d.	-	n.d.
T.M.	AA	7.3	12.9	38	4.75	81	27.5	34	-	n.d.	-	n.d.
D.M.	AX	11.0	11.8	37	4.24	85	28	32	+	+	+	+
S.M.	AX	7.7	13.3	40	4.01	98	33.5	33.5	+	+	+	+
R.M.	AA	7.9	13.0	38.5	4.68	81	28	34	-	-	-	-

TABLE II - Continued

Hematological and Hemoglobin Stability Data on 22 Members of the Family with Hb-Atlanta

Case[a]	Condition[b]	WBC $10^3/mm^3$	Hb g%	PCV %	RBC $10^6/mm^3$	MCV μ^3	MCH $\mu\mu g$	MCHC %	Heat[c] Stability	Iso-[c] propanol	Free[c] α Chains	Heinz[c] Bodies
IV. F.B.	AA	7.1	11.8	36	4.56	80	27.5	34	-	n.d.	-	-
B.B.	AA	6.8	14.1	42	4.95	85	27.5	32.5	-	-	-	-
T.B.	AA	5.9	14.6	43.5	5.00	87	28	32.5	-	-	-	-
M.B.	AX	8.2	10.9	34	3.86	87	27	31	+	+	+	+
P.B.	AA	7.0	13.0	39.5	4.50	87	28	31	-	-	-	-
J.B.	AX	7.3	11.3	35	3.99	87	27.5	32	+	+	+	+
M.B.	AX	10.2	9.2	29.5	3.98	73	22.5	30.5	n.d.	n.d.	+	+
V. A.S.	AA	6.3	11.9	35.5	4.33	81	27.5	33.5	-	n.d.	-	-

a. See Figure 13; ages of the children in generation IV vary between 1 and 26 years.

b. X refers to Hb-Atlanta

c. + refers to a positive test and - to a negative test; n.d.: not determined.

rapid method is desirable for the determination of its concentration. Red cell hemolysates can be stripped of 2,3-DPG by dialysis against 0.2 M NaCl for 24 hours followed by dialysis against a desired buffer, or by passage of the red cell hemolysate through a Sephadex G-25 column previously equilibrated with buffer used in the oxygen equilibrium analyses.

The oxygen content of blood and other test samples can be measured with the well-known Van Slyke apparatus or spectrophotometrically. Automated instruments for measuring the oxyhemoglobin content in blood are available; for instance the system IL517 of the Instrumentation Laboratory Inc., (Lexington, Mass.). This system consists of a gas mixing module, oxygen monitor, tonometer, digital pH/blood gas analyzer, and CO-oximeter, and allows the construction of an oxygen dissociation curve (eight equilibrations requiring 15 ml blood) in approximately 2 hrs. Figure 14 gives examples of two dissociation curves, both being determined in freshly collected blood samples at pH 7.38 and at $37^{\circ}C$. The curve of subject A is normal with a P_{50} value of 26 mm Hg. That of subject B is most unusual, and its shape indicates the presence of two only partially interacting hemoglobin types one of which completely lacks subunit interaction. Subject B is a 20 year old black marine with a severe erythrocytosis; he has a normal 2,3-DPG level/g Hb, but is heterozygous for Hb-Fort Gordon, a β chain variant in which tyrosyl residue in position 145 is replaced by an aspartyl residue (unpublished data).

Detection of Met(Ferri-)Hemoglobins (Hb-M). Detection of these variants can be made by starch gel electrophoresis of the ferri-derivatives of hemoglobins in red cell hemolysate using a phosphate buffer, pH 7.0 (25). However, some methemoglobin variants can be separated from normal Hb-A at pH 9.0 (40). Nearly all methemoglobin variants exhibit absorption spectra that are different from that of normal ferrihemoglobin. The absorption spectra are determined after the hemolysate is dialyzed overnight at $4^{\circ}C$ against an 0.1 M phosphate buffer, pH 6.4 or 7.1, using an automatic recording spectrophotometer. A total hemoglobin concentration of 0.6 to 0.8 mg/ml is required. Table III presents characteristic spectral maxima observed for the known methemoglobin variants. Some methemoglobin variants vary in the rate of reaction with KCN.

Structural Analyses of Hemoglobin Variants. It has become impossible to characterize nearly any abnormal hemoglobin by its electrophoretic and/or chromatographic mobility only. This is most strikingly demonstrated by the fact that over fifty different variants behave similar to Hb-S in electrophoresis. Characterization, therefore, often requires detailed structural analyses or the demonstration of a property unique to a specific variant. Some of the techniques used in these studies will be

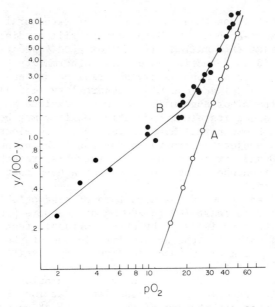

Figure 14.   Oxygen equilibrium curves of freshly collected blood samples from the author (A) and from a patient with Hb–Fort Gordon with an increased oxygen affinity (B).   Hb–Fort Gordon has been identified as $\alpha_2\beta_2$ (145 Tyr → Asp).

TABLE III

Spectral Characteristics of Methemoglobin Variants

Variants	Amino Acid Substitution	Spectroscopic Maxima at pH 7.1	Velocity of –CN Reactivity and CN–Ferri–Hb Spectrum
M–Boston	α58(E7)His→Tyr	495,600 nm	Slow & incomplete
M–Saskatoon	β63(E7)His→Tyr	490,602 nm	Fast, normal
M–Iwate	α87(F8)His→Tyr	490,610 nm	Fast, normal
M–Hyde Park	β92(F8)His→Tyr	490,610 nm	Normal
M–Milwaukee	β67(E11)Val→Glu	500,622 nm	Fast, normal

mentioned in this section and examples of structural analyses of
an α-chain variant and a β-chain variant will be discussed.

   *Structural information gained from electrophoretic proce-
dures* will aid in detecting an α-chain abnormality because such
a variant will be present as two abnormal bands, one major
abnormality ($\alpha_2{}^X\beta_2$) and one minor abnormality ($\alpha_2{}^X\delta_2$). The
absence of the minor abnormality does not exclude an α-chain
abnormality since its electrophoretic mobility may be similar
to that of a known normal hemoglobin type. The electrophoretic
pattern in a subject heterozygous for the β-chain abnormality
Hb-S or Hb-D and for the δ-chain variant Hb-A2 resembles closely
that of a person who is heterozygous for a Hb-D that is abnormal
in the α-chain.

   A detailed study of the structure of a hemoglobin variant
still requires at least 100 to 200 mg of the pure protein. The
protein can best be isolated by chromatographic techniques.

   Identification of the abnormality in one of the two types
of chains can be made by *hybridization* or by *electrophoretic
identification* of the chains. The principle of the hybridization procedure is the formation of hybrid hemoglobins from a
mixture of two hemoglobins by dissociation at low pH and subsequent random recombination of the subunits at neutral or
slightly alkaline pH. Canine hemoglobin is well suited for
hybridization experiments with human hemoglobin types. The
final products from dissociation and recombination experiments
of this hemoglobin ($\alpha_2{}^{can}\beta_2{}^{can}$) with normal human Hb-A ($\alpha_2{}^A\beta_2{}^A$)
are:

$$\alpha_2{}^{can}\beta_2{}^{can} + \alpha_2{}^A\beta_2{}^A \rightarrow \alpha_2{}^{can}\beta_2{}^{can} + \alpha_2{}^{can}\beta_2{}^A + \alpha_2{}^A\beta_2{}^{can} + \alpha_2{}^A\beta_2{}^A$$

The two hybrid hemoglobins are easily demonstrated by electrophoresis.

   The presence of individual chains in a hemoglobin variant
can also be demonstrated by electrophoresis at alkaline pH after
the protein has been dissociated into its subunits through
exposure to 6 M urea in the presence of β-mercaptoethanol. The
buffer is either a barbital buffer or a tris-EDTA-boric acid
buffer, pH 8.0 - 8.6, and contains 6 M urea and β-mercaptoethanol. Dissociation of the hemoglobin into subunits is best
accomplished in a mixture of 1 ml 10 g% Hb (or whole hemolysate),
4 ml 6 M urea barbital or tris-EDTA-boric acid buffer, and 1 to
1.5 ml β-mercaptoethanol. After 30 minutes to 1 hour the sample
is subjected to cellulose acetate or starch gel electrophoresis.
Each chain has a specific mobility and an alteration in electrophoretic mobility easily identifies the abnormal chain.
Schneider recently published a detailed description of the
technique (41).

   After it has been determined which chain in the variant is
aberrant, specific structural studies are required. Several
procedures are available which differ from one laboratory to
the other and include chain separation by column chromatography,
modification of the sulfhydryl groups through reaction with

ethylenimine, digestion of the chain with proteolytic enzymes,
separation of the resulting peptides by column chromatography
or by fingerprinting, and lastly, amino acid analyses and
sequential analyses. No detailed description of these procedures
will be given; instead, the structural analyses of two variants
will be discussed in some detail as examples of approaches that
can be followed.

Structural Analyses of Hb-St. Claude or α_2^{127}(H10)Lys→Thrβ_2
(reference 42)

This α chain variant was found in a 47 year old healthy
male under investigation for a chronic low-back complaint.
Routine hematological investigation showed a hemoglobin concentration of 15.6 g/100 ml, a packed red cell volume of 45%,
normal erythrocyte morphology, and no indication of excessive
hemolysis. The same abnormal hemoglobin was found in one son.
The propositus is one of ten children living in various parts
of Canada. While conducting the family study, it was discovered
that another part of this family (including the father, a
brother, and a niece of the propositus) was found by other
investigators to have a Hb-J$_\alpha$ with an amino acid substitution
thought to reside in the core.

This electrophoretically fast-moving variant was readily
isolated by DEAE-Sephadex chromatography. Hybridization
analyses with canine Hb confirmed the suggestion that the
abnormality was located in the α-chain. The α-chain was separated from the β-chain on 1.7 X 15 cm columns of CM-Cellulose
using the method of Clegg *et al* (43). The CM-Cellulose used
was CM-52 (Reeve Angel, Clifton, N.J.) and the developers were
8 M urea-β-mercaptoethanol phosphate buffers, pH 6.7 - 7.1.
Figure 15 shows the separation obtained. The zone containing
the α-St. Claude chain was passed through 2.5 x 50 cm columns
of Sephadex G-25 in 0.5% formic acid to remove the urea, and
the protein zone isolated and recovered by freeze-drying. The
α chain was digested with trypsin (Worthington Biochemical
Corp., TPCK trypsin) for 6 hours at room temperature in a pH
stat at pH 8.9. Trypsin equal to 0.5% of the substrate by
weight was added at 0 and at 1 hr. The pH of the digest was
lowered to 6.5, and the insoluble core separated by centrifugation and stored.

The soluble tryptic peptides of 130 mg α chain of Hb-St.
Claude were separated on 0.9 x 60 cm columns of Chromobead
resin type P (Technicon Instruments, Dowex 50-X4) at 37°C using
the procedure described earlier (16). The method uses a
gradient of volatile pyridine-acetic acid buffers of differing
molarities and pH as follows: first gradient, 666 ml 0.1 M,
pH 3.1, and 333 ml 1.0 M, pH 5.0; and second gradient, 166 ml
1.0 M, pH 5.0, and 332 ml 2.0 M, pH 5.0. The amino acid composition of isolated fragments was determined with a Spinco
model 121 automated amino acid analyzer (Beckman Instruments)

equipped with high-sensitivity cuvettes and an Infotronic model
CRS-110A integrator. Samples were hydrolyzed for 24 hr and in
some instances for 72 hr at 110°C under reduced pressure with
6 N HCl.
    Figure 16 gives the separation of the tryptic peptides.
Many fragments are eluted as single peaks. However, in some
zones at least two peptides are present, and rechromatography
on columns of Dowex 1-X2 is necessary for further purification.
Peptides T-1 through T-11 originate from the 99 residues in
NH2-terminal position and T-14 is of the Tyr-Arg dipeptide in
COOH-terminal position (see Figure 1 for the sequence of the
normal α-chain). Amino acid analyses of these peptides <u>and</u>
their location in the chromatogram usually reveal if the fragment contains a variation or not. Peptides T-12 (residues 100
through 127) and T-13 (residues 128-139) are not observed
because they form the insoluble core; however, considerable
quantities of the T-13 peptide have been observed in several
chromatograms where it is eluted in the T-1 and T-11 region.
    The insoluble core of the normal α chain consists of this
fragment:
```
100                     105                     110
Leu-Leu-Ser-His-Cys-Leu-Leu-Val-Thr-Leu-Ala-Ala-His-Leu-Pro-
115                     120                     125
Ala-Glu-Phe-Thr-Pro-Ala-Val-His-Ala-Ser-Leu-Asp-Lys-Phe-Leu-
130                     135                     139
Ala-Ser-Val-Ser-Thr-Val-Leu-Thr-Ser-Lys
```
The cysteinyl residue in the core was oxidized with performic
acid according to the method of Hirs (44), and the oxidized
core was digested with chymotrypsin for 8 hours at room temperature in a pH stat at pH 8.9. Enzyme equal to 0.5% of the
substrate by weight was added at 0 and at 2 hr. The chymotryptic
peptides were also separated by Dowex 50-X4 chromatography.
Figure 17 gives examples of separation that have been obtained.
From the peptide fragments of the normal α chain listed in the
figure it becomes evident that splits have occurred between
residues 101-102, 109-110, 117-118, 122-123, 127-128, 128-129,
and 136-137, and that all fragments were recovered. The same
is true for the chymotryptic peptides of the core of the α chain
of Hb-St. Claude. However, one extra zone (see arrow) is
observed and two zones (see arrows) are missing. The latter
two correspond to residues in positions 123-127 and 123-128,
respectively. The amino acid composition of the extra zone was
the same as that of the first missing zone except for a replacement of the normally occurring lysyl residue for a threonyl
residue; thus, the α chain of Hb-St. Claude had a Lys→Thr substitution in position 127 which corresponds to the 10th position
of the H-helix. The substitution does not affect the stability
nor the function of the protein and the presence of the variant
in the heterozygote does not have clinical consequences. The
substitution explains the electrophoretic and chromatographic

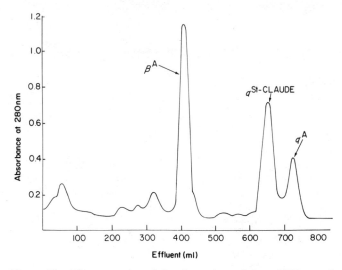

Figure 15.   The separation of the chains from globin of 280 mg of partially purified Hb–St. Claude on a 1.7 × 15 cm column of carboxymethylcellulose in 8M urea

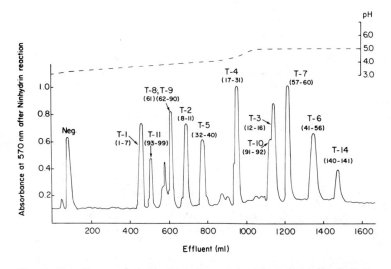

Figure 16.   Chromatographic separation of peptides of a tryptic hydrolysate of the α chain of Hb–St. Claude on a 0.9 × 60 cm column of Chromobead resin type P at 37°C. The pH gradient is indicated by the broken line. T-1, T-2, etc. refer to the tryptic peptides and the numbers underneath to the positions in the chain. Several peptides are pure and give satisfactory analyses without further purification.

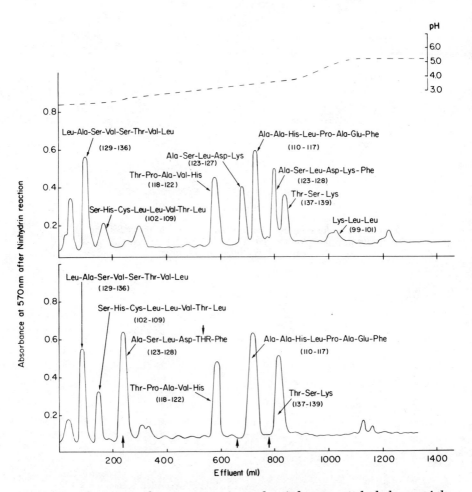

Figure 17. Chromatographic separation of peptides of chymotryptic hydrolysates of the oxidized cores of the α-chain of Hb–A (top panel) and of the α-chain of Hb–St. Claude (bottom panel) on 0.9 × 60 cm columns of Chromobead resin type P at 37°C. The pH gradient is indicated by the broken line. Peptides are identified by their sequences and by the positions they occupy in the α-chain.

properties of the variant.
Structural Analyses of Hb-Shepherds Bush or $\alpha_2\beta_2^{74}$(E18)Gly→Asp

---

The variant was found in a 22 year old woman with chronic
hemolytic anemia characterized by a persistent reticulocytosis,
development of gallstones requiring cholecystectomy, frequent
episodes of jaundice, dark urine, and falling PCV value. Her
mother, maternal grandfather, and sister have a similar clinical
picture. In all patients red cell enzymes are elevated with a
reticulocytosis of about 10%, and 2,3-DPG levels are normal.
Heinz body preparations are positive as is the heat stability
test. Electrophoretic examination of hemolysate showed the
presence of a fast-moving variant which was readily separated
from Hb-A by chromatography on DEAE-Sephadex. The abnormal β-
chain was isolated by CM-Cellulose chromatography as described
before, and converted into the S-2-aminoethyl (AE) derivative
(45). Treatment of the β-chain with ethylenimine converts the
-SH groups into the $-S-CH_2-CH_3$ groups. The structure of AE-
cysteine is similar enough to that of lysine that peptide bonds
involving this derivative will also serve as a substrate for
trypsin. An added advantage is that the peptides containing
the AE-cysteinyl residue have a greatly increased solubility.

Tryptic peptides from a digest of 120 mg AE-β-chain were
separated by Dowex 50-X4 chromatography; the chromatogram is
depicted in Figure 18. Many peptides were eluted in single
zones, but several occurred together. However, all peptides,
T-1 through T-15, were recovered (residues 1-146; see Figure 2).
Peptide T-12 occurred in two fragments; T-12a is the NH_2-terminal
fragment with a AE-cysteinyl residue in COOH-terminal position.
Some larger fragments (T-10, T-11, T-14, 15; T-7, 8) were also
observed in small quantities indicating an incomplete tryptic
digestion. Several zones required rechromatography using 0.6 X
60 cm columns of Dowex 1-X2 according to the method of Schroeder
(46). Figure 19 gives an example of the separation of two
peptides that occurred together in the original Dowex 50 chromatogram.

Peptide T-9 was eluted from the Dowex 50 column in front
of the T-14 peptide instead of between the T-14 and T-1 peptides.
Amino acid analysis indicated that one of the two normally
occurring glycyl residues (in positions 69 and 74, respectively)
was replaced by an aspartyl residue. To decide which glycyl
residue was replaced, two approaches were followed. First,
degradation of the isolated peptide by the phenylthiohydantoin-
dansylation procedure (47, 48) determined its NH_2-terminal
sequence (a Val-Leu-Gly-Ala-NH_2-terminus was established, thus
suggesting that glycyl residue in position 74 was involved).
Second, the peptide was digested with thermolysin for 3 hr at
37°C in a volatile buffer at pH 7.4; this enzyme will hydrolyze
peptide bonds with alanyl, aspartyl, leucyl, and asparaginyl
residues in COOH-terminal position. The thermolytic fragments

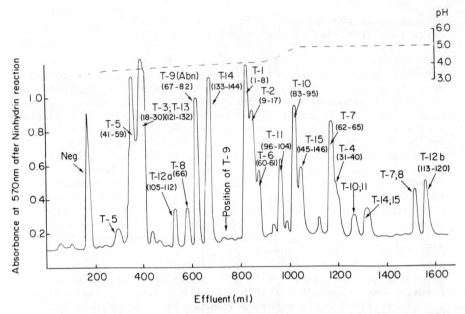

Figure 18. *Chromatographic separation of peptides of a tryptic digest of the AE–β-chain of Hb–Sheperds Bush on a 0.9 × 60 cm column of Chromobead resin type P at 37°C. The pH gradient is indicated by the broken line. Peptides are identified by the positions occupied in β-chain.*

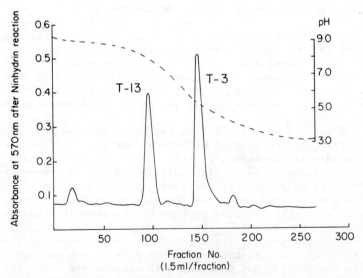

Figure 19. *Chromatographic separation of peptides βT-3 and βT-13 on a 0.6 × 60 cm column of Dowex 1-X2. The broken line indicates the pH gradient.*

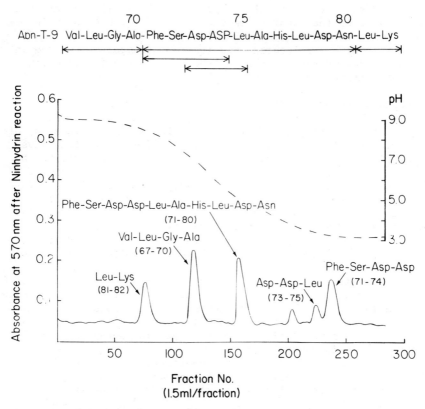

Figure 20. Chromatographic separation of thermolytic fragments of peptide T-9 isolated from the tryptic digest of the AE–β-chain of Hb–Sheperds Bush. The Dowex 1-X2 column was 60 cm long and had an internal diameter of 0.6 cm. The pH gradient is indicated by the broken line. The fragments are identified by their sequences and the positions they occupy in the β-chain. The sequence of the abnormal T-9 is given at the top of the figure.

were separated on a column of Dowex 1-X2, and five fragments
were recovered as indicated in Figure 20. Examination of the
amino composition of these fragments left no doubt as concerns
the introduction of a charged amino acid residue in the heme
pocket causing considerable disruption to this internal structure and an instability of the protein. It is likely that the
side chain of the aspartyl residue at E18 of the β-chain interferes with threonyl residue β84 (EF8) and phenylalanyl residue
β85 (F1) which are located opposite to the aspartyl residue in
position 74, probably weakening the hydrophobic forces which
hold the heme pocket together (49).

Concluding Remarks

There are many important reasons for an intensive study of
hemoglobin variants. First, the number of variants that have
been discovered is steadily increasing, and it may well be that
some 100 million persons have a variant of Hb-A or a type of
thalassemia. Second, homozygosity and even heterozygosity for
some variants and the thalassemias, may cause considerable
health problems because these conditions (Hb-S, Hb-E, β-thalassemia, α-thalassemia in particular) affect several million
persons in various racial and/or ethnic groups. Third, identification of hemoglobin variants in persons suffering from unexplained hemolytic anemias or from an unexplained erythrocytosis has aided in explaining these conditions. Fourth, analyses of structural variants have offered data of great importance
for an insight in the structure-function relationships of the
hemoglobin molecule. Fifth, the discovery of several unusual
variants has given insight into the genetic mechanisms that
control protein synthesis in man.

It seems likely that these investigations when continued
will uncover additional variants of importance for the understanding of basic biological phenomena and disease states.

Literature Cited

1. Perutz, M. F.; Muirhead, H.; Cox, J. M.; and Goaman, L. C.
    G.; "Three-dimensional Fourier Synthesis of Horse Oxyhemo-
    globin at 2.8 Å Resolution: (II) The Atomic Model". Nature
    (1968), 219, 131.
2. Bolton, W.; and Perutz, M. F.; "Three Dimensional Fourier
    Synthesis of Horse Deoxyhaemoglobin at 2.8 Å Resolution".
    Nature (1970), 228, 551.
3. Huisman, T. H. J.; "Normal and Abnormal Human Hemoglobins".
    Advan. Clin. Chem. (1972), 15, 149.
4. Capp, G. L.; Rigas, D. A.; and Jones, R. T.; "Evidence for
    a New Haemoglobin Chain (ζ-Chain)". Nature (1970), 228,
    278.
5. Jones, R. T.; Personal communication (1974).

6. Pauling, L.; Itano, H. A.; Singer, S. J.; and Wells, I. C.; "Sickle Cell Anemia, a Molecular Disease". Science (1949), 110, 543.

7. Perutz, M. F.; and Lehmann, H.; "Molecular Pathology of Human Haemoglobin". Nature (1968), 219, 902.

8. Schroeder, W. A.; "Hemoglobin Structure and Function. The Proteins", H. Neurath and R. Hill, Eds., Academic Press, New York, in press.

9. Hollán, S. R.; Szelényi, J. G.; Brimhall, B.; Duerst, M.; Jones, R. T.; Koler, R. D.; and Stocklen, Z.; "Multiple Alpha Chain Loci for Human Haemoglobins: Hb J-Buda and Hb G-Pest". Nature (1972), 235, 47.

10. Brimhall, B.; Duerst, M.; Hollán, S. R.; Stenzel, P.; Szelényi, J.; and Jones, R. T.; "Structural Characterizations of Hemoglobins J-Buda [α 61 (E 10) Lys→Asn] and G-Pest [α 74 (EF 3) Asp→Asn]". Biochim. Biophys. Acta., (1974), 336, 344.

11. Gajdusek, D. C.; Guiart, J.; Kirk, R. L.; Carrell, R. W.; Irvine, D.; Kynoch, P. A. M.; and Lehmann, H.; "Haemoglobin J Tongariki (α 115 Alanine→Aspartic Acid): The First New Haemoglobin Variant Found in a Pacific (Melanesian) Population". J. Med. Genet. (1967), 4, 1.

12. Abramson, R. K.; Rucknagel, D. L.; and Shreffler, D. C.; "Homozygous Hb J Tongariki: Evidence for Only One Alpha Chain Structural Locus in Melanesians". Science (1970), 169, 194.

13. Weatherall, D. J., guest editor; "The Haemoglobinopathies". Clinics in Haematology (1974), 3, No. 2.

14. Williams, W. J.; Beutler, E.; Allan, J. E.; and Rundles, R. W.; "Hematology", Chapter 11, "Erythrocyte Disorders - Anemias Related to Abnormal Globin", McGraw-Hill Book Company, New York, 1972.

15. Huisman, T. H. J.; Wilson, J. B.; Gravely, M.; and Hubbard, M.; "Hemoglobin Grady: the First Example of a Variant with Elongated Chains Due to an Insertion of Residues". Proc. Natl. Acad. Sci., (1974), 71, 3270.

16. Huisman, T. H. J.; Wrightstone, R. N.; Wilson, J. B.; Schroeder, W. A.; and Kendall, A. G.; "Hemoglobin Kenya, the Product of Fusion of γ and β Polypeptide Chains". Arch. Biochem. Biophys. (1972), 153, 850.

17. Kendall, A. G.; Ojwang, P. J.; Schroeder, W. A.; and Huisman, T. H. J.; "Hemoglobin Kenya, the Product of a Gamma-beta Fusion Gene: Studies of the Family". Am. J. Hum. Genet., (1973), 25, 548.

18. Clegg, J. B.; Weatherall, D. J., and Milner, P. F.; "Haemoglobin Constant Spring - A Chain Termination Mutant?" Nature (1971), 234, 337.

19. Efremov, G. D.; Wrightstone, R. N., Huisman, T. H. J.; Schroeder, W. A.; Hyman, C.; Ortega, J.; and Williams, K.; "An Unusual Hemoglobin Anomaly and its Relation to

α-Thalassemia and Hemoglobin - H Disease". J. Clin.
Invest., (1971), 50, 1628.

20. Flatz, G.; Kinderlerer, J. L.; Kilmartin, J. V.; and
Lehmann, H.; "Haemoglobin Tak: A Variant with Additional
Residues at the End of the β-Chains". Lancet, (April 10,
1971), 732.

21. Huisman, T. H. J.; Schroeder, W. A.; Efremov, G. D.;
Duma, H.; Mladenovski, B.; Hyman, C. B.; Rachmilewitz,
E. A.; Bouver, N.; Miller, A.; Brodie, A. R.; Shelton,
J. R.; Shelton, J. B.; and Apell, G.; "The Present Status
of the Heterogeneity of Fetal Hemoglobin in β-Thalassemia;
An Attempt to Unify Some Observations in Thalassemia and
in Related Conditions". Proc. Third Cooley's Anemia Conf.
April, 1973. Ann. N. Y. Acad. Sci., (1974), 232 107.

22. Huisman, T. H. J.; "Normal and Abnormal Hemoglobins".
Advan. Clin. Chem. (1963), 6, 231.

23. Huisman, T. H. J.; "Human Hemoglobins in Biochemical
Methods in Red Cell Genetics", Ed. Y. Yunis, p. 391,
Academic Press, New York, 1969.

24. Jonxis, J. H. P.; and Huisman, T. H. J.; "A Laboratory
Manual on Abnormal Haemoglobins", Second Edition, Blackwell,
Oxford, 1968.

25. Efremov, G. D.; and Huisman, T. H. J.; "The Laboratory
Diagnosis of Hemoglobinopathies". Clinics in Haematology,
(1974), 3, No. 2, 527.

26. Schmidt, R. M.; and Brosious, E. M.; "Laboratory Methods
of Hemoglobinopathy Detection", U. S. Department of Health,
Education, and Welfare, Public Health Service, 4th Edition,
April 1973.

27. Schroeder, W. A.; Jakway, J.; and Powars, D.; "Detection
of Hemoglobins S and C at Birth: A Rapid Screening Procedure by Column Chromatography". J. Lab. Clin. Med.,
(1973), 82, 303.

28. Schroeder, W. A.; Huisman, T. H. J.; Powars, D.; Evans, L.;
Abraham, E. C.; and Lam, H.; "Microchromatography of
Hemoglobins". IV. "An Improved Procedure for the Detection of Hemoglobins S and C at Birth". J. Lab. Clin. Med.,
in press.

29. Efremov, G. D.; Huisman, T. H. J.; Bowman, K.; Wrightstone,
R. N.; and Schroeder, W. A.; "Microchromatography of
Hemoglobins". II. "A Rapid Method for the Determination
of Hemoglobin A_2". J. Lab. Clin. Med., (1974), 83, 657.

30. Huisman, T. H. J.; Schroeder, W. A.; Brodie, A. R.;
Mayson, S. M.; and Jakway, J.; "Microchromatography of
Hemoglobins". III. "A Simplified Procedure for the
Determination of Hemoglobin A_2". J. Lab. Clin. Med., in
press.

31. Betke, K.; and Kleihauer, E. F.; "Fetaler und bleibender
Blutfarbstoff in Erythrozyten und Erythroblasten von
menschlichen Feten und Neugeborenen". Blut, (1958), 4, 241.

32. Kleihauer, E.; "Fetales Hämoglobin und fetale Erythrocyten". Archiv. Kinderheilk. Beih., 53, F. Enke-Verlag, Stuttgart, Germany, 1966.

33. Kleihauer, E.; "Determination of Fetal Hemoglobin: Elution Technique", in "The Detection of Hemoglobinopathies", p. 20, R. M. Schmidt, T. H. J. Huisman, and H. Lehmann, editors. CRC Press, publishers, 1974.

34. Betke, K.; Marti, H. R.; and Schlicht, I.; "Estimation of Small Percentages of Foetal Haemoglobin". Nature, (1959), 184, 1877.

35. Schroeder, W. A.; Huisman, T. H. J.; Shelton, J. R.; and Wilson, J. B.; "An Improved Method for Quantitative Determination of Human Fetal Hemoglobin". Anal. Biochem., (1970), 35, 235.

36. Itano, H. A.; "Solubilities of Naturally Occurring Mixtures of Human Hemoglobin". Arch. Biochem. and Biophys., (1953), 47, 148.

37. Carrell, R. W.; and Kay, R.; "A Simple Method for the Detection of Unstable Hemoglobins". Br. J. Haematol., (1972), 23, 615.

38. Bucci, E.; and Fronticelli, C.; "A New Method for the Preparation of α and β Subunits of Human Hemoglobin". J. Biol. Chem., (1965), 240, 551.

39. Hubbard, M.; Winton, E.; Lindeman, J. G.; Dessauer, P. L.; Wilson, J. B.; Wrightstone, R. N.; and Huisman, T. H. J.; "Hemoglobin Atlanta or $\alpha_2\beta_2^{75Leu\rightarrow Pro}$ (E19) an Unstable Variant Found in Several Members of a Caucasian Family". Biochim. Biophys. Acta, (1975), 386, 538.

40. Efremov, G. D.; Huisman, T. H. J.; Stanulovic, M.; Zurovec, M.; Duma, H.; Wilson, J. B.; and Jeremic, V.; "Hemoglobin M Saskatoon and Hemoglobin M Hyde Park in Two Yugoslavian Families". Scand. J. Haematol., (1974), 13, 48.

41. Schneider, R. G.; "Differentiation of Electrophoretically Similar Hemoglobins - Such as S, D, G, and P; or A_2, C, E, and O - by Electrophoresis of the Globin Chains". Clin. Chem., (1974), 20, 1111.

42. Vella, F.; Galbraith, P.; Wilson, J. B.; Wong, S. C.; Folger, G. C.; and Huisman, T. H. J.; "Hemoglobin St. Claude or $\alpha_2^{127(H10)}$ Lys→Thrβ_2". Biochim, Biophys. Acta., (1974), 365, 318.

43. Clegg, J. B.; Naughton, M. A.; and Weatherall, D. J.; "Abnormal Human Haemoglobins. Separation and Characterization of the α and β Chains by Chromatography, and the Determination of Two New Variants, Hb-Chesapeake and Hb-J-Bangkok". J. Mol. Biol., (1966), 19, 91.

44. Hirs, C. H. W.; "Performic Acid Oxidation", in "Methods in Enzymology", p. 197, Vol. XI, "Enzyme Structure", C. H. W. Hirs, Editor, Academic Press, New York, 1967.

45. Jones, R. T.; "Structural Studies of Aminoethylated

Hemoglobins by Automatic Peptide Chromatography". Cold
Spring Harbor Symp. Quant. Biol., (1964), 29, 297.

46.   Schroeder, W. A.; "Separation of Peptides by Chromatography
      on Columns of Dowex 1 with Volatile Developers", in
      "Methods in Enzymology", p. 214, Vol. XXV, "Enzyme
      Structure, Part B", C. H. W. Hirs and S. N. Timasheff,
      Editors, Academic Press, New York, 1972.

47.   Gray, R.; "Sequence Analysis with Dansyl Chloride", in
      "Methods in Enzymology", p. 333, Vol. XXV, "Enzyme
      Structure, Part B", C. H. W. Hirs and S. N. Timasheff,
      Editors, Academic Press, New York, 1972.

48.   Woods, R.; and Wang, Kung-Tsung; "Separation of Dansyl
      Amino Acids by Polyamide Layer Chromatography". Biochim.
      Biophys. Acta., (1967), 133, 369.

49.   White, J. M.; Brain, M. C.,; Lorkin, P. A.; Lehmann, H.;
      and Smith, M.; "Mild 'Unstable Haemoglobin Haemolytic
      Anemia' caused by Haemoglobin Shepherds Bush (β74 (E18)
      Gly$\rightarrow$Asp)". Nature, (1970), 225, 939.

Acknowledgment

Supported in part by U.S. Public Health Service Grants
HL-05168 and HL-15158.

Measurement of Calciotropic Hormones in Clinical Medicine

CLAUDE D. ARNAUD, JAMES A. FLUECK, and FRANCIS P. Di BELLA

Mineral Research Unit, Mayo Clinic, Rochester, Minn. 55901

Parathyroid Hormone (PTH)

Methodology. The radioimmunoassay of PTH is currently difficult to carry out. It requires meticulous attention to the vagaries of ^{131}I or ^{125}I labeling of the polypeptide, to its adsorption to glassware, to techniques of separation of bound and free $[^{131}I]$- or $[^{125}I]$-labeled PTH, and to nonspecific factors in serum which interfere with immune reactions. Extensive quality control measures are essential because of the clinical significance attached to increased values for PTH in serum by clinicians (i.e. recommending surgical exploration of the neck). Because of this latter important consideration, it is probably crucial for laboratories performing PTH radioimmunoassay for clinical purposes to maintain a consultation service to aid physicians in the interpretation of results.

The development of an individual assay for PTH requires great effort and dependence on chance. To provide a complete and competent service, it is important to have both an extremely sensitive assay, and also assays specific for amino terminal (NH_2-) and carboxyl terminal (COOH-) regions of the PTH molecule (see below). Sufficient human PTH is not available at the present time for even a single large immunization effort. Antisera must be produced with either bovine or porcine PTH with the hope of obtaining a high affinity cross reacting antiserum. Both bovine and procine PTH (crude extracts) are extremely expensive unless extraction and purification is done in individual laboratories, and procedures available for the latter are time consuming and difficult. The commercial availability of "good" bovine PTH for labeling is limited and only a few research laboratories have preparations of standard human PTH.

It is hoped that current work being carried out on the amino acid sequence of human PTH (1-4) will be successful, so that synthetic preparations of important regions of the hormone can become commercially available. This would partially solve some of the reagent problems. Although large programs for the collection of human parathyroid adenomas and hyperplastic glands are ongoing for the purpose of obtaining sufficient human PTH for complete amino acid sequence analysis, the availability of this tissue is clearly the central, rate-limiting problem in making progress in chemically characterizing human PTH; the expansion of gland collection efforts is important.

Circulating Immunoreactive PTH (iPTH) and Different Uses of NH2- and COOH-Specific Assays. The major secretory product of parathyroid tissue is the native 9,500 M.W. polypeptide (5), although it is possible that fragments of this molecule are secreted also (6,7). Once secreted, the 9,500 M.W. PTH is metabolized into amino terminal and carboxyl terminal fragments (8). In fact, the COOH fragments predominate over the 9,500 M.W. PTH in the circulation to the extent of 5:1 to 20:1 (7,9,10). This predominance is probably due to the long survival time of COOH-fragments in serum (hours) as compared with the 9,500 M.W. PTH (minutes) (11,12). The 9,500 M.W. PTH and its synthetic (bovine), amino terminal, (1-34) polypeptide are biologically active, but its carboxyl terminal region is biologically inert (13).

These relationships are confirmed by direct measurements on serum, using assays, which are specific for either "NH2-PTH" or "COOH-PTH". Concentrations of COOH-iPTH are 5-20 times higher than NH2-iPTH (9-10). However, the clinical utility of the two assays differs markedly (4,10,14). Assays specific for "COOH-PTH" are superior to "NH2" assays in assessing the chronic state of parathyroid function and conversely, "NH2" assays are superior to "COOH" assays in assessing the acute secretory status of the parathyroid glands as well as in the demonstration of step-up changes in iPTH levels in serum samples obtained during differential venous catheterization of the neck and mediastinum for localization of hyperfunctioning parathyroid tissue. Although the reasons for these differences are not entirely clear, they are probably related to the marked differences in the survival times of 9,500 M.W. PTH and -COOH fragments in the circulation and to the fact that the major secretory product of parathyroid tissue is the 9,500 M.W. species of PTH.

In a practical sense, routine fasting serum samples are examined in our laboratory using a very sensitive COOH-specific PTH assay (antiserum GP 1M, guinea pig anti-porcine PTH). It distinguishes between normal and hyperparathyroid individuals with 90% efficiency, and patients with primary hyperparathyroidism (HPT) and ectopic hyperparathyroidism due to non-parathyroid cancer (EHPT) with 80% efficiency; iPTH values are lower for a given degree of hypercalcemia in EHPT than in HPT because, in general, the quantity of COOH fragments in the serum of EHPT patients is lower (15,16,17). Additionally, the COOH-specific assay yields low or undetectable values in hypercalcemia of nonparathyroid origin (i.e., sarcoid, vitamin D intoxication, and hyperthyroidism).

On the other hand, serum samples obtained during provocative and suppression tests of parathyroid function by means of differential venous cateterization of the neck and mediastinum are examined with a very sensitive NH_2-specific assay (antiserum CH 14M, chicken anti-bovine PTH). Unfortunately, we do not yet know how to interpret provocative and stimulation tests in patients with hyperparathyroidism with respect to determining the degree of autonomy of hyperfunctioning parathyroid tissue. Using NH_2-specific assays, serum iPTH increases with induced hypocalcemia and decreases variably with induced hypercalcemia in patients with parathyroid adenoma. We are currently carring out systematic comparative studies of "COOH" and "NH_2" assays of sera obtained during stimulation and suppression of serum iPTH levels in normal individuals and patients with either primary parathyroid adenoma or hyperplasia. It is hoped that significant differences will be observed which will allow the separation of normals from patients with mild hyperparathyroidism as well as the preoperative separation of patients with parathyroid adenoma and parathyroid hyperplasia.

Calcitonin (CT)

Methodology. Several radioimmunoassays of human calcitonin (hCT) have been developed in the past 5 years (18-20). Their greatest utility has been in the definitive diagnosis of patients with medullary carcinoma of the thyroid gland (MTC) and, recently, in identifying family members of these patients who have occult MTC.

Synthetic hCT is not commercially available now. Most assays have been developed by using hormone supplied as gifts from the CIBA-Geigy Co., Basel, Switzerland for ^{131}I or ^{125}I labeling, immunization and standards although several useful antisera have been produced by immunization with crude extracts of medullary carcinoma tissue.

Utility. There is general agreement that the concentration of immunoreactive CT in normal serum is extremely low (< 200 pg/ml). However, there is evidence for immunoheterogeneity of calcitonin in the serum of MTC patients (21) and it is possible that studies in the future will demonstrate this phenomenon in normal sera as well. This might explain some reports of higher concentrations of immunoreactive CT in normal subjects (22).

Basal values for serum immunoreactive CT in patients with overt MTC are almost always increased above 1000 pg/ml, and relatively insensitive assays are capable of measuring these levels. However, many MTC patients' relatives with occult MTC have values below 100 pg/ml (20 pg/tube if serum concentrations in incubation mixtures are 20%). This is particularly true when systematic examination of family members of a patient with proved MTC with provocative testing is anticipated since some of these family members may have normal basal concentrations (23).

Provocative testing has centered on the ability of calcium infusion and pentagastrin administration to increase serum immunoreactive hCT. With most assays, increases in immunoreactive CT greater than 500 pg/ml are not observed in normal subjects with either of these secretagogues; increases above this level are generally considered to be consistent with the presence of MTC and sufficient evidence (especially in a family member) to recommend thyroidectomy. Recently, the preliminary results of a systematic comparison between the calcium infusion and pentagastrin test in 4 patients with proved MTC were reported by Sizemore and Go (24). Although further studies will be required, the data suggested that the pentagastrin test produces more definitive increases in immunoreactive hCT and has the advantage of eliciting much earlier responses (1-5 minutes for pentagastrin vs. 1-5 hours for calcium infusion).

Vitamin D and Metabolites

Methodology. Vitamin D, a sterol, occurs naturally in plants as vitamin D_2 (ergocalciferol) and is produced by ultraviolet irradiation of ergosterol. In man vitamin D_3 (cholecalciferol), the natural form of the vitamin, is produced by ultraviolet irradiation of 7-dehydrocholesterol in the skin. The fact that vitamin D_2 is a major food additive and the over-the-counter therapeutic form of vitamin D produces a serious problem in evaluating endogenous vitamin D_3 and its metabolites in human serum. Available ligand binding assay techniques generally fail to distinguish between D_2 and D_3; special chromatographic techniques (long column, 60 Cm, Sephadex LH-20) are required to do this (25).

Vitamin D_3 enters the skin microcirculation after formation and is bound to a specific globulin in the serum. It and vitamin D_2 which is absorbed from the gut are subsequently metabolized to the 25-hydroxy derivative (25-OH-D) in the liver by an enzyme system which may or may not be regulated. The subsequent release of 25-OH-D from the liver is not well understood. There is evidence that it is secreted into the bile and subsequently reabsorbed by the intestine. The relative importance of this "enterohepatic" process and the release of this metabolite directly into the circulation from the liver is not known (26). It is clear however, that 25-OH-D_3 is the major circulating metabolite of vitamin D_3. It circulates almost completely bound to a specific serum globulin.

The methods now used to measure 25-OH-D are competitive protein-ligand binding assays that use either serum globulin (diluted rat serum) (27,28) or a vitamin D-deficient rat kidney cytosol preparation (29,30) as binding proteins, crystaline 25-OH-D$_3$ as standard and ^{3}H-25-OH-D$_3$ as radioactive ligand. Both methods require that the serum or plasma be extracted (after addition of ^{3}H-25-OH-D$_3$ for recovery and marker purposes) with either chloroform-methanol or ether and that the extracts be chromatographed on silicic acid or Sephadex LH-20 columns. The column fractions containing previously added ^{3}H-25-OH-D are dried over N$_2$, taken up in ethanol, and assayed. Recovery of labeled or stable 25-OH-D is 65-85%.

The sensitivity of these competitive binding assays for 25-OH-D$_3$ (0.1 - 0.5 ng) is sufficient for the measurement of the large quantities of this metabolite circulating in serum in normal subjects (range 11-55 ng/ml, mean 27 ng/ml).

The 25-OH-D is further metabolized in the kidney to 1,25 dihydroxycholecalciferol (1,25(OH)$_2$D) which is considered to be the major physiologically important, tissue-active metabolite of vitamin D. It circulates in extremely low concentrations (< 100 pg/ml of serum). Assay of 1,25(OH)$_2$D is extremely tedious. It is done by competitive binding technique using a combined intestinal cell cytosol and chromatin binding system, biosynthetic ^{3}H-1,25(OH)$_2$D$_3$ as labeled ligand and synthetic 1,25(OH)$_2$D$_3$ as standard (31).

Utility. Insufficient data is available on the measurement of 1,25(OH)$_2$D$_3$ for evaluation of its utility in clinical medicine. A major breakthrough in methodology will be needed before routine application will be possible. This could come with the development of a battery of radioimmunoassays for the measurement of all of the vitamin D metabolites. So far, however, the development of antibodies to vitamin D and its metabolites has been limited by apparently irreversable changes in the important B ring of the sterol which occur during its conjugation to immunogenic proteins.

The basic clinical tool used at the present time is the competitive ligand binding assay for 25-OH-D. Although concentrations are low in the serum of patients with osteomalacia and vitamin D deficiency rickets, we have recently noted the interesting paradox that levels can be only 1/2 normal in the face of overt bone disease (32). This had led us to propose that substrate levels of 25-OH-D$_3$ available to the hydroxylase in kidney which is responsible for the conversion of 25-OH-D$_3$ to the tissue active metabolite, 1,25(OH)$_2$D$_3$, may be rate limiting for this enzyme.

One of the major problems in the treatment of patients with vitamin D compounds (i.e., patients with hypoparathyroidism) has been the unpredictable development of hypercalcemia and the syndrome of vitamin D intoxication. Although this problem may become less serious when some of the faster-acting metabolites and analogues of metabolites of vitamin D become available for clinical use, it is likely that monitoring of serum levels of

25-OH-D3 may prove to be helpful in anticipating overdosage.
However, systematic studies which correlate vitamin D dosage,
25-OH-D3 serum concentrations, and serum calcium in patients such
as these, have not yet been reported.

<u>Literature Cited</u>

1. Brewer, H. B.; Fairwell, T.; Ronan, R.; Sizemore, G. W.;
    Arnaud, C. D.; "Human Parathyroid Hormone: Amino-Acid
    Sequence of the Amino-Terminal Residues 1-34". Proc. Natl.
    Acad. Sci. USA, (1972), <u>69</u>, 3585-3588.
2. Niall, H. D.; Sauer, R. T.; Jacobs, J. W.; Keutmann, H. T.;
    Segre, G. V.; O'Riordan, J. L. H.; Aurbach, G. D.; Potts,
    J. T. Jr.; "The Amino-Acid Sequence of the Amino-Terminal
    37 Residues of Human Parathyroid Hormone". Proc. Natl.
    Acad. Sci. USA, (1974), <u>71</u>, 384-388.
3. Brewer, H. B.; Fairwell, T.; Rittel, W.; Littledike, T.;
    Arnaud, C. D.; "Recent Studies on the Chemistry of Human,
    Bovine and Porcine Parathyroid Hormones". Am. J. Med.
    (1974), <u>56</u>, 759-766.
4. Arnaud, C. D.; Brewer, H. B. Jr.; "Parathyroid Hormone:
    Structure and Immunoheterogeneity" in "Methods in Radio-
    immunoassay, Toxicology and Related Areas". Progress in
    Analytical Chemistry, pp. 45-75, Vol. 8, Simmons, I. L. and
    Ewing, G. W., Editors, Plenum Press, New York and London,
    1974.
5. Habener, J. F.; Powell, D.; Murray, T. M.; Mayer, G. P.;
    Potts, J. T. Jr.; "Parathyroid Hormone: Secretion and
    Metabolism in Vivo". Proc. Natl. Acad. Sci. USA, (1971),
    <u>68</u>, 2986-2991.
6. Arnaud, C. D.; Sizemore, G. W.; Oldham, S. B.; Fischer,
    J. A.; Tsao, H. S.; Littledike, T.; "Human Parathyroid
    Hormone: Glandular and Secreted Molecular Species". Am. J.
    Med. (1971), <u>50</u>, 630-638.
7. Silverman, R.; Yalow, R. S.; "Heterogeneity of Parathyroid
    Hormone: Clinical and Physiologic Implications". J. Clin.
    Invest. (1973), <u>52</u>, 1958-1971.
8. Segre, G. V.; Niall, H. D.; Habener, J. F.; Potts, J. T. Jr.;
    "Metabolism of Parathyroid Hormone: Physiologic and Clinical
    Significance". Am. J. Med. (1974), <u>56</u>, 774.
9. Segre, G. V.; Habener, J. F.; Powell, D.; Tregear, G. W.;
    Potts, J. T. Jr.; "Parathyroid Hormone in Human Plasma:
    Immunochemical Characterization and Biological Implications".
    J. Clin. Invest. (1972), <u>51</u>, 3163-3172.
10. Arnaud, C. D.; Goldsmith, R. S.; Bordier, P. J.; Sizemore,
    G. W.; Larsen, J. A.; Gilkinson, J.; "Influence of Immuno-
    heterogeneity of Circulating Parathyroid Hormone on the
    Results of Radioimmunoassays of Serum in Man". Am. J. Med.
    (1974), <u>56</u>, 785-793.
11. Canterbury, J. M.; Riess, R.; "Multiple Immunoreactive

Molecular Forms of Parathyroid Hormone in Human Serum".
Proc. Soc. Exp. Biol. Med. (1972), 140, 1393-1398.

12. Goldsmith, R. S.; Furszyfer, J.; Johnson, W. J.; Fournier,
A. E.; Sizemore, G. W.; Arnaud, C. D.; "Etiology of Hyper-
parathyroidism and Bone Disease During Chronic Hemodialysis.
III. Evaluation of Parathyroid Suppressability". J. Clin.
Invest. (1973), 52, 173-180.

13. Potts, J. T. Jr.; Keutman, H. T.; Niall, H. D.; Tregear,
G. W.; Habener, J. F.; O'Riordan, J. L. H.; Murray, T. M.;
Powell, D.; Aurbach, G. D.; "Parathyroid Hormone: Chemical
and Immunochemical Studies of the Active Molecular Species"
in "Endocrinology 1971" (Proceedings of the Third International Symposium), pp. 333-349, Taylor, S., Editor,
William Heinemann, London, 1972.

14. Arnaud, C. D.; "Parathyroid Hormone: Coming of Age in
Clinical Medicine". Am. J. Med. (1973), 55, 577-581.

15. Riggs, B. L.; Arnaud, C. D.; Reynolds, J. C.; Smith, L. H.;
"Immunologic Differentiation of Primary Hyperparathyroidism
From Hyperparathyroidism Due to Nonparathyroid Cancer".
J. Clin. Invest. (1971), 50, 2079-2083.

16. Benson, R. C.; Riggs, B. L.; Pickard, B. M.; Arnaud, C. D.;
"Radioimmunoassay of Parathyroid Hormone in Hypercalcemic
Patients With Malignant Disease". Am. J. Med. (1974), 56,
821.

17. Benson, R. C.; Riggs, B. L.; Pickard, B. M.; Arnaud, C. D.;
"Immunoreactive Forms of Circulating Parathyroid Hormone in
Primary and Ectopic Hyperparathyroidism". J. Clin. Invest.
(1974), 54, 175-181.

18. Tashjian, A. H. Jr.; Howland, B. G.; Melvin, K. E. W.;
Hill, C. S. Jr.; "Immunoassay of Human Calcitonin: Clinical
Measurement, Relation to Serum Calcium and Studies in
Patients With Medullary Carcinoma". N. Engl. J. Med. (1970),
283, 890-895.

19. Deftos, L. J.; "Immunoassay of Human Calcitonin, I Method".
Metabolism (1971), 20, 1122.

20. Sizemore, G. W.; Go, V. L. W.; Kaplan, E. L.; Sanzenbacher,
L. J.; Holtermuller, K. H.; Arnaud, C. D.; "Relations of
Calcitonin and Gastrin in the Zollinger-Ellison Syndrome and
Medullary Carcinoma of the Thyroid". N. Engl. J. Med.
(1973), 288, 641-644.

21. Sizemore, G. W.; Heath, H. III; "Immunochemical Hetero-
geneity of Calcitonin in Plasma of Patients With Medullary
Carcinoma of the Thyroid". J. Clin. Invest. (1975), In
Press.

22. Sanman, N. A.; Hill, C. S. Jr.; Beceiro, J. R.; Schultz,
P. N.; "Immunoreactive Calcitonin in the Thyroid and in
Maternal and Cord Serum". J. Lab. Clin. Med. (1973), 81,
671.

23. Melvin, K. E. W.; Miller, H. H.; Tashjian, A. H. Jr.;
"Early Diagnosis of Medullary Carcinoma of the Thyroid Gland

By Means of Calcitonin Assay". N. Engl. J. Med. (1971), 285, 1115-1120.

24. Sizemore, G. W.; Go, V. L. W.; "Stimulation Tests For Diagnosis of Medullary Carcinoma". Mayo Clin. Proc. (1975), 50, 53-56.

25. Haddad, J. G.; Hahn, T. J.; "Natural and Synthetic Sources of Circulating 25-Hydroxyvitamin D in Man". Nature (1973), 244, 515-517.

26. Arnaud, S. B.; Goldsmith, R. S.; Lambert, P.; Go, V. L. W.; "25-Hydroxyvitamin D3: Evidence of an Enterohepatic Circulation in Man". Proc. Soc. Exp. Biol. and Med., In Press.

27. Belsey, R.; De Luca, H. F.; Potts, J. T. Jr.; "Competitive Binding Assay for Vitamin D and 25-OH-Vitamin D". J. Clin. Endocrinol. Metab. (1971), 33, 554-558.

28. Belsey, R.; Clark, M. B.; Bernat, M.; Nold, J.; Holick, M. F., De Luca, H. F.; Potts, J. T. Jr.; "The Physiologic Significance of Plasma Transport of Vitamin D and Metabolites". Am. J. Med. (1974), 57, 50-56.

29. Haddad, J. G.; Chuy, K. J.; "Competitive Protein-Binding Radioassay for 25-Hydroxycholecalciferol". J. Clin. Endocrinol. Metab. (1971), 33, 992-995.

30. Haddad, J. G.; Stamp. T. C. B.; "Circulating 25-Hydroxyvitamin D in Man". Am. J. Med. (1974), 57, 57-62.

31. Brumbaugh, P. F.; Haussler, D. H.; Bressler, R. Houssler, M. R.; "Radioreceptor Assay for 1α25-Dihydroxyvitamin D3". Science (1973), 183, 1089-1091.

32. Arnaud, S. B.; Arnaud, C. D.; Bordier, P. J.; Goldsmith, R. S.; Flueck, J. A.; "The Interrelationships Between Vitamin D and Parathyroid Hormone in Disorders of Mineral Metabolism in Man" (Proceedings of 2nd Vitamin D Symposium), Weisbaden, West Germany, Oct., 1974, In Press.

Supported in Part by Grants from the NIH (AM 12302 and CA 11911) and from the Mayo Foundation.

Practical Concepts of Competitive Protein Binding Assays

LAWRENCE J. CROLLA[1] and EDWARD W. BERMES, JR.

Departments of Pathology and Biochemistry and Biophysics,
Loyola University Medical Center, Maywood, Ill. 60153

The terminology used in the field of competitive protein binding procedures has become very complex and may be confusing for a newcomer in this area. It will therefore be necessary to define a few of the commonly used terms.

Antigens may be defined as substances which, when injected into an animal, will elicit an immunologic response resulting in the production of antibodies. Molecules with a molecular weight less than 10,000 usually will not elicit such a response. An example of this type of compound would be cortisol. To make cortisol antigenic it is coupled to albumin thereby resulting in a complex with a molecular weight greater than 10,000. When this complex is injected into an animal, antibodies that will bind to cortisol will be produced. In this case, cortisol is termed a hapten, that is, a molecule which on its own cannot elicit the production of antibodies but which can react with certain preformed antibodies. The term ligand may be used as a general term to include both antigens and haptens.

Antibodies are a group of serum proteins called gamma globulins or immunoglobulins, that are produced by an animal in response to exposure to foreign substances (antigens). The antibody molecules produced will react in vitro with a great degree of specificity towards the antigens. However, some substances structurally similar to the antigen that originally produced the antibodies may also react with them. This is termed a cross-reaction. For example, the antibodies produced against insulin will cross-react with proinsulin.

Radioimmunoassay is a competitive protein binding assay which utilizes an antibody as the binding protein. This assay also employs a highly purified antigen which has been radio-labeled (tagged).

[1] Present address: Department of Pathology, Columbus-Cuneo-Cabrini Medical Center, 2520 N. Lakeview, Chicago, Ill. 60614

Radioassay is a competitive protein binding assay which employs a natural binding protein instead of an antibody. For example, transcortin is the binding protein for cortisol in nature and also in the radioassay procedure for cortisol.

Titre is a term used to express the strength of an antiserum. Thus, an antiserum with a high titre would indicate that it would be able to be diluted and used to perform a large number of assays.

Sensitivity may be defined as the lowest concentration of the material being assayed that can be distinguished from zero concentration.

Specificity may be defined as the freedom from interferences by substances other than those intended to be measured.

Principle (1,2)

The basic theory of competitive protein binding assays employing a radioactive label is as follows:

P = Material to be measured

P* = Radioactive label of this material

Q = Binding protein (natural binding protein or antibody, depending on the assay).

Combining components P & Q and P* and Q in equal quantities yields:

$$P + Q \rightleftharpoons PQ \qquad\qquad (1)$$

$$P* + Q \rightleftharpoons P*Q \qquad\qquad (2)$$

Thus, it can be seen that by adding P or P* to Q individually, a complex PQ or P*Q is obtained. By combining both P and P* with Q simultaneously the following situtation obtains:

$$P + P* + Q \rightleftharpoons PQ \,\&\, P*Q \qquad (3)$$

In this one reaction both PQ and P*Q are generated simultaneously. These complexes can be referred to as either the bound fraction of P or P*. However in radioassay and radioimmunoassay techniques, the concern is with the bound fraction of P* (i.e., P*Q), since it is this complex that is measured. If a fixed amount of Q and P* is used and the amount of Q is adjusted so that it can only bind 50% of the P* added, the following equilibrium is obtained:

$$P + P* + Q \rightleftharpoons PQ + P*Q + P + P* \quad (4)$$

This equation illustrates the components of a competitive protein binding assay system. That is, the reaction system contains both radioactive and non-radioactive free ligand (P* and P) and both radioactive and non-radioactive protein bound ligand (P*Q and PQ). This type of assay assumes that binding protein will have the same affinity for the labeled or non-labeled material that is being measured. Although this assumption is not always completely valid, it usually causes no problems of consequence with most radioassays or radioimmunoassays.

In order to obtain reproducible results, near equilibrium must be established in the reagent system. This is usually accomplished by combining the material to be measured with the binding protein under fixed conditions. The time required to achieve this equilibrium may vary from several hours to days depending on the system used (3,4).

After the addition of the non-radioactive material, the labeled material is added to the mixture and the mixture allowed to proceed toward equilibrium. In equilibrium analysis the order of addition of reagents is not critical as long as sufficient time is allowed for establishing equilibrium of the complete mixture (3,4).

Furthermore, from equation (4) it can be seen that when the amount of P* and Q are fixed, the more P added the smaller will be the quantity P*Q. Therefore, if various known amounts of P are added and P*Q is measured in a suitable counter, the relationship between radioactivity and concentration of P can be established. From this a standard curve can be drawn and used to determine the amount of P in an unknown solution.

In order to quantitate P*Q by counting, it must be separated from the reagent mixture so that it can be counted in the absence of free P*.

Separation Techniques

Four types of techniques for separating the bound fraction P*Q from the reagent mixture are in common usage, loosely termed: double antibody, solid phase, charcoal adsorption and solution precipitation. The first type is used with radioimmunoassay methods specifically, while the other three types can be used with both radioassay and radioimmunoassay methods.

In the double antibody method of separation, a second antibody, produced by injecting the first antibody into another animal, is utilized. This antibody is used to combine with and form an insoluble complex with the first antibody. After allowing sufficient time for the precipitation reaction, separation of the precipitate from the reagent mixture is accomplished by centrifugation and decantation or aspiration of the supernatant. Although this method of separation is the most specific, a problem arises here in that the precipitate is of low density, thus requiring a minimum centrifugal force of about 2500 to 3000 x g to achieve separation. In addition, the centrifugation should be performed in the cold since heat tends to break up antibody complexes.

In the solid phase type of separation the antibody or binding protein is bound to an inert material such as Sephadex or glass beads yet is still free to react with the ligand. Once equilibrium in the reagent mixture is attained, centrifugation in a common laboratory centrifuge, followed by decantation of the supernatant is all that is required for separation of bound and free label.

The precipitation method of separation involves the addition of salts such as ammonium sulfate or solvents such as polyethylene glycol to the reagent mixture to cause precipitation of the large molecular weight bound species. These methods of precipitation lack specificity and work well only when there is a large difference between the molecular weight of the material being measured and that of the bound complex of it.

A fourth separation technique employs charcoal. Charcoal has adsorption characteristics such that most organic molecules will adhere to its surface. However, charcoal is also very porous, thereby allowing smaller molecules to enter into its pores and become trapped in them. The charcoal is first coated with dextran or hemoglobin which covers its outer surface. Since both of these compounds are very large they cannot enter the pores, thus the pores are still free to hold small molecules. When the coated charcoal is added to the assay reagent mixture, the free (unbound) material is adsorbed while the larger bound fraction is not. Final separation is accomplished by centrifugation and decantation of the supernatant.

In the first three methods of separation discussed, the bound label has been contained in the precipitate and it is this radioactivity which is measured in the assay. In the charcoal method, the bound label fraction is in the supernatant and thus it is the supernatant which is counted. From a theoretical point of view the best method of separation is the double antibody method due to its specificity. However, because of the need for a high capacity refrigerated centrifuge, this method is not used as commonly as would be expected. The most convenient type of separation from an operational point of view is the solid phase technique. This type of separation also has a good degree of specificity because of the fact that the binding protein is the only material attached to the solid material which may then be separated by centrifugation. This method is limited, however, by the technology needed to attach

the binding proteins to the solid material in a workable form.
The other two types of separation procedures can be used
adequately after some experience; however, they are prone to
other problems and are not as specific as the double antibody
or solid phase separation methods. There are, however, a great
many commercially available kits utilizing charcoal separation
and one should therefore become familiar with this technique
and its problems. The coated charcoal can lose its adsorption
properties after a period of time in solution, and one has to
be extremely careful in making sure that the charcoal suspension
is kept homogeneous so that a uniform amount is dispensed to
the assay mixture.

Standard Curves

After separating the bound label from the free label and
counting the former in a gamma or beta counter depending upon
the isotope used, a standard curve is plotted. The standard
curve may be presented in a number of ways. The most common
forms of presentation are shown in Figures 1 and 2. These
are, in Figure 1, a plot of the percent bound vs. log of the
concentration (dose) of a series of standards. Percent bound
may be represented as B/B_0, B being defined as the ligand bound
at any concentration of standard and B_0 defined as the zero
dose tube, that is the tube that contains no non-radioactive
ligand. This form of data expression is referred to as a plot
of B/B_0 vs log dose, and yields a sigmoid shaped curve. In
doing an assay the values for B/B_0 are determined for each
standard and unknown and then the standard curve is plotted.
The concentration of the unknown is then read off the standard
curve opposite its B/B_0 value. This sigmoid shaped standard
curve, because of its linear portion, simplifies data handling.
A mathematical transform of the B/B_0 vs log dose is shown in
Figure 2.   This logit of B/B_0 vs log dose is a widely used
method of standard curve presentation (5,6,7). Logit B/B_0
is defined as follows:

$$\text{logit } (B/B_0) = \ln \ (B/B_0)/(1 - B/B_0)$$

This latter transform is used to linearize the usual sigmoid
curve produced in plotting B/B_0 vs log dose. This transform
may be accomplished by using a computer, logit paper or a table
of logit values.

Counting Equipment

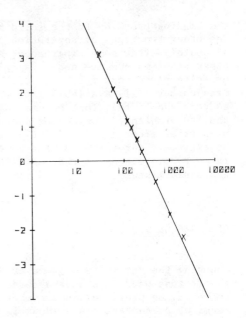

Figure 1. Plot of the percent bound vs. log of the concentration of a series of standards (dose)

LOGIT VS LOG CONCENTRATION

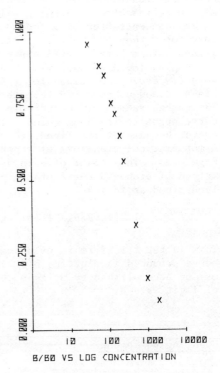

Figure 2. Mathematical transformation of the B/B₀ vs. log dose

B/B0 VS LOG CONCENTRATION

The counting equipment used to establish quantitation is
radioassay and radioimmunoassays may be either a gamma counter
or a liquid scintillation counter depending upon the isotope
being used. Most assays use ^{125}I as a label and require a
gamma counter; however, a few of the steroid hormones are
tritium labeled and require a liquid scintillation counter.
If only one counter can be purchased, then a gamma counter is
the instrument of choice since most assays are now performed
with gamma emitting isotopes. Table I lists the isotopes in
common usage for competitive protein binding assays.

There are several manufacturers of counting equipment and
most manufacturers will be able to supply manual, semi-auto-
matic or completely automatic counting equipment.

With a manual counter each tube has to be positioned by
hand. This system would be used for low volume or small batch
sized assays. The decision most people have to make is whether
to get a counter capable of counting only 100 tubes or counters
capable of handling 300 to 500 samples. With the 100 tube
counters usually a lister printer is included which places the
printout on adding machine tape with the tube number next to
it. This type of instrument is suitable for a laboratory that
is involved in a limited number of assays, say 3 or 4 at the
most. The reasons are that counting time can be slow since
the changing cycle, that is the time to go from one sample to
the next, is not always fast on these instruments. Another
factor is that the efficiency of these small counters may not
be as reliable as the more expensive counters, therefore, requiring more counting time per sample to acquire good counting
statistics. Finally, a lister printer is used which necessi-
tates manual data handling. This usually means that even blank
tube counts must be subtracted by hand from each sample tube
count. In the larger counter, printout is via a teletype with
a paper tape punch. These counters are usually very efficient
and have fast sample changing times. They usually can automatically subtract out background and most can even give you the
dose response factor, B/B_0, as the print out, thereby eliminating the need to calculate this.

Data Handling

After counting the samples and obtaining a printout from
the counter the data must be arranged into a standard curve
of some type from which patient results can be determined.
In order to do this, a simple calculator may be used to aid
in the mathematical manipulations. A desktop computer into
which the data is entered may be used to generate a standard
curve automatically along with the unknown values which are
automatically read from the curve. If a paper tape print out

TABLE I

COMMON ISOTOPES USED IN

COMPETITIVE PROTEIN BINDING ASSAYS

Nuclide	Half Life	Type of Emmission
$^{125}_{53}I$	60 d	γ
$^{3}_{1}H$	12.3 y	β
$^{57}_{27}Co$	270 d	γ
$^{75}_{34}Se$	120 d	γ

is available from the teletype output of the counter, data handling is made even easier in that the tape can be read by a
tape reader and fed automatically into the computer. This eliminates the time it takes to enter numbers manually. The only
other consideration is whether to keep the computer on line
with the counter and eliminate the paper tape. This system
is predicated only if a counter is running continually day and
night since the cost of the computer itself is approximately
the same, whether on line or off line. By being on line the
computer can be used for nothing else in the laboratory.

Miscellaneous Equipment

Besides counting equipment, automatic pipettes and dilutors
are also needed in doing competitive protein binding assays.
These can range from a manual pipetter ($\simeq \$65$), semi-automatic
dilutor-pipetter ($\simeq \$2,000$) or fully automatic diluting-pipetting
station ($\simeq \$18,000$). When only a few assays, consisting of
a small number of samples, are run in a laboratory, the manual
type pipette can be used. When several different assays of
between 10 and 25 patients per assay are being done, the semi-
automated pipettes are time saving and enhance precision. The
fully automated pipette stations are recommended if the number
of samples run is very large. If it is not, the time and inconvenience of cleaning these systems between runs and of using
a large amount of reagent to prime them tends to preclude their
use.

Assay Set Up

Assays are usually set up according to the instructions
provided with the reagents. These directions are usually very
detailed and should be referred to in establishing an assay.
However, the following illustrates the most common type of assay
and may be helpful in explaining some of the various nomenclature
used in the field of competitive protein binding assays.

1. Total activity tubes: These tubes contain only
   the isotope used in the assay in the same volume
   as that in each of the remaining tubes of the
   assay. These tubes are run to assess total
   activity (T) used in the assay and to determine
   $B_0/T \times 100$ which usually should be between 35%
   and 50% in order to assure that the assay has
   a useable sensitivity.

2. NSB (non-specific binding) tubes: These tubes con-
    tain all reagents except the binding protein. They
    will therefore show those counts that cause an
    error in that they are due to free label being
    counted as bound.

3. Zero dose tubes (B_0): These tubes contain all com-
    ponents except unlabeled material being assayed.

4. Finally, tubes for the standard curve are followed
    by the quality control tubes and the unknown tubes.

The background for each particular system should be determined periodically. This can be accomplished by counting an
empty tube overnight in the counter and then by determining
the counts per minute. This background is then substracted
from all tubes before any calculations are performed.

In evaluating different assay systems it is convenient
to use a table of B/B_0 vs dose. By comparing these values for
different assays a comparison of the sensitivity of the assay
can be made. Thus an insulin assay with 50% binding at a concentration of 40 microunits would show much more sensitivity
than an assay with a 50% binding occuring at 100 microunits,
since the more the dose is lowered, the greater the percent
binding becomes.

Isotope Safety (8)

Since the amount of radiation present in most radioassay
methods is quite small, relatively few special precautions are
needed. The basic factors to be kept in mind in dealing with
isotopes are time, distance and shielding. The isotope storage
should be located as far from personnel as possible. Radiation
can be reduced by proper shielding. Normally gamma sources
exceeding 10 μCi are packaged in small lead containers and
should be kept in these containers except when material is being
withdrawn. Each laboratory should have an isotope safety officer
who has the responsibility of knowing and enforcing the safety
rules which will vary with the type and amount of isotope used.
This person would be responsible for monitoring the radiation
areas with a portable radiation detector (Geiger Mueller Counter).
Radiation workers who are working with gamma emitters or with
beta emitters having a maximum energy greater than 0.2 Mev should
wear film badges (these badges are provided by various companies). This badge is a sealed photographic film to measure
exposure to ionizing radiation. The badges are then sent to
the company and the exposure in rems is calculated and reported
each month.

Disposal of Radioactive Waste

The level of radioactivity encountered in the usual radio-immunoassay procedures is low enough so that liquid wastes may be disposed of in the sink with running water. In calculating the amount of radioactive material that may be disposed of via the sewage system from one building, one must know the water usage. This may be obtained from the water bill. The allowable quantity of ^{125}I in sewage is 4.0×10^{-5} μ Ci/ml of water usage. This is equal to 1.13 μ Ci per cubic foot of water usage.

Radioisotope Licensing:

This rule varies from state to state. Some materials are exempt from Nuclear Regulatory Commission or State licensing requirements. Most institutions already have an institutional license which would specify the safety officer. It would be well for the clinical chemistry laboratory to check with this individual before beginning to use radioactive materials. If there is no license, many manufacturers of isotope materials will assist the laboratory in obtaining the proper license.

Conclusion

While much care has to be used in performing competitive protein binding assays, most well-equipped and staffed clinical laboratories should have no serious problem in undertaking such assays. The biggest problem that may be encountered is the selection of a dependable and reliable manufacturer for reagents. Problems that may arise are non-purity of standards and label non-specificity of antibodies or the inability to maintain any of these characteristics from lot to lot. It therefore is a good practice to evaulate a few manufacturers before selecting one for routine use.

Literature Cited

1. Besch, P.K.; Clinical Radioassay Procedures: A Compendium. AACC (1975).
2. Odiell, W. D.; and Daughaday, W.; Principles of Competitive Protein-Binding Assays. J. B. Lippincott (1971).
3. Zettner, A.; Principles of Competitive Binding Assays (Saturation Analyses) I Equilibrium Techniques. Clin. Chem. (1973), 19, 699.
4. Zettner, A; and Duly, P.; Principles of Competitive Binding

      Assays (Saturation Analyses) II Sequential Saturation.
      Clin. Chem. (1974), 20, 5.
5.   Rodbard, D. et al.; Statistical Quality Control of
      Radioimmunoassays. J. Clin. Endocrinol. and Metab. (1968),
      28, 1412.
6.   Rodbard, D.; Statistical Quality Control and Routine Data
      Processing for Radioimmunoassays and Immunoradiometric
      Assays. Clin. Chem. (1974), 20, 1255.
7.   Rodgers, R. C.; Radioimmunoassay Theory for Health Care
      Professionals. Hewlett Packard (1974).
8.   Bermes, E.W., Jr.; and Forman, D.T.; "Basic Laboratory
      Principles and Procedure" Fundamentals of Clinical Chemistry,
      2nd ed., pp. 1-59, N.W. Tietz (ed.), W. B. Saunders,
      Philadelphia (1976).

Supported in part by a NIH Research Training Grant in Clinical
Chemistry 5 TO1 GM02122-02.

Prenatal Detection of Genetic Diseases

CHARLES J. EPSTEIN

Department of Pediatrics, University of California, San Francisco, Calif. 94143

Perhaps the most important development in the general area of genetic counseling in the past several years has been the development of techniques for the prenatal diagnosis of genetic diseases. These techniques have made it possible to convert genetic counseling from an essentially passive endeavor to one in which the counselors and parents, working together, can take steps to alter the genetic risks to which the latter are exposed (1). This discussion, which will deal with the broad aspects of prenatal diagnosis, will be divided into two parts. The first will constitute a general background and theoretical introduction to the subject, while the second will describe the experience which we and others have had in the application of the various techniques of prenatal diagnosis. For further background and detail, the reader is referred to several other recent reviews of the subject (2-6).

As the name implies, the objective of making a prenatal diagnosis of a genetic disease is to determine whether a fetus believed to be at risk for having some genetic disease actually does have that disorder. For the most part the information which is obtained is used by the parents to decide whether they wish to continue the pregnancy or have it terminated. In the beginning stages of the introduction of prenatal diagnosis into medical practice, it was a general policy not to undertake prenatal diagnosis unless the family seemed committed to terminating the pregnancy if the fetus were abnormal. The principal reason for this policy was to protect the interests of the fetus in view of the uncertainty about the risks associated with the procedure. However, as time has passed and the safety of the procedure has been better established, more prenatal diagnoses are being performed to reassure the parents that the fetus is normal without necessarily providing information leading to termination of the pregnancy (7). In numerical terms, this still represents a very small proportion of the procedures which are actually done.

Frequency and Types of Genetic Disease

When the newborn population is examined it is found that between 2 and 4% of individuals, depending on how the figures are calculated, have some type of birth defect which is considered to be genetic in origin (8,9). The term "birth defect" is used in a general sense and encompasses all types of structural, metabolic, and other abnormalities which derive from genetic or other prenatal causes. The birth defects detected postnatally represent only a small fraction of the totality of abnormalities which result from genetic aberrations, but most of the latter result in early spontaneous abortions (10) and do not constitute indications for prenatal diagnosis.

The genetic disorders of the newborn can be divided into three general categories, and these are shown in Table I. The first category is that of the chromosomal disorders compatible with viability, and they affect about 0.6% of the newborn population. The second is the group of mendelian disorders which result from abnormalities of single genes. It is estimated that approximately 0.4% of the newborn population are affected with such conditions. This figure does not, however, include the large number of individuals who would be affected by erythroblastosis fetalis due to Rh incompatibility if anti-Rh-immune globulin were not administered. Likewise, it does not include those genetic conditions which have particularly high frequencies in restricted ethnic or racial groups. The best examples of the latter are glucose-6-phosphate dehydrogenase (G6PD) deficiency and sickle cell anemia (0.25% incidence) in the Black population, thalassemia in certain Mediterranean and Oriental populations, and Tay-Sachs disease in Ashkenazi Jews (0.04% incidence). While many of the single gene disorders are biochemical in nature, at least in so far as is possible to define specific biochemical abnormalities, not all can be so characterized. Several of them represent disorders of morphogenesis, with malformation of one or several organs, or disorders in function for which biochemical explanations do not presently exist. In absolute numbers, therefore. the frequency of frankly biochemical genetic disorders, often designated as the inborn errors of metabolism, is quite low.

The third category of genetic disorders includes these conditions in which the genetic components are less well defined and are influenced by non-genetic or "environmental" factors which are poorly understood. These conditions are referred to as the polygenic or multifactorial disorders and can be further subdivided into two groups. The first is the group of the common congenital malformations, including cleft palate and lip, spina bifida and anencephaly, club feet,

congenital heart defects, pyloric stenosis, congenitally
dislocated hips, and renal anomalies. In the aggregate, these
disorders affect over 1% of the newborn population. The second
group of multifactorial disorders, and the one for which it is
impossible to obtain accurate incidence figures, is the group of
relatively common diseases of adulthood which have genetic
components to them. Included in this group are diabetes
mellitus, schizophrenia, allergies, and certain forms of
malignancy.

In terms of their suitability for prenatal diagnosis, the
first two categories of genetic diseases, the chromosome
abnormalities and single gene defects, especially those that
are biochemical in nature, constitute the conditions most
amenable to the techniques presently available. However, at
least one of the multifactorially determined congenital
malformations (the neural tube defects) can also be diagnosed
prenatally.

The major impetus to the development of methods for the
prenatal detection of genetic disorders derives, in historical
terms, from the roughly simultaneous development of three major
techniques (11-14). One was the technique, and the willingness
to use it, for obtaining samples of amniotic fluid early in
gestation. The second was the development of techniques for the
culture of human cells in vitro, and the third was the
development of better techniques for cytogenetic analysis. As
will be described below, with the availability of these three
techniques it became possible first to work out methods for the
examination of fetal chromosomes, and then, by extension, to
devise ways of determining other characteristics of the fetus.

If the object of prenatal diagnosis is to determine the
state of the fetus who is suspected of having some genetic
abnormality, how can its condition actually be assessed? The
range of possibilities for making such assessments will be
outlined in the next section, starting with the most direct and
going to the least direct. Although discussions of prenatal
diagnosis are not usually presented in this way, this approach
should help the reader conceptualize the problems associated
with attempting to learn about an organism which cannot readily
be approached.

Fetal Visualization

Direct Visualization. The most direct way of examining a
fetus is to look directly at it, and an instrument has been
developed for this purpose -- the fetoscope (15). This
instrument is a modified endoscope which can be inserted into
the amniotic cavity through a 14 gauge needle. Since this
needle is fairly large in diameter, there is a significant
possibility of uterine or placental bleeding associated with its
introduction. In addition, lack of flexibility interferes with

Table I

Frequency of genetic disorders in the English newborn population

Chromosomal Disorders
  Autosomal
    Trisomy 21**   0.13%
    Trisomy 18**   0.03
    Trisomy 13**   0.02
    Translocations**   0.01
    Deletions**   0.01
  Total autosomal   0.20%

  Sex chromosome
    XO and X deletions**   0.02
    Other "severe" defects**   0.01
    XXY**   0.1
    XXX**   0.1
    XYY**   0.1
    Others**   0.015
  Total sex chromosome   0.35%

  Total chromosomal disorders   0.55%

Monogenic (mendelian) Disorders
  Autosomal recessive
    Mental retardation, severe   0.08%
    Cystic fibrosis   0.05
    Deafness, severe (several forms)   0.05
    Blindness, severe (several forms)   0.02
    Adrenogenital syndrome   0.01
    Albinism   0.01
    Phenylketonuria   0.01
    Other amino acidurias*   0.01
    Mucopolysaccharidoses, all forms**   0.005
    Tay-Sachs disease**   0.001
    Galactosemia**   0.0005
    Others*   0.05
  Total autosomal recessive   0.30%

Table I   (Continued)

X-linked
  Duchenne muscular dystrophy***   0.02%
  Hemophilias A and B***   0.01
  Others*, ***   0.02
Total X-linked   0.05%

Autosomal dominant
  Blindness (several forms)   0.01%
  Deafness (several forms)   0.01
  Marfan syndrome   0.005
  Achondroplasia   0.005
  Neurofibromatosis   0.005
  Myotonic dystrophy   0.005
  Tuberous sclerosis   0.005
  All others   0.015
Total autosomal dominant   0.06%

Total monogenic disorders   0.41%

Multifactorial Disorders
  Congenital malformations
    Spina bifida and anencephaly**   0.45%
    Congenital heart defects   0.4
    Pyloric stenosis   0.3
    Talipes equinovarus (club feet)   0.3
    Cleft lip and palate   0.1
    Dislocated hips   0.1
    Others   0.2
  Total congenital malformations   1.85%

  "Common diseases"   ?   (>>1%)

Total multifactorial disorders   >>1.85%

     Total frequency of genetic disorders   >>2.81%

---

  *Diagnosable in utero (some)
 **Diagnosable in utero
***Fetal sex can be determined

manipulation of the instrument once it is within the uterus, and
the narrow field of vision makes it difficult to adequately
examine all parts of the fetus. Neverless, it has been possible
with such an instrument to visualize fetal fingers and other
aspects of the external surface of the fetus, and in theory such
examination should be useful in diagnosing major structural
abnormalities. However, because of the difficulties already
mentioned, the fetoscope does not presently enjoy much
popularity as a practical tool for prenatal diagnosis, although
it is being used to assist in the sampling of fetal blood from
placental vessels (16,17). Before the fetoscope can be more
widely used, it will be necessary to develop a very fine
flexible instrument with a wide field of vision.

Visualization by Radiological and Ultrasound Techniques.
Other less direct visualization systems have also been and are
being used, with varying degrees of success. At the present
time, radiological (x-ray) examinations of the fetus are mainly
limited to a determination of the structure of fetal bones.
This is of potential usefulness in those disorders which are
characterized by the absence or gross structural abnormality of
a specific bone or bones (18), but such examinations have not
always proved to be reliable. Again, it will be necessary to
have improvements in radiologic technique, such as are
exemplified by xerography and image intensification, before
radiologic examination of the fetus will attain the degree of
usefulness that it might have for prenatal diagnosis.
   The method of fetal visualization that has thus far been
the most helpful makes use of ultrasonic scanning. In regular
obstetrical practice this technique is used to diagnose twin
pregnancies, to localize the placenta, and to determine fetal
age by measuring the width of the fetal head. The ability to
examine the fetal head by the currently available techniques
makes ultrasonic scanning useful for the prenatal diagnosis of
anencephaly, one of the multifactorially determined congenital
malformations (19). In this condition, the cranium and brain
are not properly formed, and it is the absence of the cranium
which is detected by ultrasonic scanning. While this disorder
is relatively infrequent in the general population, its
frequency is greater than 1% in the offspring of couples who
have already had a child affected with the same or a related
(spina bifida) neural tube disorder. Coupled with a determination of amniotic fluid α-fetoprotein concentrations (see below),
ultrasonic scanning leads to a secure diagnosis of anencephaly.
However, like the other methods, the present techniques of
ultrasonic scanning are still capable of considerable improvement, and one such improved method, gray scale scanning, is now
being introduced (20). In theory, this technique has the
capability of providing much sharper resolution of fetal
structures, both external and internal.

Sampling of Fetal Blood and Tissues

Even if visualization techniques were developed to the point of allowing a complete and accurate examination of the external aspects of the fetus, many genetically determined disorders would still not be diagnosable, either because they did not produce any external physical abnormalities or because the abnormalities would not as yet have become apparent. Therefore, the next most direct method of examining the fetus is to obtain a sample of fetal tissue. As might be imagined, the direct sampling of tissues of an infant or child is not always an easy thing to do, and the direct sampling of fetal tissues is even less so. The most readily accessible and easily sampled tissue after birth is blood, and it is not surprising that the most serious attempts to sample fetal tissues have also been concerned with the obtaining and examination of fetal blood. The prenatal situation is particularly favorable for this since it is not really necessary to obtain blood from the fetus itself. With suitable techniques, fetal blood can be obtained from the placenta, either by puncture of a placental vessel under direct visualization or by aspiration from the placenta with ultrasonic guidance (15-17,21,22). The principal abnormalities which have so far come under investigation and seem to be amenable to this approach are those of hemoglobin structure and synthesis. While the major hemoglobin synthesized by the fetus after the first few months in utero is fetal hemoglobin (hemoglobin F), which is composed of α- and γ-chains, the fetus also makes β-chains from very early on. Therefore, in addition to being able to detect all of the α-chain abnormalities, it is also possible to make the diagnosis of β-chain abnormalities as well. Of the latter, the most common are sickle cell anemia, a structural abnormality of the β-chain, and β-thalassemia, a condition characterized by decreased β-chain synthesis. To diagnose hemoglobin abnormalities, small quantities of fetal blood are obtained from the placenta and incubated with radioactive amino acids in vitro. Since there is usually an admixture of maternal blood, it is necessary to determine the relative proportions of maternal and fetal red cells and to make the appropriate corrections to the data. After incubation, the hemoglobin is isolated, fractionated by chromatographic techniques, and the radioactivity in the individual chains determined (22,23). With these methods it is possible to assess whether the various chains are made in normal amounts and whether abnormal chains are being synthesized. Because of changes in the relative rates of chain synthesis -- for example, the ratio of β- to γ-chains in normal fetuses increases from 7.5 to 10% between the 6th and 16th weeks of development -- it is necessary to have well defined control information if a decision is to be made about whether a significant decrease in the rate of synthesis of a particular chain has occurred (22).

At the present time the sampling of fetal blood is still problematic at best. Fetal blood in sufficient amounts for analysis cannot be obtained with absolute certainty and with the degree of safety associated with the sampling of amniotic fluid (17). Therefore, we are still not yet at the stage of being able to analyze fetal blood with the same ease that we can analyze other biochemical properties of the fetus from cultured cells and amniotic fluid. And, to date, the obtaining of fetal serum, as opposed to red cells, has been even less satisfactory. Since many of the constituents that could be assayed for in the prenatal detection of genetic disorders are present in maternal serum in relatively large concentrations, even a small contamination of the fetal serum would make reliable assessment of the latter quite difficult. Therefore, while it would be desirable to be able to determine the amounts of antihemophilic globulin (factor VIII) and other coagulation factors to diagnose the clotting disorders an of Cl'-esterase inhibitor, to diagnose hereditary angioneurotic edema, such determinations are not presently feasible. Similarly, other serum proteins of future genetic interest would be α_1-antitrypsin, ceruloplasmin, complement, and the immunoglobulins.

The direct sampling of other fetal tissues such as skin (24) and possibly even the internal organs has been discussed but has not been used in practice. Likewise, biopsying and analyzing the placenta has been advocated but not used for prenatal diagnosis (25). Therefore, for most types of information, indirect sampling of the fetus through analysis of the amniotic fluid and its constituents is commonly used. It must be emphasized that amniotic fluid and its constituents are a few biochemical and physiological steps removed from the fetus itself, and results obtained from their examination must be interpreted with caution.

Amniocentesis

The amount of amniotic fluid which surrounds the fetus increases with fetal size and age. The ability to obtain amniotic fluid for analysis is basically a mechanical problem of having an amniotic cavity large enough to enable the obstetrician to safely insert a needle and withdraw an amount of fluid sufficient for study. With current techniques it is considered reasonably safe to do so at 13 or more weeks of fetal development, at which time there is 150 ml or more of amniotic fluid (26). The amount of fluid withdrawn is generally of the order of 10 to 15 ml, 10% or less of the total amniotic fluid volume, and this volume is rapidly replaced by the fetus. The amniotic fluid is obtained by inserting a needle into the uterus through the midline of the lower abdomen. This procedure, referred to as amniocentesis, is relatively non-traumatic physically, and if handled properly, psychologically. The

risks to the mother and to the fetus seem to be minimal, but
absolute safety cannot be claimed and the possibility of
inducing a miscarriage cannot be dismissed (see below).

Direct Analysis of Amniotic Fluid Constituents

In most instances, the cellular component of the amniotic
fluid, which consists of diverse cells of fetal origin, are
placed in culture and used for further analysis. However, there
are instances in which uncultured cells have been used for
direct cytologic or biochemical analysis and in which the
soluble components of the fluid have been directly analyzed
(27-29). The biochemical analysis of uncultured cells has not
proven to be highly reliable (30,31). The cell population
itself is quite heterogeneous in composition and variable with
regard to the proportion of viable and nonviable cells. The
use of uncultured cells for ultrastructural examinations has
also been advocated, especially for the diagnosis of the lysosomal storage diseases, and there is evidence that amniotic
cells of fetal origin will show the presence of various bodies
characteristic of lysosomal storage (27,32). However, this
requires the availability of an appropriate electron microscope
facility, and most groups do not have such facilities at their
disposal.

Uncultured cells have also been used to a limited extent
for fetal sex determination. This is possible because the cells
can be appropriately stained and examined for the presence of
sex chromatin, characteristic of female cells, and for the
fluorescent Y-body, characteristic of male cells (33,34).
However, these cytologic techniques are not completely reliable,
and it is still desirable to determine fetal sex by direct
chromosome analysis (35).

The soluble components of the amniotic fluid have also
been subjected to various types of analyses. Thus far, examination of the concentrations of various metabolites or degradation
products in the fluid have not proven to be useful for the
diagnosis of inborn errors of amino acid or mucopolysaccharide
metabolism (36,37). Likewise, it has not been possible to make
specific diagnoses of disorders associated with deficiencies of
particular proteins by examination of amniotic fluid. While
certain proteins, deficiencies of which are associated with
inherited disease, are present in amniotic fluid (38,39) -- for
example, α_1-antitrypsin, Cl'-esterase inhibitor, ceruloplasmin,
β-lipoprotein, and immunoglobulin G (IgG) -- it still has to be
determined how much of these materials are fetal in origin as
opposed to being maternal, and how well the concentration in the
amniotic fluid reflects the actual state of the fetus (40). The
one constituent of the cell-free amniotic fluid which has proven
to be very useful for prenatal diagnosis is α-fetoprotein, and
this will be discussed below. A few prenatal diagnoses have

been made by analyses of enzymes in cell-free amniotic fluid.
However, such methods are not considered highly reliable (41)
and are little used.

Cultured Amniotic Fluid Cells

As a result of these difficulties, most of the work with
amniotic fluid is concerned with the analysis of cultured cells.
At the present time it is believed that three types of cells
can be grown from the amniotic fluid: an epithelioid type of
cell, a fibroblast-like cell, and a so-called "amniotic fluid
cell" (AF cell) intermediate in characteristics between the
other two (42). While the AF and fibroblast-like cells grow
reasonably well in culture, the epithelioid cells grow very
slowly and are difficult to work with. Of all of the cells
originally applied to a culture plate when a culture is initiated, relatively few (on the order of several hundred) actually
attach and grow out. Therefore, cultures derived from amniotic
fluid represent a set of cell clones rather than a mass population (42). The media and general techniques for culturing
amniotic fluid are not greatly different from those used for
the culturing of other human cells, and success seems to be
more a function of the skill of the person handling the cells
than of any particular culture condition.
     Two types of information can be obtained from cultured
amniotic fluid cells. The first, which constitutes the major
proportion of the work done in the area of prenatal diagnosis
of genetic disorders, is the chromosome constitution of the
fetus. The second is the biochemical status of the fetus, at
least in so far as certain defined enzyme pathways are concerned.

Cytogenetic Analysis and Sex Determination. Since amniotic
fluid cells are fetal in origin, they have the chromosome
complement of the fetus itself. Therefore, the chromosomes of
the fetus can be examined by karyotyping the cultured amniotic
fluid cells. There are two principal reasons for examining
fetal chromosomes. One, the numerically less frequent reason,
is to determine the sex of the fetus; the other is to determine
whether the fetus has a chromosome abnormality. Fetal sex
determination is not, at present, performed so that couples can
chose the sex of their baby. While there may not be any significant ethical or sociological (43) reasons to oppose sex determination for this reason, the lack of sufficient facilities has
made this an indication of extremely low priority. The reason
for ascertaining the sex of a fetus, in so far as the prenatal
diagnosis of genetic disease is concerned, is to determine
whether the fetus is a male or female in situations in which
the parents are at risk of having a child with an X-linked
disorder which affects only males. If the fetus is a male, it
will have a 50% risk of being affected. This risk, in such

conditions as Duchenne muscular dystrophy, hemophillia A, and
some of the other serious X-linked disorders, is considered to
be quite high (see 44 for complete list). If the fetus is
female, the risk of being affected is extremely low (except in
the rare situation in which the father is affected), and families
which undertake to have the sex of the fetus determined because
of X-linked problems do so because they are anxious to prevent
the birth of a male who might be affected.

The more general reason for examining the chromosomes of the
fetus and the single most important indication for prenatal
diagnosis is to determine whether some type of chromosome abnormality is present. Several of the more common chromosome abnormalities are listed in Table I. The chromosome abnormalities can
be divided into two broad categories, those of the autosomes
(non-sex chromosomes) and those of the sex chromosomes. Of the
autosomal abnormalities, by far the most common is trisomy 21, the
presence of an extra chromosome 21. This abnormality is associated with Down's syndrome (mongolism), a condition characterized
by mental retardation and major and minor congenital malformations. The other autosomal trisomies, trisomies 18 and 13, are
less frequent but considerably more severe than trisomy 21 and
usually result in early death. Abnormalities involving other
autosomes are also infrequent, but can produce a wide variety of
abnormalities and are generally always associated with significant
mental retardation.

The sex chromosome abnormalities are generally less severe
in terms of their effects on mental development, but two of them,
the XO and XXY abnormalities, are associated with sterility and
other abnormalities in individuals who develop as females or
males, respectively. The two other sex chromosome abnormalities,
XXX and XYY, are more problematic. The XXX constitution does
not produce significant abnormalities in the females who have it
but can, in some individuals, be associated with a modest degree
of mental slowness (45). The XYY constitution, in the males who
have it, appears to be associated with increased stature and,
at least in some individuals, with a tendency toward antisocial
behavior (46, 47). While the absolute incidence of such behavior
of XYY individuals is probably quite low, it is still thought to
be higher than in a chromosomally normal population. These two
sex-chromosome abnormalities have been specifically mentioned
because they have engendered considerable concern about what
types of counseling should be given in situations in which they
are detected prenatally.

While all chromosomal abnormalities can in principle be
detected by prenatal diagnosis, fetal karyotyping is not at
present being done as a general screening procedure. Rather,
it is done under circumstances in which there appears to be a
significantly increased risk of having a child with a chromosome
abnormality. For the most part, this increased risk is associated with trisomy 21, although it can, in certain rare instances,

be associated with other chromosomal abnormalities as well.
While the overall population incidence of trisomy 21 is between
1 in 700 and 1 in 600 live births (48, 49), the frequency of its
appearance in any given family is determined by two factors.
One is the age of the mother at the time of the infant's birth.
The mean figure of about 1 in 600 live births is representative
of the risk to a mother who is 35 years of age at the time the
child is born. For women in the third decade, the risk is considerably less, 1 in 1000 or lower. However, by the time a
women reaches 40 years of age, the risk of having a child with
Down's syndrome is between 1 and 2% (based on the newborn population) and this risk may reach as high as 4% by the time she
is 45. Although it is impossible to define what constitutes a
high risk for having a child with Down's syndrome, it is commonly
accepted that a women of age 40 or greater is in a high risk
category. However, for many families and physicians this period
of high risk begins even as early as age 35.

The second major factor which influences the frequency of
Down's syndrome is the prior birth of a child with the same
disorder (50). In such instances, the chance of having another
affected child is considerably greater than the age-specific
incidence of the disorder, and is generally in the range of 1
to 2%. Again, for the individuals involved, this is considered
to be a high risk, particularly in view of the fact that they
have already had an abnormal child. Down's syndrome can occur
with even higher frequencies, sometimes reaching as high as 20%,
in the relatively rare families in which one of the parents,
usually the mother, is the carrier of a balanced translocation
involving chromosome 21.

As has already been mentioned, all chromosome abnormalities
can be detected in the fetus. For that reason, some individuals
have suggested that wide-scale routine prenatal screening be
carried out (51). However, the greater the population screened,
the lower will be the proportion of fetuses found to be affected.
In economic terms, this would elevate the cost of case detection
to high, perhaps prohibitive, levels. Putting economics aside,
the most cogent reason for not undertaking wide-scale screening,
at least at this time, may be the still undefined upper limit
of complications of the procedure, whether these be induction
of miscarriage, misdiagnosis, or the like. It has generally
been felt, at least to this time, that prenatal diagnosis should
not be undertaken in circumstances in which the risk of having
an affected child is significantly less than the risk of the
procedure itself. As confidence in the safety of the procedure
has increased there has been a relaxation in the age restrictions
for prenatal diagnosis. But, it is not at all clear that the
overall complication rate will even reach a point of being significantly below 0.1 to 0.2%, the risk to a 30 to 35 year old
mother of having a child with a chromosome abnormality.

Biochemical Analysis. The second principal use of cultured
amniotic fluid cells is to determine the biochemical status of
the fetus. Again, it should be pointed out that the individual
biochemical disorders are quite low in incidence, but many of
them are very serious in their manifestations and can occur with
relatively high frequencies in specific families. If two parents
are carriers of a gene for an autosomal recessive condition, then
the risk to each child of having the disorder is 25%.
       The biochemical disorders diagnosable in utero are those
which have enzymatic representations in the types of cells which
can be cultured from the amniotic fluid. At the present time
approximately 25 to 30 disorders have actually been diagnosed
(table II) and another 35 are capable of diagnosis (52,53). Many
of the disorders which have already been diagnosed are those in
the lysosomal storage disease group, conditions which frequently
cause early neurologic degeneration, sometimes in association
with skeletal abnormalities and visceral enlargement. In nearly
all instances, the diagnosis is made by direct determination of
the activity of the enzyme involved in the disorder, although
occasionally a somewhat more indirect approach can be used. For
example, cystinosis is detected in cultured cells by assessment
of the ability of the cells to handle cystine, even though the
precise enzymatic defect is not known (54).
       There are important methodologic considerations which apply
to the use of cultured amniotic fluid cells for the detection of
biochemical disorders. The first is that the enzymes which can
be sampled are those which are usually present in fibroblasts or
fibroblast-like cells. Therefore, conditions such as phenylketonuria and glycogen storage disease type I, which are associated with deficiencies of enzymes present only in liver and
kidney, are not amenable to this approach. The same also per-
tains to enzyme deficiencies affecting other specific tissues.
The one present exception to this is histidase, an enzyme
characteristic of epithelial cells. In this instance, it has
been possible to select clones of epithelioid cells from the
mixed cell population of the amniotic fluid cell cultures and to
analyse them for this enzyme (55).
       The second methodologic consideration relates to the type
of cells which are used as controls for the biochemical determinations. While less a problem now, there was a tendency in
some early investigations to use cultured skin fibroblasts or
similar cells as controls for the cultured amniotic fluid cells.
It has been demonstrated that such controls are not valid and
that there may be significant differences in enzyme concentrations between two cell types (56). For this reason, normal
amniotic fluid cells themselves must be used as controls for
amniotic fluid cell cultures being subjected to enzymologic
investigation.
       The third and potentially most severe methodologic problem

Table II

Biochemical Disorders Diagnosed Prenatally (Second Trimester)

Disease	Metabolic Defect	Reference
Acid phosphatase deficiency	Lysosomal acid phosphatase deficiency	73
Adenosine deaminase deficiency (combined immunodeficiency)	Adenosine deaminase deficiency	74
Argininosuccinic aciduria	Argininosuccinase deficiency	75
Cystinosis	Cystine accumulation	54
Fabry disease	Ceramidetrihexoside α-galactosidase deficiency	76
Galactokinase deficiency	Galactokinase deficiency	77
Galactosemia	Galactose-1-phosphaturidyltransferase deficiency	78
G_{M_1} gangliosidosis, type I (generalized)	β-Galactosidase deficiency	79
G_{M_1} gangliosidosis, type II (juvenile)	β-Galactosidase deficiency	80
Gaucher disease	β-Glucosidase deficiency	70
Glycogen storage disease, type II (Pompe)	α-1,4 Glucosidase deficiency	81
Hunter syndrome	α-L-Iduronic acid-2 sulfatase deficiency	82, 83
Hurler syndrome	α-L-Iduronidase deficiency	82, 83
Hypophosphatasia	Alkaline phosphatase deficiency	84
Krabbe disease	Galactocerebroside-β-galactosidase deficiency	69, 72
Lesch-Nyhan syndrome	Hypoxanthine guanine phosphoribosyltransferase deficiency	85
Maple syrup urine disease	Branched-chain keto-acid decarboxylase deficiency	86
Metachromatic leuko-	Arylsulfatase A deficiency	87

Table II (Continued)

Disease	Metabolic Defect	Reference
dystrophy		
Methylmalonic aciduria (B_{12}-resistant)	Methylmalonyl-CoA mutase deficiency	88
Mucolipidosis II (I-cell disease)	Multiple lysosomal enzyme deficiencies	89
Niemann-Pick disease	Sphingomyelinase deficiency	68, 71
Sandhoff disease	β-N-Acetyl-hexosaminidase A and B deficiency	27
Sanfilippo disease, type A	Heparin sulphamidase deficiency	90
Tay-Sachs disease	β-N-Acetylhexosamidase A deficiency	28
β-thalassemia	Decreased hemoglobin β-chain synthesis	22
Xeroderma pigmentosum	Endonuclease deficiency	91

is that which relates to the amount of material required for
analysis. For most of the conditions that have been studied,
conventional methods of enzyme analysis have been employed. This
has necessitated the growing of fairly large quantities of cells,
a procedure frequently requiring between 4 and 8 weeks of culture
(57). There is a limited time available between the earliest
period at which an amniocentesis can be performed and the latest
at which a pregnancy can be terminated. As a result, such long
culture periods can lead to great difficulties, psychologic and
otherwise, for both the patients and the physician. For this
reason, micromethods have been developed for the assay of
enzymes in limited numbers of cells. Such methods have been
applied to cultured amniotic cells and make use of microspect-
rophotometry and/or microfluorometry. The amniotic fluid cells
are generally grown directly on thin plastic foils, and after
a relatively short time in culture (5-10 days), are freeze dried
and their number or dry mass determined. They are then incubated
with substrates in very small quantities of medium and examined
with the appropriate instrumentation. By this means, it has
been possible to make the diagnosis of several conditions using
fewer than a thousand cells, sometimes even fewer than 100,
rather than the several million cells which are generally needed
at present (58,59). Since the instrumentation for such micro
assays is expensive and the techniques highly specialized, it
would seem reasonable to have centralized laboratories which can
make this methodology available to those who need it. While such
laboratories exist in Europe, these methods are not readily
available at the present time in the United States.

α-Fetoprotein Determinations

Perhaps the most indirect way of sampling the fetus is to
assess something which the fetus causes to happen even though it
is not itself an intrinsic part of the birth defect. Such
sampling has become the basis of the diagnosis of the neural
tube abnormalities, spina bifida with anencephaly and meningo-
myelocele, and mention has already been made of determination of
α-fetoprotein in the amniotic fluid. This protein is made by
the fetus and is present in only low centrations in amniotic
fluid and maternal serum during pregnancy. However, in the
presence of open neural tube defects, as well as of a limited
number of other defects (such as omphalocele or the fetal nephro-
tic syndrome), large quantities of α-fetoprotein appear in the
amniotic fluid (60-62). Using sensitive immunochemical methods
for assaying α-fetoprotein concentrations, it has been possible
to reliably make the diagnosis of the open neural tube defects
during the second trimester of pregnancy. This diagnostic
procedure is gradually being introduced as a screening procedure
in all cases in which amniocentesis is performed, since ample
amniotic fluid is available after the cells are removed for

culture.

While the concentration of α-fetoprotein in the maternal serum is also frequently elevated when the mother is carrying a fetus with an open neural tube defect, such elevations occur only about 65% of the time (63). Therefore, the determination of α-fetoprotein in maternal serum cannot be used as a specific diagnostic procedure. However, it has been suggested that it might be a useful screening procedure for all pregnant women, particularly those who are not undergoing amniocentesis for some other indication. While not all affected fetuses would be detected, a sizable proportion would, and this could lead to a significant reduction in the incidence of a condition associated with significant disability.

Experience with Prenatal Diagnosis

The San Francisco Series. With the above as background, the experience in San Francisco and the accumulated experience of several groups throughout the world will be discussed. At the time of this writing, over 700 patients have undergone amniocentesis in San Francisco for the prenatal diagnosis of a wide variety of genetic disorders. The figures to be discussed here are based on the fully analyzed first 500 cases (64)(earlier reports of the first 50 and 100 cases have already appeared) (65, 66). Before giving actual outcomes, there are two technical points worthy of mention. First, an attempt was made to determine whether the time required to obtain a cytogenetic diagnosis was a function of the stage of pregnancy at which the amniotic fluid was obtained. Over the time span of 14 weeks to 21 weeks after the last menstrual period, there did not appear to be any significant relationship between stage of gestation and time to diagnosis, and the mean time to diagnosis was approximately 3 1/2 weeks (65). Likewise, this time was not affected by the experience of the technician who was doing the work and seemed to be more related to inherent differences in the proliferative capacity of the amniotic cells derived from different individuals (65). For biochemical investigations, as already mentioned, considerably longer periods of time were required.

A total of 448 of the 500 pregnancies were monitored for cytogenetic indications exclusive of fetal sex. Of these, 332 were for advanced maternal age, with 172 of that group being between 35 and 39 years of age and 160 being 40 years or over. Of the former group, four fetuses had Down's syndrome, while of the latter, two had Down's syndrome, two had other autosomal trisomies, and one had an unidentified centromeric fragment. Taken together, and keeping in mind the limited size of the sample, these figures indicate a 2.7% frequency of chromosomal abnormalities in the age group 35 years and older. Of this group, 1.8% had Down's syndrome, with the frequency of Down's syndrome being 2.3% in the 35 to 39 year old group and 1.3% in the 40 and over

group. If the other abnormalities are included, the frequency
of chromosomal aberrations in the 40 and older group was 3.1%.
However they are interpreted, these figures are higher than would
be expected from the usual newborn population survey statistics,
particularly in the age group between 35 and 39. The reasons for
this are unclear. It does not seem to be a statistical artifact,
since similar results have been obtained in the cumulative experience of many centers. It is possible that some sort of bias of
which we are presently unaware is operating.

The second most frequent group being monitored for cytogenetic indications was that composed of women who had a previous
child with Down's syndrome due to a simple trisomy 21. Of that
group, one fetus had an XO karyotype, one had Down's syndrome
and one had an abnormal karyotype with an extra band on the short
arm of chromosome 7 (7p+). Again, keeping the size of the sample
in mind, this gives a frequency of Down's syndrome of 1% and of
all chromosome abnormalities of 3.2%. The former figure is within the expected range but the latter is higher than might have
been expected. Twenty-one other women underwent amniocentesis
for a variety of different cytogenetic indications, and no abnormal fetuses were detected. In one case, however, the fetal
karyotype was quite abnormal, with a previously unrecognized
translocation involving chromosomes 2 and 14. When this abnormality was first recognized in the cultured cells, it was
impossible to determine whether the fetus would be normal or not.
The parents elected to carry the pregnancy to term, and a normal
fetus with the previously detected chromosome abnormality was
delivered.

Nineteen women underwent amniocentesis for the determination
of fetal sex. Several different X-linked abnormalities constituted the indications for this procedure, and these included
hemophilia A, hemophilia B, Duchenne muscular dystrophy, optic
albinism, X-linked mental retardation, the Lesch-Nyhan syndrome
(due to dificiency of hypoxanthine-guanine phosphoribosyltrans-
ferase, and Fabry's disease (due to deficiency of an α-galact-
osidase). Fourteen of the fetuses were male, including one
which turned out to be a set of twins, and most of the male
pregnancies were terminated. The sex determination being carried
out for Fabry's disease is of particular interest, since in this
case it was desired to find out whether the fetus was a female.
The father of the child was affected, and the family was concerned about having a female who would by necessity be heterozygous for the condition and subject to manifesting the disorder.
Of the X-linked disorders, muscular dystrophy was the most common
indication. While it was not possible in our cases to determine
whether the fetuses were or were not affected, it may, on the
basis of a recent report, be possible to do so (67).

Although, as has been mentioned, inherited biochemical disorders are rare, 17 out of the 500 pregnancies have been monitored
because of a possibility of having a child with a hereditary

biochemical defect. In two instances, a woman underwent aminocentesis in more than one successive pregnancy. In our series,
prenatal diagnosis was undertaken for the following conditions:
Niemann-Pick disease (sphingomyelinase deficiency), Gaucher
disease (β-glucosidase deficiency), Krabbe disease (galacto-
cerebroside-β-galactosidase deficiency), Pompe disease or glycogen storage disease type II (α-glucosidase deficiency), metachromatic leukodystrophy (arylsufatase A deficiency), galactosemia (galactose-1-phosphate uridyltransferase deficiency), maple
syrup urine disease (branched chain ketoacid decarboxylase deficiency), cystinosis (abnormal storage of cystine), and β-
thalassemia (decreased synthesis of hemoglobin β chains). Of
this group, six affected individuals were detected, not statist-
ically different from the five expected for a 25% recurrence
risk (22, 68-70). Of considerable interest were the results of
the pathologic examination of three fetuses affected with lysosomal storage diseases, Niemann-Pick disease, Gaucher disease,
and Krabbe disease (70-72). Each of these fetuses presented
unequivocal chemical and ultrastructural evidence for the disease
process and indicated that even a fetus midway through gestation
is demonstrably affected by the genetic abnormality.

The monitoring of pregnancies for neural tube defects is the
most recent of the indications for prenatal diagnosis. In
families in which one child has been affected, the risk of
recurrence is approximately 4%. Of the 16 pregnancies in which
amniocentesis was done to determine the level of α-fetoprotein,
no affected fetuses were found.

In these 500 cases, there were 26 culture failures, an incidence of about 5%. Nine women of this group underwent a second
aminocentesis, and successful cultures were obtained. The
other 17, or 3.4% of the total, did not obtain any results,
either because of spontaneous abortions prior to the time a
second amniocentesis could be performed (in four) or because
the family elected not to proceed. There were no instances of
severe or significant fetal injury, although small linear "scars"
were noted on four fetuses. Three fetuses had abnormalities
which were not related to the procedure itself, including spina
bifida, osteogenesis imperfecta, and congenital heart disease.
One set of undetected triplets also occurred, in addition to the
twins already mentioned. Ten abortions occurred following amniocentesis, three occurring within one week of the procedure and
associated with fever, and seven not associated with fever and
occurring between 18 and 50 days after amniocentesis itself, the
former group which comprises 0.4% of the total, must be considered a direct complication. However, even this conclusion must be
tempered by the fact that in the week prior to a scheduled amniocentesis, 20 women had spontaneous abortions.

Since the introduction of the prenatal diagnosis in San
Francisco in 1970, there has been virtually an exponential
increase in the demand for this service. This demand has been

almost entirely for chromosomal indications and mainly by women
in the older childbearing years. With the introduction of the
determination of α-fetoprotein concentrations for the detection
of neural tube abnormalities, there has also been a similar increase, although numerically much less great, in the requests
for prenatal diagnosis of neural tube defects. The number of
cases monitored for fetal sex determination and for biochemical
indications has remained fairly constant since 1971.

Finally, it is of some interest to examine the cumulative experience of many prenatal diagnostic centers. These figures
have been gathered and analyzed by Dr. Mitchell S. Golbus. A
total of 3,452 pregnancies have been studied and reported, 2,889
for cytogenetic indications, 181 for sex determination, 155 for
biochemical disorders, and 227 for neural tube defects. For
women 35 to 39 and 40 and over, the frequencies of abnormal
fetuses were 2.3% and 3.8%, respectively. When previous trisomy
21 was the indication, 1.5% of the fetuses were affected, but
18.9% were affected when one of the parents carried a balanced
translocation. Of the pregnancies monitored for fetal sex determination, 45.3% had male fetuses, and 20% of fetuses at risk
for biochemical disorders were found to be affected. The overall incidence of fetal abnormality, including all male fetuses
in the sex determination group, was 6.4%. If the latter group
is removed and only specific diagnoses are considered, 4.3% of the
tested fetuses were abnormal.

Literature Cited

1. Epstein, C. J.; "Genetic Counseling - Past, Present and
    Future" in "Birth Defects and Fetal Development, Endocrine
    and Metabolic Factors", ed. K. S. Moghissi, Charles C.
    Thomas Publisher, Springfield, Illinois, 1974.
2. Nadler, H. L.; "Prenatal Detection of Genetic Disorders".
    Adv. Hum. Genet., (1972), 3, 1-37.
3. Dorfman, A., ed.; "Antenatal Diagnosis", University of
    Chicago Press, Chicago, 1972.
4. Milunsky, A.; "The Prenatal Diagnosis of Hereditary Dis-
    orders", Charles C. Thomas, Springfield, 1973.
5. Symposium on Intrauterine Diagnosis; "Birth Defects: Ori-
    ginal Article Series", (1971), 7, 5.
6. Epstein, C. J.; "Prenatal Diagnosis". Adv. Int. Med.,
    (1975), 20, 325-344.
7. Garlinger, P.; Hecht, F.; Prescott, G. H.; Wyandt, H. E.;
    Tolby, B. E.; Milbeck, R. L.; and Overton, K.; "Restrictive
    Consent and Amniocentesis". New Eng. J. Med., (1973), 288,
    1028.
8. Edwards, J. H.; "The Mutation Rate in Man". Prog. Med.
    Genet., (1974), 10, 1-16.
9. Carter, C. O.; "Genetics of Common Disorders". Brit. Med.
    Bull., (1969), 25, 52-57.

10. Boué, J.; Boué, A.; and Lazar, P.; "The Epidemiology of
     Human Spontaneous Abortions with Chromosomal Abnormalities",
     Aging Gametes, Int. Symp. Seattle, (1975), 330-348.
11. Fuchs, F.; and Riis, P.; "Antenatal Sex Determination".
     Nature (Lond.), (1956), 177, 330.
12. Steele, M. W.; and Breg, W. T.; "Chromosome Analysis of
     Human Amniotic Fluid Cells". Lancet, (1966), 1, 383-385.
13. Jacobson, C. B.; and Barter, R. H.; "Intrauterine Diagnosis
     and Management of Genetic Defects". Am. J. Obstet. Gynecol.,
     (1967), 99, 796-807.
14. Nadler, H. L.; "Antenatal Detection of Hereditary Disorders".
     Pediatrics, (1968), 42, 912.
15. Levine, M. D.; McNeil, D. E.; Kaback, M. M.; Frazer, R. E.;
     Okada, D. M.; and Hobel, C. J.; "Second-Trimester Fetoscopy
     and Fetal Blood Sampling: Current Limitations and Problems".
     Amer. J. Obstet. Gynecol., (1974), 120, 937-943.
16. Valenti, C.; "Antenatal Detection of Hemoglobinopathies".
     Am. J. Obstet. Gynecol., (1973), 115, 851-853.
17. Hobbins, J. C.; and Mahoney, M. J.; "Fetal Blood Drawing".
     Lancet, (1975), 2, 107-109.
18. Omenn, G. S.; Figley, M. M.; Graham, C. B.; and Heinrichs,
     W. L.; "Prospects for Radiographic Intrauterine Diagnosis -
     The Syndrome of Thrombocytopenia with Absent Radii". N.
     Engl. J. Med., (1973), 288, 777-778.
19. Campbell, S.; Johnston, F. D.; Holt, E. M.; and May, P.;
     "Anencephaly: Early Ultrasonic Diagnosis and Active Manage-
     ment". Lancet, (1972), 2, 1226-1227.
20. Campbell, S.; "The Prenatal Detection of Fetal Abnormality
     by Ultrasonic Diagnosis" in Birth Defects, Proc. 4th Int.
     Conf., ed. A. G. Motulsky and W. Lenz, Excerpta Medica,
     Amsterdam, (1974), 234-239.
21. Kan, Y. W.; Valenti, C.; Guidotti, R.; Carnazza, V.; and
     Rieder, R. F.; "Fetal Blood Sampling in Utero". Lancet,
     (1974), 1, 79-80.
22. Kan, Y. W.; Golbus, M. S.; Klein, P.; and Dozy, M.;
     "Successful Application of Prenatal Diagnosis in a Pregnancy
     at Risk for Homozygous β-thalassemia". New Engl. J. Med.,
     (1975), 292, 1096-1099.
23. Hollenberg, M. D.; Kaback, M. M.; and Kazazian, H. H. Jr.;
     "Adult Hemoglobin Synthesis by Reticulocytes from the Human
     Fetus at Mid-Trimester". Science, (1971), 174, 698-702.
24. Kadotani, T.; Sato, H.; Ohama, K.; and Takahara, H.; "A
     Technical Note on the Antenatal Chromosome Analysis by Trans-
     abdominal Fetal Skin Biopsy". Jap. Jour. Human Genet.,
     (1971), 16, 42-47.
25. Hahnemann, N.; "Early Prenatal Diagnosis; A Study of Biopsy
     Techniques and Cell Culturing from Extraembryonic Membranes".
     Clin. Genet., (1974), 6, 294-306.
26. Lind, T.; and Hytten, F. E.; "Relation of Amniotic Fluid
     Volume to Fetal Weight in the First Half of Pregnancy".

Lancet, (1970), 1, 1147-1149.

27. Desnick, R. J.; Krivit, W.; and Sharp, H. L.; "In Utero
     Diagnosis of Sandhoff's Disease". Biochem. Biophys. Res.
     Commun., (1973), 51, 20-26.

28. O'Brien, J. S.; Okada, S.; Fillerup, D. L.; Veath, M. L.;
     Adornato, B.; Brenner, P. H.; and Leroy, J. G.; "Tay-Sachs
     Disease: Prenatal Diagnosis". Science, (1971), 172, 61-64.

29. Nadler, H. L.; and Gerbie, A. B.; "Enzymes in Noncultured
     Amniotic Fluid Cells". Am. J. Obstet. Gynecol, (1969), 103,
     710-712.

30. Cox, R. P.; Douglas, G.; Hutzler, J.; Lynfield, J.; and
     Dancis, J.; "In-utero Detection of Pompe's Disease". Lancet,
     (1970), 1, 893.

31. Sutcliffe, R. G.; and Brock, D. J. H.; "Enzymes in Uncul-
     tured Amniotic Fluid Cells". Clin. Chim. Acta, (1971), 31,
     363-365.

32. Hug, G.; Schubert, W. K.; Soukup, S.; "Prenatal Diagnosis of
     Type-II Glycogenosis". Lancet, (1970), 1, 1002.

33. Mukherjee, A. B.; Blattner, P. Y.; and Nitowsky, H. M.;
     Quinacrine Mustard Fluorescence of Sex Chromatin in Human
     Amniotic Fluid Cell Cultures". Nature (New Biol.), (1972),
     235, 226-229.

34. Valenti, C.; Lin, C. C.; Baum, A.; Massobrio, M.; and
     Carbonara, A.; "Prenatal Sex Determination". Am. J. Obstet.
     Gynecol., (1972), 112, 890-895.

35. Tishler, P. V.; Lamborot-Manzur, M.; and Atkins, L.; "Poly-
     morphism of the Human Y Chromosome: Fluorescence Micro-
     scopic Studies on the Sites of Morphological Variation".
     Clin. Genet., (1972), 3, 116-122.

36. Matalon, R.; Dorfman, A.; and Nadler, H. L.; "A Chemical
     Method for the Antenatal Diagnosis of Mucopolysaccharidoses".
     Lancet, (1972), 1, 798-799.

37. Elsas, L. J.; Priest, J. H.; Wheeler, F. B.; Danner, D. J.;
     and Pask, B. A.; "Maple Syrup Urine Disease: Coenzyme
     Function and Prenatal Monitoring". Metabolism, (1974), 23,
     569-579.

38. Gitlin, D.; and Biasucci, A.; "Development of γG, γA, γM,
     $\beta_1 C/\beta_1 A$, C'1 Esterase Inhibitor, Ceruloplasmin, Transferrin,
     Hemopexin, Haptoglobin, Fibrinogen, Plasminogen, α_1-Anti-
     trypsin, Orosomucoid, β-Lipoprotein, α_2-Macroglobulin, and
     Prealbumin in the Human Conceptus". J. Clin. Invest., (1969)
     48, 1433-1446.

39. Kohler, P. F.; "Maturation of the Human Complement System.
     I. Onset Time and Sites of Fetal C1q, C4, C3, and C5
     Synthesis". J. Clin. Invest., (1973), 52, 671-677.

40. Cedergvist, L. L.; Queenan, J. T.; Gadow, E. C.; and Litwin,
     S. D.; "The Origin of Gamma G Globulins in Human Amniotic
     Fluid". Am. J. Obstet. Gynecol., (1972), 113, 838-840.

41. Nadler, H. L.; Bigley, R. H.; and Hug, G.; Prenatal Detec-
     tion of Pompe's Disease". Lancet, (1970), 2, 369-370.

42. Hoehn, H.; Bryant, E. M.; Karp, L. E.; and Martin, G. M.;
     "Cultivated Cells from Diagnostic Amniocentesis in Second
     Trimester Pregnancies. I. Clinical Morphology and Growth
     Potential". Pediat. Res., (1974), 8, 746-754.
43. Westhoff, C. F.; and Rindfuss, R. R.; "Sex Preselection in
     the United States: Some Implications". Science, (1974),
     184, 633-636.
44. McKusick, V. A.; "Mendelian Inheritance in Man", 4th ed.,
     Baltimore, John Hopkins Press, 1975.
45. Krone, L. R.; Prichard, L. L.; Bradshaw, C. L.; Jones, O.
     W.; Peterson, R. M.; and Dixson, B. K.; "Antenatal Diagnosis
     of an XXX Female. A Dilema for Genetic Counseling". West.
     J. Med., (1975), 123, 17-21.
46. Hook, E. B.; "Behavioral Implications of the Human XYY Geno-
     type". Science, (1973), 179, 139-150.
47. Noël, B.; Duport, J. P.; Revil, D.; Dussuyer, I.; and Quak,
     B.; "The XYY Syndrome: Reality or Myth?" Clin. Genet.,
     (1974), 5, 387-394.
48. Penrose, L. S.; and Smith. A. F.; "Down's Anomaly".
     Churchill, London, 1966.
49. Zellweger, H.; and Simpson, J.; "Is Routine Prenatal Karyo-
     typing Indicated in Pregnancies of Very Young Women?"
     J. Pediatr., (1973), 82, 675-677.
50. Mikkelsen, M.; and Stene, J.; "Genetic Counselling in Down's
     Syndrome". Hum. Hered., (1970), 20, 457-464.
51. Stein, Z.; Susser, M.; Guterman, A. V.; "Screening Programme
     for Prevention of Down's Syndrome". Lancet, (1973), 1,
     305-310.
52. Golbus, M. S.; "The Antenatal Diagnosis of Genetic Disorders,"
     in "Office Gynecology," ed. R. Glass, Williams & Wilkins,
     Baltimore, in press.
53. Littlefield, J. W.; Milunsky, A.; and Atkins, L.; "An Over-
     view of Prenatal Genetic Diagnosis", in Birth Defects, Proc.
     4th Int. Conf., ed, A. G. Motulsky and W. Lenz, Excerpta
     Medica, Amsterdam, 1974, 234-239.
54. Schneider, J. A.; Verroust, F. M.; Kroll, W. A.; Garvin,
     A. J.; Horger, E. O., III; Wong, V. G.; Spear, G. S.;
     Jacobson, C.; Pellett, O. L.; and Becker, F. L. A.; "Pre-
     natal Diagnosis of Cystinosis". Abst., Pediatr. Res.,
     (1973), 7, 291.
55. Gerbie, A. B.; Melancon, S. B.; Ryan, C.; and Nadler, H. L.;
     "Cultivated Epithelial-Like Cells and Fibroblasts from
     Amniotic Fluid: Their Relationship to Enzymatic and Cyto-
     logic Analysis". Am. J. Obstet. Gynecol., (1972), 114,
     314-320.
56. Kaback, M. M.; and Howell, R. R.; "Infantile Metachromatic
     Leukodystrophy. Heterozygote Detection in Skin Fibroblasts
     and Possible Application to Intrauterine Diagnosis". New
     Engl. J. Med., (1970), 282, 1336-1340.
57. Galjaard, H.; Fernandes, J.; Jahodova, M.; Koster, J. F.;

and Niermeijer, M. F.; "Prenatal Diagnosis of Genetic
Disease". Bull. Europ. Soc. Hum. Genet., (1972), November,
79-91.

58. Haljaard, H.; Hoogeveen, A.; Keijzer, W.; DeWit-Verbeek,
E.; and Vlek-Noot, C.; "The Use of Quantitative Cytochemical
Analysis in Rapid Prenatal Detection and Somatic Cell
Genetic Studies of Metabolic Diseases". Histochem. J.,
(1974), 6, 491-509.

59. Hösli, P.; "Microtechniques for Rapid Prenatal Diagnosis in
Early Pregnancy", in Birth Defects, Proc. 4th Int. Conf.,
ed. A. G. Motulsky and W. Lenz, Excerpta Medica, Amsterdam,
1974, 234-239.

60. Brock, D. J. H.; and Sutcliffe, R. G.; "Alpha-Fetoprotein
in the Antenatal Diagnosis of Anencephaly and Spina Bifida".
Lancet, (1972), 2, 197-199.

61. Kjessler, B.; Sherman, M.; Johansson, S. G. O.; Gustavson,
K. H.; and Hultquist, A.; "Alpha-Fetoprotein in Antenatal
Diagnosis of Congenital Nephrosis". Lancet, (1975), 1,
432-433.

62. Milunsky, A.; Macri, J. N.; Weiss, R. R.; Alpert, E.;
McIssac; and Joshi, M. S.; "Prenatal Detection of Neural
Tube Defects. Comparison Between Alpha Fetoprotein and
Beta-Trace Protein Assays". Amer. J. Obstet. Gynecol,
(1975). 122, 313-315.

63. Wald, N. J.; Brock, D. J. H.; and Bonnar, J.; "Prenatal
Diagnosis of Spina Bifida and Anencephaly by Maternal Serum
- Alpha-Fetoprotein Measurement. A Controlled Study".
Lancet, (1974), 1, 765-767.

64. Golbus, M. S.; Personal Communication.

65. Epstein, C. J.; Schneider, E. L.; Conte, F. A.; and
Friedman, S.; "Prenatal Detection of Genetic Disorders".
Am. J. Hum. Genet., (1972), 24, 214-226.

66. Golbus, M. S.; Conte, F. A.; Schneider, E. L.; and Epstein,
C. J.; "Intrauterine Diagnosis of Genetic Defects: Results,
Problems, and Follow-up of 100 Cases in a Prenatal Genetic
Detection Center". Am. J. Obstet. Gynecol., (1974), 118,
897-905.

67. Toop, J.; and Emery, A. E. H.; "Muscle Histology in Fetuses
at Risk for Duchenne Muscular Dystrophy". Clin. Genet.,
(1974), 5, 230-233.

68. Epstein, C. J.; Brady, R. O.; Schneider, E. L.; Bradley,
R. M.; and Shapiro, D.; "In Utero Diagnosis of Niemann-Pick
Disease". Amer. J. Hum. Genet., (1971), 23, 533-535.

69. Suzuki, K.; Schneider, E. L.; and Epstein, C. J.; "In Utero
Diagnosis of Globoid Cell Leukodystrophy (Krabbe's Disease)".
Biochem. Biophys. Res. Commun., (1971), 45, 1363-1366.

70. Schneider, E. L.; Ellis, W. G.; Brady, R. O.; McCulloch,
J. R.; and Epstein, C. J.; "Infantile (Type II) Gaucher's
Disease: In Utero Diagnosis and Fetal Pathology". J.
Pediatr., (1972), 81, 1134-1139.

71. Schneider, E. L.; Ellis, W. G.; Brady, R. O.; McCulloch, J. R.; and Epstein, C. J.; "Prenatal Niemann-Pick Disease: Biochemical and Histologic Examination of a 19 Gestational Week Fetus". Pediatr. Res., (1972), 6, 720-729.

72. Ellis, W. G.; Schneider E. L.; McCulloch, J. R.; Suzuki K.; and Epstein, C. J.; "Fetal Globoid Cell Leukodystrophy (Krabbe's Disease): Pathological and Biochemical Examination". Arch. Neurol., (1973), 29, 253-257.

73. Nadler, H. L.; and Egan, T. J.; "Deficiency of Lysosomal Acid Phosphatase; a New Familial Metabolic Disorder". N. Engl. J. Med., (1970), 282, 302-307.

74. Hirschhorn, R.; Beratis, N.; Rosen, F.; Parkman, R.; Stern, R.; and Palmer, S.; "Adenosine-Deaminase Deficiency in a Child Diagnosed Prenatally". Lancet, (1975), 1, 73.

75. Goodman, S. I.; Mace, J. W.; Turner, B.; and Garrett, W. J.; "Antenatal Diagnosis of Argininosuccinic Aciduria". Clin. Genet., (1973), 4, 236-240.

76. Brady, R. O.; Uhlendorf, B. W.; and Jacobson, C. B.; "Farby's Disease: Antenatal Detection". Science, (1971), 172, 174-175.

77. Donnell, G.; Personal Communication.

78. Fensom, A. H.; Benson, P. F.; and Blunt, S.; "Prenatal Diagnosis of Galactosemia". Brit. Med. J., (1974), 4, 386-387.

79. Lowden, J. A.; Cutz, E.; Conen, P. E.; Rudd, N.; and Doran, T. A.; "Prenatal Diagnosis of GM_1 - Gangliosidosis". N. Engl. J. Med., (1973), 288, 225-228.

80. Booth, C. W.; Gerbie, A. B.; and Nadler, H. L.; "Intrauterine Detection of GM_1 - Gangliosidosis, Type 2". Pediatr., (1973), 52, 521-524.

81. Nadler, H. L.; and Messina, A. M.; "In-Utero Detection of Type-II Glycogenosis (Pompe's Disease). Lancet, (1969), 2, 1277-1278.

82. Fratantoni, J. C.; Neufeld, E. F.; Uhlendorf, B. W.; and Jacobson, C. B.; "Intrauterine Diagnosis of the Hurler and Hunter Syndromes". N. Engl. J. Med., (1969), 280, 686-688.

83. Neufeld, E. F.; "Mucopolysaccharidoses" in "Antenatal Diagnosis", ed. A. Dorfman, University of Chicago Press, Chicago, 1972, 217-228.

84. Benzie, R.; Doran, T. A.; Escoffery, W.; Gardner, H. A.; Hoar, D. I.; Hunter, A.; Malone, R.; Miskin, M.; and Rudd, N. L.; "Prenatal Diagnosis of Hypophosphatasia". Birth Defects Conference, 1975 (abstract).

85. Boyle, J. A.; Raivio, K. O.; Astrin, K. H.; Schulman, J. D.; Seegmiller, J. E.; and Jacobson, C. B.; "Lesch-Nyhan Syndrome: Preventive Control by Prenatal Diagnosis". Science, (1970), 169, 688-689.

86. Dancis, J.; "Maple Syrup Urine Disease", in "Antenatal Diagnosis", ed. A. Dorfman, University of Chicago Press, Chicago, 1972, 123-125.

87. Nadler, H. L.; and Gerbie, A. B.; "Role of Amniocentesis
    in the Intrauterine Detection of Genetic Disorders".
    N. Engl. J. Med., (1970), 282, 596-599.
88. Mahoney, M. J.; Rosenberg, L. E.; Waldenstrom, J.;
    Lindbald, B.; and Zetterstrom, R.; "Prenatal Diagnosis
    of Methylmalonicaciduria". Pediatrics Res., (1973), 7,
    342.
89. Warren, R. J.; Condron, C. J.; Hollister, D.; Huijing, F.;
    Neufeld, E. F.; Hall, C. W.; McLeod, A. G. W.; and
    Lorincz, A. E.; "Antenatal Diagnosis of Mucolipidosis II
    (I-cell disease)". Pediatrics Res., (1973), 7, 343.
90. Harper, P. S.; Lawrence, K. M.; Parkes, A.; Wusteman, F. S.;
    Kresse, H.; Von Figura, K.; Ferguson-Smith, M. A.;
    Duncan, D. M.; Logan, R. W.; Hall, F.; and Whiteman, P.;
    "Sanfilippo A Disease in the Fetus". J. Med. Genet.,
    (1974), 11, 123-132.
91. Ramsay, C. A.; Coltart, T. M.; Blunt, S.; Pawsey, S. A.;
    Gianelli, F.; "Prenatal Diagnosis of Xeroderma Pigmentosum".
    Lancet, (1974), 2, 1109.

The Analytical Laboratory of Neonatology

SAMUEL NATELSON

Department of Biochemistry, Michael Reese Medical Center, Chicago, Ill. 60616

Functions of the Pediatric Laboratory

Objectives. The objectives of the chemical laboratory of the Neonatology Division of a hospital are to:

1. Supply data obtained by analysis of various biological materials from the newborn.
2. To develop new procedures for improving the service to the Pediatric Department.
3. To act as an advisory and consultant center for problems related to clinical chemistry for the Department of Neonatology; and
4. To carry on an active program in research and development in order to improve the procedures for the understanding and the diagnosis of the disease process in the newborn.

The Newborn Infant. Figure 1 is a photograph showing the appearance of a 2-1/2 kilo premature infant as compared to a nurse's hand. This infant is not the smallest infant one has to contend with since premature infants weighing 600 grams with no genetic abnormalities are occasionally seen.

Figure 2 shows a similar infant that has become dehydrated as a result of not receiving any fluids for approximately 36 hours after birth. In another infant who weighed 1 kilo at birth, no fluids were administered for 27 hours. During that period of time, 144 grams of body weight was lost which comprises approximately 19% of the original weight of the infant.

The Newborn and the Laboratory. The wellbeing of the premature infant can be ascertained by measuring blood pH, electrolytes and other blood components on a routine basis. The maintenance of these infants' electrolyte balance and normal pH is shown in Figure 3. An infant placed on a high protein diet milk formula developed an acidosis, and when brought to normal pH

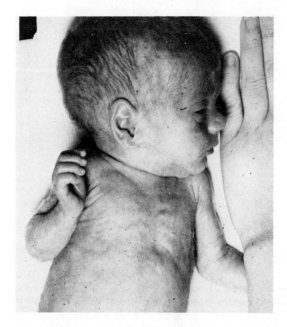

Figure 1. Premature infant, well hydrated at birth

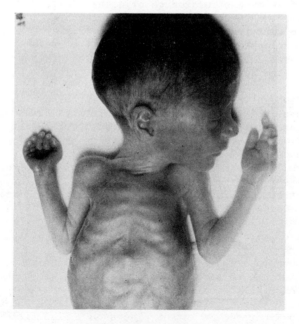

Figure 2. Premature infant similar to Figure 1, but deprived of fluids for 36 hr showing symptoms of dehydration

responded with a rapid recovery of his initial weight and weight
gain(1).

From the above, derives the fundamental concept that the
newborn infant must be maintained in an adequate degree of hy-
dration and in electrolyte balance in order for the infant to
thrive. In some cases, where for one reason or other, the infant is not able to take fluids by mouth in the normal manner,
one may need to resort to supplementary fluid therapy by vein.
For a rational approach to this problem one needs to have available from the clinical chemical laboratory, rapid response in
order to continuously monitor changes in electrolyte levels
so that fluids can be modified so as to correct these abnormalities.

Parenteral Fluids. During the past ten years interest
has been renewed in the total alimentation of the infant by vein
(2). The motivation for this is the fact that neonates may
suffer from some congenital malformation of the intestinal tract
which would require surgical resection. If this is done, then
one needs some outside way for alimentation, bypassing the intestine, until the intestine is able to heal and recover its
normal function. This may take many weeks. A second source
of motivation is the small premature infant weighing less than
a kilogram, whose immature central nervous system and gastrointestinal tract make it difficult to establish nutrition by oral
intake soon after birth. These also require total intravenous
nutrition for a substantial period of time.

A major breakthrough occurred in intravenous alimentation
in 1966 when it was shown in puppies that not only could one
maintain an animal in fluid and electrolyte balance by total
intravenous alimentation, but also that one could achieve
weight gain, approaching that of the normal while the animals
received nothing other than fluids intravenously (3). This was
accomplished by the use of hyperosmotic glucose and protein
hydrolysate solutions, along with the required amount of salt
and vitamins to maintain the infant. An important contribution
to this development was the development of materials such as the
silicones, which could lie in the vein or artery of the infant
without producing a tissue reaction. Because of the use of
hypertonic solutions in this procedure some refer to this method
of fluid administration as hypertonic alimentation. Figure 4
illustrates the route used for administering fluids for total
alimentation.

In addition to these two applications, intravenous nutrition and fluid therapy has been given for many years to newborns
with chronic diarrhea, malabsorption for various reasons, and
other problems associated with disease.

Laboratory Service. As a minimum, the physician requires
that a laboratory be available on a 24 hour a day basis, which

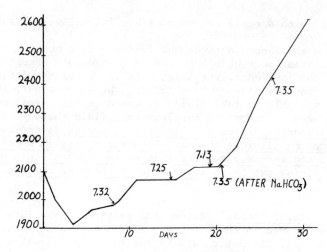

Figure 3. Effect of adjustment of pH to the normal range
on weight gain in a premature infant

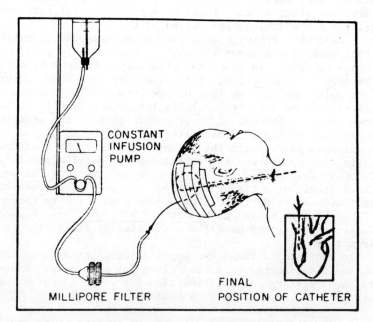

Figure 4. Total intravenous alimentation. Demonstration of method
of I.V. administration (after Winters, et al.).

is capable of analyzing blood and urine samples for, at least,
sugar, urea, protein, sodium, potassium, chloride, calcium,
magnesium, and blood pH. With the small premature, and even
with full term neonates, respiration may be a problem, it is
important that the laboratory have available, on an emergency
basis, methods for the analysis for pCO_2, pO_2, total CO_2, oxygen
content, hemoglobin and hematocrit values. It is advantageous
to calculate P_{50} values from the data so as to aid the physician
in determining whether he is dealing with an abnormal oxygen
transport system (4).

In addition, the physician with the aid of the clinical
chemist, needs to calculate salt and water requirements for
the newborn infant. Of prime importance is the determination
of how much sodium bicarbonate is required to correct an acidosis, or in rare cases, how much ammonium chloride might be required to correct an alkalosis (5).

During the administration of fluids, the newborn infant
requires that one periodically assay for the various components
discussed above, so as to see whether the fluids being administered are serving their purpose or need to be changed. The
newborn infant does not have the reserve capacity that the adult
has in being able to buffer and adjust for various problems
which may arise during fluid therapy. For this reason, the
newborn infant during acute treatment may require repetitive
analyses, at relatively short intervals. Even when the condition is stabilized it is customary for the pediatrician to
require analyses for electrolytes at periodic intervals for
the security of the patient.

In addition to the above, the laboratory of Neonatology
needs to be equipped so as to screen newborn infants for the
various genetic diseases. In the case of phenylketonuria, many
states, including the State of Illinois, require that every
infant be screened for this defect. Further, many hospitals
are screening, in general, for aminoacidopathies in serum and
urine of newborn infants. In some areas, screening is being
done for the glycogenoses (6), lipidoses (7), and mucopolysaccharidoses (8). Screening for biochemical defects in the
erythrocytes, such as the various enzymes of the Embden-Meyerhof
sequence, and also the Shunt Mechanism (9), are required to
be part of the armamentarium of the laboratory of Neonatology.

In certain areas, such as Chicago, where there is a high
percentage of certain ethnic groups, certain defects, such as
glucose-6-phosphate dehydrogenase are more common, and screening
is useful in explaining some of the unexplained non-spherocytic
hemolytic anemias and other abnormalities. In addition, the
laboratory of Neonatology needs to be prepared to analyze for
numerous metabolic intermediates which appear in increased
amounts with certain genetic abnormalities. These include the
porphyrins (10), porphobilinogen and ethanolamine phosphate
(11), as typical examples.

Along with an effective electrolyte and screening program
for genetic disease, the laboratory of Neonatology needs to
have the capability of analyzing for other components in blood
serum, which aid in the diagnosis of disease. These include
such determinations as alkaline phosphatase, and various other
enzymes, creatinine, uric acid and a host of other components
which are normally assayed by the main clinical laboratory.

Toxicological problems among infants are relatively common.
For example, it is now routine to follow the course of changes
in Dilantin levels of patients who are being treated for various
convulsive disorders (12). It is also important to be able
to detect and assay for other drugs that are used in the newborn,
such as various other anticonvulsants, salicylates, and a host
of others.

Need for a Separate Pediatric Laboratory. From the above
discussion, one can see that one may divide the analytical
activities of the laboratory of Neonatology into four major
classes.

1. Those associated with the acute and chronic
   treatment of newborns for respiratory, fluid
   and electrolyte problems.
2. Those associated with the screening of newborns
   for genetic diseases and for determining genetic
   diseases in newborns after some abnormalities
   are noted.
3. Those associated with drugs which may have been
   administered in excess to the infant or, more
   commonly, may have been administered correctly,
   where the physician requires that he be assured
   that the drug level is in the range that he intended.
4. Those associated with general clinical laboratory service assaying for numerous other components which are also done in the main laboratory
   of clinical chemistry.

It should be apparent from the above, that the problems
of the laboratory of Neonatology are distinct from the main
laboratory, and it would always be advisable that it be maintained as a separate unit, or at least in a separate section
of the clinical laboratory of the institution in which clinical chemistry is being practiced.

The Pediatric Laboratory As A Micro Analytical Unit

The Fundamental Analytical Problem. There is a problem,

which is unique to the laboratory of Neonatology and distinct
from that of the main laboratory, that is the problem of the
size of the sample to be analyzed. If one assumes that approximately 9% of the weight of the newborn is blood, and if the
newborn weighs one kilogram, then one has a total volume of 90 ml
of blood, of which about half is plasma. This should be compared to the 9 liters available from an adult who weighs 100
kilo. To withdraw 5 ml of blood from a 1 kilo premature, would
then be almost equivalent to drawing 500 ml from an adult. One
is therefore necessarily limited to the amount of blood to be
drawn repetitively. Even if one is able to get into the vein
of the newborn, one prefers to limit the total volume of blood
that is drawn to less than 1 ml.

   From the fingertip, earlobe or heel prick, one would like
to stay within the limits of 100 - 200µl as a maximum. If
one then draws 100µl of blood, then one cannot hope to have
more than approximately 40µl of plasma, since the hematocrit
of newborn infants is relatively high. This volume would be
substantially lowered, in the dehydrated infant, with which
one is working, normally.

   Assuming that one had 50µl , and one were to use 10µl per
analysis, then one could do 5 tests, which might be sodium,
potassium, chloride, sugar and urea. However, experience has
taught us that unless we do all of the tests required to evaluate the well-being of the infant, as far as his electrolyte
balance is concerned, then it often turns out that the one
test that we did not do is the most important. For example,
in the experience of the author, in one case, a glucose level
was not done on an infant who was admitted dehydrated. Subsequently, it turned out that the infant was suffering from
hypoglycemia and was the offspring of a diabetic mother. In
another case, the hematocrit value was not obtained for certain
reasons. Subsequently, it was shown that even at birth, this
newborn had a hematocrit value of only 28%, and had a severe
hemolytic anemia. It is therefore the practice, in many laboratories of Neonatology, to set up a goal for determinations
that need be done on the first sample of blood drawn from the
infant. This would require as a minimum approximately 10 components. In order to meet this need one may resort to two
different solutions:

1. A larger specimen, of the order of 0.5 ml
   may be routinely drawn. This in effect requires that this be taken by vein.
2. One may decrease the volume required per
   test so that fingertip blood may be utilized
   if one desires. This approach is the subject
   of subsequent discussion.

Measuring the sample. The question arises as to what the

lower limit of specimen volume can be sampled conveniently
with a degree of accuracy required for the particular component being analyzed. In actual practice, there are at least
two ways in which one may measure a small quantity of liquid.
In the first method, a small quantity of material may be sampled directly for each test. Alternatively, this may then be
mixed with a diluting fluid of larger volume, say of the order
of 1 or 2 ml. In this case, if 10 μl were sampled, and diluted
to 1 ml, then each 100 μl would actually contain 1 μl of specimen. This could then be measured with an accuracy of better
than 1 or 2%.

In order to indicate the accuracy that can be obtained
from a capillary pipette, one may refer to the so called Sahli
pipette, which is approximately 80 mm from mark to tip. This
pipette is used as a washout pipette and can measure samples
which are readily reproducible to 1 part in 80, since it is
a relatively simple thing for the eye to see 1 mm. On the other
hand, if one places a bulb in the tube, and cuts the bore down
at the mark by 50%, then this would decrease the error by a
factor of 4. It is thus practicable to sample from a micro-
pipette, which is used as a washout pipette, with greater accuracy than one can sample from a conventional macro pipette,
which delivers 1 ml by blowout, or to deliver. Figures 5 and 6
illustrate various designs of micropipets (13,14).

It is advantageous to attach the micropipet to a sampler
diluter. In this manner, the sample is aspirated by means of
a plunger. The technician is not required to adjust the volume
nor to make a judgement, because this is being done by a plunger, and accuracy is a function of the sampler diluter. If then
one wipes off the tip and then ejects a diluting fluid, one
could then proceed to measure out very small samples limited
only on the nature of the tip. This can be seen in the
sequence of events in Figure 7.

From a glass tip it is impracticable to measure specimens
smaller than 10 μl . This is so because the holdback of the
wetted glass, on the outside, is a significant portion of the
volume sampled. If the tip is then dipped into the solution
and then used as a washout pipet, a serious error would be introduced.

For these reasons, the plastic tip, or the siliconed glass
tip have been used for micro measurements. With a plastic tip, there is no limit to the size of the specimen which
may be sampled. For example, it is possible to sample amounts
of the order of nanoliters, provided one resorted to a micromanipulator. While the clinical chemist has not availed himself
generally of this technique, the physiologist, has for many
years, been measuring samples from within a single cell, or from
perhaps, a renal tubule, so that the sample can then be subsequently analyzed. It awaits only an intelligent manufacturer
to adapt the micromanipulator as a routine tool in the Pediatric

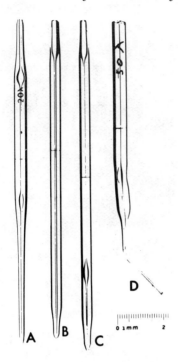

Figure 5. Examples of micro-pipets. A, pipet with slender tip; B, Sahli pipet; C, Accupipet with bulb; D, pipet with bulb and bent tip.

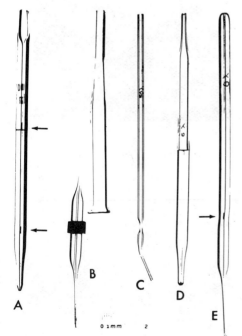

Figure 6. Self zeroing ultramicro pipets. A, constriction at two marks; B, overflow type with constriction at both ends; C, Lang–Levy pipet; D, another type of constriction pipet; E, Speedipet of Natelson.

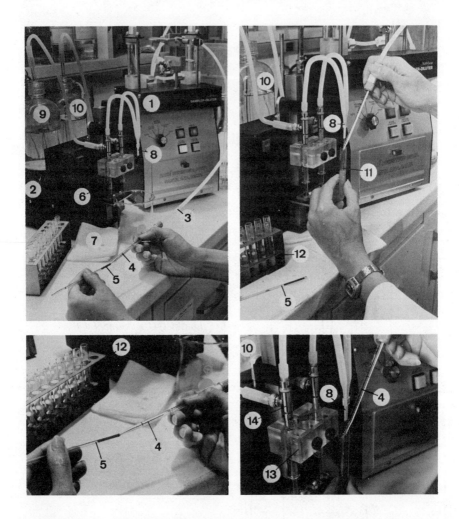

Figure 7. Demonstration of the method of sampling from a capillary with a sampler–diluter and dispensing with a simultaneous dispenser for two reagents, so as to prepare a protein precipitate of the Somogyi type in two steps. 1, sampler–diluter; 2, dispenser (both made by Rohé Scientific Co., Santa Ana, Calif.); 3, connecting tube; 4, Sahli pipet; 5, blood collecting tube; 6, syringe for dispensing one of the reagents; 7, gauze for wiping off the tips of the pipet; 8, ganged tips for dispensing the two reagents; 9 and 10, zinc sulfate and barium hydroxide reagents, respectively; 11, test tube to receive the specimen and the reagent; 12, rack of test tubes already sampled; 13, block holding the two syringes; 14, valve.

Laboratory. This will eventually come about because this is the
practical solution to the sampling of minute specimens. The
micromanipulator, may be adapted to a sampler-diluter where
amounts of the order of a few nanoliters are being sampled
followed through the same tip by a diluting solution of
several microliters.

At present, several of the instruments which are being
utilized for enzyme analysis, such as the centrifugal analyzers (15), have been measuring samples of the order of 5 µl.
But this is deceptive, for the simple reason that in order to
sample the 5 microliters, one requires 100 microliters or more
to be present in the cup. Therefore, the sample size required
is not the size that is being sampled, but the size that is
needed in the sampling cup. This problem may be approached
in several ways. The problem of sample control will now be
discussed.

Sample Control. In figure 7, the technician is sampling
with a sampler diluter from the capillary. Here we see what
is called "sample control". None of the specimen is being
wasted on the walls of a cup. All of it is being taken eventually into the capillary and then dispensed. With a setup as
shown in Figure 7, synchronized with this diluter, is a multiple dispenser, which can dispense several reagents at the same
time that the specimen is added to the tube.

In the particular example shown, zinc sulfate and barium
hydroxide are being dispensed into the test tube so as to precipitate the proteins. The filtrate obtained is the filtrate
from 10 microliters of serum. This can be used for several
purposes and in the application being referred to, an amount
equivalent to 3 microliters is being used for sugar determination, by the hexokinase procedure and an amount equivalent
to 3 microliters is being used for urea estimation with
diacetylmonoxime (15).

Figure 7, therefore, illustrates several practical methods
of sampling. First, the sampling of a relatively large initial
volume (10 µl). This has the advantage that it can be measured
with precision by the particular instrument employed; second,
the removal of protein from the specimen, and, third, the
taking of aliquots so that smaller volumes of sample can be
removed with the same accuracy with which the initial sample
was measured.

A similar procedure is used in the SMAC system of Technicon, where a modest sample of several hundred microliters is
diluted and then aliquots are fed to various channels for analysis.

In summary, as far as measuring the initial specimen, it
is recommended that the ordinary micro pipettes be aspirated
by automatic means. It is also recommended that where large
numbers of tests are to be performed on a single sample that

the initial specimen be diluted so as to have a reservoir from
which to measure large numbers of aliquots. If this is followed, then with present technology it is not very difficult
to set up procedures for determining sugar, urea, uric acid,
creatinine enzymatically, and the various enzymes and electrolytes, on approximately 1 microliter aliquots. With this
approach, a single drop of blood, which represents approximately 50 microliters would yield 20 microliters of plasma,
which could then be utilized for 20 distinct tests.

It must be pointed out, that at present, this type of
equipment cannot be readily purchased, but must be assembled
from materials which are commercially available. The cost of
a sampling station would be less than $3,000. This would in-
clude 3 or 4 multiple dispensers, a single sample diluter and
possibly a micromanipulator. If the micromanipulator is
omitted, then the cost would be less than $2,000.

Another approach to this problem is to use the type of
syringe commonly referred to as the Eppendorf syringe. This
is based upon the concept, originally introduced by Sanz, that
plastic which does not wet, can be used to sample from
different specimens without cross contamination (16). In the
original Sanz system, he used a small bottle, which was pressed
and then released to create a negative pressure, and aspirate
the specimen, and then by positive pressure on the bottle,
expel the specimen. In the Eppendorf system this is done with
a plunger. The plunger retreats, aspirating the specimen, it
then advances a greater distance than it retreated originally,
expelling the specimen. The tip is disposable, so that a tip
can be changed with each specimen, or can be changed after it
becomes wetted by long use. This system is not very reproducible. It is difficult to measure an exact specimen volume and
it is difficult to reproduce the volume but if one is satisfied
with an accuracy of approximately ±5%, this is useful. For
this reason it has found wide use with the procedures using
competitive binding systems of analysis. There the accuracy
of the procedure is approximately ±12% and the error introduced
by the Eppendorf pipette is acceptable.

Obtaining The Specimen. Up to this time, the assumption has
been made that a specimen in a capillary tube has been presented
to the laboratory of Neonatology for analysis. I would like to
address myself now to the problem of obtaining a specimen.

This problem is by far the most difficult of all problems
presenting themselves to the laboratory of clinical chemistry.
It is relatively simple to analyze a specimen for a host of components, as compared to the obtaining of the specimen in a dehydrated infant, particularly one who is in circulatory collapse.

The Pediatric Chemistry Committee of the AACC is now turning
its attention to this particular problem as a separate study.

The procedures generally recommended are as follows. First, the blood collector must prepare himself for obtaining the blood. This includes the same procedure which one would undergo if one were initiating a surgical process. In other words, the operator needs to scrub his hands thoroughly to remove any contaminants which may be injurious to the infant. While a surgeon uses rubber gloves, it is not customary for the blood collector to do so. If the hands are properly washed, this is perfectly satisfactory, since one is not going to do extensive surgery.

The patient then needs to be prepared. In the case of the heel prick, a leg of the infant is massaged or warmed so as to increase circulation to the heel where the puncture is to be made. The site from which the collection of blood is made, is determined by the size of the infant. In prematures, where the fingers are extremely tiny, one has no choice but to obtain the specimen from the heel. In older children, the large toe may be used. In using the heel, one does not use the bottom of the heel because here the capillaries lie deep. One uses instead the back of the heel, where the capillaries come near the surface. Generally, sterile scapel blades or lances are used to puncture the skin and obtain the blood flow. Figure 8 illustrates the process of obtaining the specimen.

In Figure 8, it is noted that the blood is being taken from the bottom of the heel. This is not the correct technique. However, the principles discussed above are shown in the picture.

It is best to allow a drop to accumulate at the site where the puncture has taken place and then use the collecting tube which is held in a downward position to aspirate the specimen by a combination of capillarity and gravity. This can be seen in Figure 8. Note that the operator does not aspirate with suction. As each drop enters the capillary, the operator then moves the blood to the back of the capillary and then forward again, by rotating his wrists, while the second drop is collecting on the heel. In this way, the heparin that lines the wall of the capillary is equally distributed throughout the blood, and clotting is prevented. Prior to touching to the second drop, the blood is brought to the tip of the collecting tube so as to produce a continuous flow of blood.

If adequate flow does not occur after a reasonably deep puncture, sometimes massaging the leg downward will start the flow, sometimes merely waiting will start the flow. At the initial incision, there is a short period when the capillaries constrict. After a few minutes they relax and open up again. If one is patient, the blood flow will start. However, where no flow occurs, then one needs to resort to the bottom of the lobe of the ear, because while the blood flow may be restricted to the extremities in certain severe conditions, the flow to the head and the brain is not, and one can usually get an adequate amount of capillary blood from the ear. Once the blood

is collected, the bottom of the capillary is capped, with a
plastic cap, which is commercially available, and the samples
are brought to the laboratory where they are processed.

In the case of the capillary blood, it is extremely important that the specimen not be allowed to stand for extensive
periods of time before centrifugation. If the blood is to be
transferred to the pH meter, then the collecting tube is sealed
at both ends during transportation. It is then aspirated into
the pH instrument as soon as practicable since one needs a
smooth even flow in order to aspirate a specimen into the conventional micro pH meter. After the whole blood has been sampled for various purposes, it is important that the remaining
blood be centrifuged promptly. If not, it will clot. Subse-
quentially, centrifuging with a clot will tend to hemolyze the
blood. Erythrocytes will adhere to the wall and as they are
pulled down by the clot, they will be ruptured. Those who do
not observe these precautions will find that it is rather difficult to obtain unhemolyzed blood.

In the small premature, if the collection of capillary
blood has been unsuccessful, then one needs to obtain
blood from the scalp or the jugular vein. This is never
attempted by the technician, but is done by the resident or
member of the medical staff.

Generally, it is wise to rely on those individuals for
obtaining capillary blood who are successful in doing so. Not
everyone can obtain blood by fingertip from newborns readily,
and this is particularly true for residents. If one finds a
technician who is successful regularly in obtaining capillary
blood from the infants, then that technician is the one who
should be entrusted exclusively with that job. It is one area
where skill is not always teachable. Certain individuals have
a certain knack for obtaining blood where others do not.

After the capillary has been filled, it is necessary to
transport the capillary, usually, to the laboratory. For this
purpose it is sealed at bedside. Most commonly it is capped
with a plastic cap which is commercially available. However,
it can be sealed with either sealing wax or with Kronig's cement,
and then be brought to the laboratory. This sealing of the
tube is shown in Figure 9.

After the tube has been sealed, it is brought to the laboratory and centrifuged. Usually, it is then cut by means of a
file or an ampoule file at the interface, between the plasma and
the cells. In Figure 10, the operator has just cut and broken
the capillary above the plasma. Some prefer to do this first
before cutting at the interface between the plasma and cells
in order to remove any adhering blood particularly at the narrow
tip of the capillary.

In Figure 11, the capillary with the plasma, is held in
the left hand of the operator and the aspirating pipet is held
in the right hand. Notice that the operator tilts the tube to

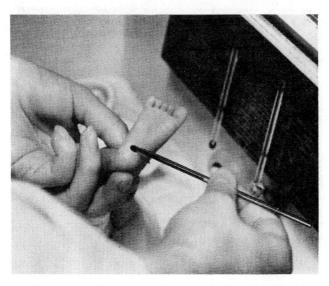

Figure 8. *Collecting the specimen from the infants heel*

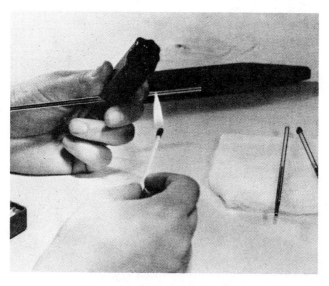

Figure 9. *Sealing the specimen*

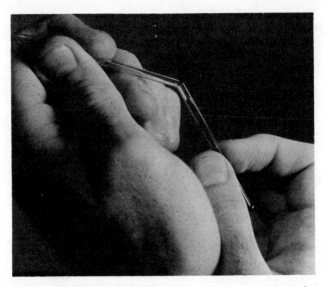

Figure 10. Breaking the tube to separate the serum from the erythrocytes

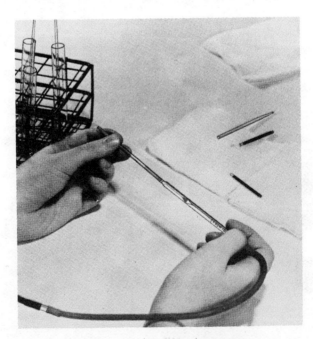

Figure 11. Sampling from the cut tube

bring the plasma to the end and then allows the plasma to run
in by gravity and capillarity into the sampling pipette. As
shown earlier, in Figure 7, this pipet could be used to sample
with a sampler diluter.

   The Specimen. One must keep in mind that the specimen
to be analyzed, which is the blood of a premature or newborn
infant, has certain characteristics of its own, which distinguishes it from blood which one normally obtains from the normal
adult. First, bilirubin concentration is generally elevated.
Values as high as 60 mg/l are not uncommon in normal infants,
especially on the third day of life, when adjustment is taking
place by extensive destruction of hemoglobin. Second, the
erythrocytes of the neonate are rather fragile, and it is not
uncommon to encounter blood which is partially hemolyzed. Third,
with the destruction of the erythrocytes, and especially in
view of the fact that the blood one obtains is not necessarily
fasting blood, it is not uncommon for the blood of the premature to be turbid. All of these factors affect the choice of
methodology which can be utilized in the laboratory of Neonatology.
   The methodology selected for the laboratory of Neonatology
needs to have as its prime objective, accuracy, that is specificity for what it is analyzing. This automatically eliminates many of the commercial automatic systems which are in
common use, and which do not process the specimen adequately
to remove interfering substances before analysis. The methodology discussed below is selected as being applicable to the
type of specimen that is supplied to the analyst in the laboratory of Neonatology.
   In addition to blood, certain types of specimens are submitted to the Pediatric laboratory which would not be commonly
seen elsewhere. An example of this is sweat for analysis of
chloride. The process of obtaining the sweat by iontophoresis
usually falls to the personnel of the Laboratory of Neonatology (17). Stool for analysis of lipids and trypsin is more
commonly submitted to the Laboratory of Neonatology than to
the laboratory which services the adult population. The reason
for this is that one is screening for certain intestinal
diseases characteristic of infants and newborns which are rare
in adults. Such conditions would be celiac disease, cystic
fibrosis and others.
   In addition to the specimens discussed above, it is common
for the laboratory of Neonatology to process the erythrocytes
and the leukocytes for enzymatic defects of genetic origin including aberrant hemoglobin identification. The laboratory
which services the adult would be called upon to do these
tests much less commonly.
   In summary, the specimens which are submitted to the laboratory of Neonatology require that more extensive processing

be performed to remove interfering substances before the substance is assayed. However, as newer techniques develop, which are more specific, it is practicable to assay directly for the component in which one is interested. Examples of this would be the use of glucose analyzers which measure the oxygen generated with glucose oxidase and certain other specific ion electrodes which will react directly with the substances sought. Amperometric titration for chloride is an example where processing of the sample is not required.

The specimens submitted to the Laboratory of Neonatology, are also more varied and are usually analyzed on an individual basis. All of these factors need to be taken into account in setting up and operating a Pediatric Laboratory of clinical chemistry.

Instrumentation and Methodology. The instrumentation and methodology as applied to the Pediatric laboratory will now be discussed in relationship to particular components which are being assayed. The sequence choosen has no significance other than that these are the tests which are most frequently requested.

Before discussing these most commonly applied tests in detail, certain general principles should be presented. Converting a macro-method to a micro-method sometimes involves no more effort than decreasing all the volumes used in the procedure. This general procedure is well known to clinical chemists. A typical example would be the Folin method for doing sugar analysis, where a final volume of 25 ml was obtained. Since only 2 ml of solution are required for reading in a colorimeter, it is obvious that more than a 12 fold increase in sensitivity and decrease in sample size can be achieved merely by measuring out volumes which are smaller.

Dr. Sanz, from Switzerland, has, in the past, designed a system which was marketed commercially. The system was based on the philosophy that by keeping concentrations high a greater accuracy would be achieved. This was done by using very small volumes of sample of the order of $10 - 25 \mu l$, and then adding reagents, of approximately $100 \mu l$ in volume. For this purpose, ultramicro cuvettes were designed which maintained the same light path. These are still in use today, the latest application being to the Perkin-Elmer Enzyme System. Figure 12 illustrates this principle.

In contradistinction to this philosophy, is the philosophy proposed by the author, for many years, even antidating Sanz's system, that the only micro specimen to be measured need be the original sample. Subsequent to that, methodology could be devised which would permit the sampling of larger volumes. These could then be handled more conveniently.

In order to bring this about, it was necessary to take advantage of certain fundamental principles of analytical chem-

istry. It was advocated that narrower band pass filters be
used for increased sensitivity. For example, for the diacetyl
method, for urea determination, the sensitivity with an interference filter is approximately 8 fold over that with a conventional colored piece of glass with a wide band pass. This
can be seen in Figure 13.

Along the same lines it was advocated that colors be read
at the absorption maximum rather than at some other convenient
point. An example of this is the increase in absorbance one
obtains when analyzing for bromide by means of gold chloride
(18). As can be seen from Figure 14, the peak with gold bromide
increases by a factor of more than 2 when the color is extracted
into octanol and read at its absorption maximum (18).

Figure 14 also demonstrates the principle that sometimes
extraction into an organic solvent increases the intensity of
the color. This is true, for example, for ferric thiocyanate,
where extraction into an organic solvent will increase the
sensitivity of iron determination to that obtainable with the
phenanthrolines. The advantage of the iron ferric thiocyanate
method in organic solvents is the fact that it is insensitive
to pH changes, which is not true for the phenanthroline procedures (19).

Another method that is commonly used for increasing sensitivity of a system is to increase the length of the light path.
This is shown in Figure 15. In this case, the same volume is
now read through a longer light path.

In Figure 15, comparison is made of the absorbance obtainable with a 1 centimeter light path as compared to an increased
light path, with various instruments. Sensitivity is directly
proportional to the length of the light path. This principle
has become extremely important in the determination of trace
gases. For example, if an individual has been exposed to a
particular gas, such as fluorohydrocarbons, and has then left
the area for substantial periods of time, up to as many as 2
or 3 days, it is possible to have him breathe into a cuvette
which is several meters long, and is then placed in the path
of an infrared beam. The gas can then readily be detected
and identified by means of a spectrum drawn for the major lines.

In the authors experience, the amount of carbon dioxide
in 10 microliters of blood can readily be determined by adding
the blood to an acid, through which bubbles an inert gas. The
CO_2 is then brought into the field of a long cuvette, of approximately 20" in length, and the carbon dioxide measured at
the near infrared with a filter instrument. Instrumentation
can be designed readily for measurement of the carbon dioxide
content of as little as $1\,\mu l$ of plasma with this principle at
the rate of approximately 40-60 per hour.

There are many techniques, which in their very nature
permit the assay of very minute amounts of components in solution. The atomic absorption instrument is an example of such

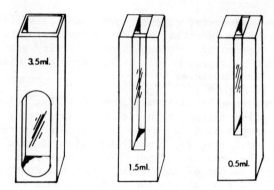

Figure 12.   Maintenance of the same light path of
10 mm with smaller volumes

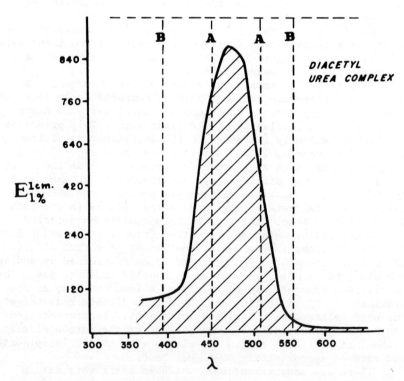

Figure 13.   Demonstrating that a narrow band pass filter will increase
sensitivity

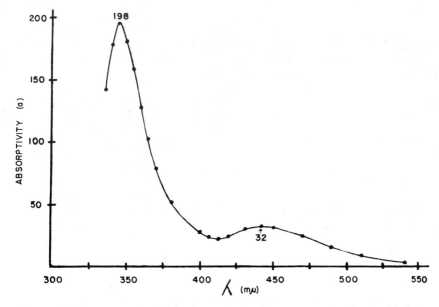

Figure 14.   *Increase in sensitivity by extraction into an organic solvent and choice of a high absorbance peak for bromide*

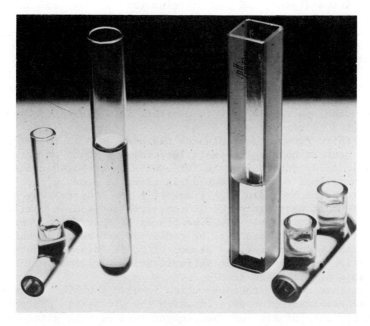

Figure 15.   *Increasing sensitivity by lengthening the light path*

a device. In addition, fluorescence techniques readily measure
concentrations of the order of 0.02 micrograms/ml for many
substances. If fluorescence is measured in place of absorbance,
increase in sensitivity of a factor of approximately 20 can
be achieved when NADPH is being used.

Certain ion selective electrodes, such as the iodide and
the chloride electrode, permit the assay of minute quantities
if the electrode is properly designed for the purpose (20).
Long range, many determinations which are presently being performed by chemical procedures, will be performed in the future
with specific ion electrodes. Using the iodide electrode the
high sensitivity of iodimetry is augmented manyfold.

How these and other principles are used in the Pediatric
laboratory will now be discussed in connection with specific
methodology which is recommended by the author for use in the
laboratory of Neonatology.

Assay for Specific Components

Glucose. There are four basic principles utilized for
glucose analysis. The most widely used depends upon the reduction of some element such as copper or iron. This is the
principle of the Folin-Wu method, the ferricyanide method, used
on the Autoanalyzer, and the cupreine (21) method used on the
SMA-12/60.

A second principle used widely for glucose analysis, is
that of the oxidation of glucose enzymatically, mediated by
the action of glucose oxidase with the formation of gluconic
acid and hydrogen peroxide (22). In this procedure it is the
hydrogen peroxide which is usually assayed for determination
of glucose. This method suffers from the action of inhibitors
which occur, particularly with patients in a diabetic coma and
these need to be removed.

A third general method which has been used in the past,
is the conversion of glucose to furfural, by means of strong
sulfuric acid, condensing the furfural with certain substances
such as orcinol or anthrone (23) in order to produce a color.
While these methods are highly specific for glucose they suffer
from the fact that traces of glucose from any source whatsoever
will react. An example would be traces of dust which contain
paper fragments. These will be converted and react in the same
way as the glucose from the serum. Also in this procedure one
is dealing with very strong sulfuric acid solutions, which are
sometimes difficult to handle.

Another common procedure which is used for glucose assay
is the hexokinase procedure in which the glucose is phosphory-
lated by means of ATP and then dehydrogenated with glucose-
6-phosphate dehydrogenase measuring the abosrption of NADPH

generated at the wavelength at 340nm, or by fluorescence. This method requires deproteinization by means of the Somogyi method in order to remove interference from hemoglobin (24). Figure 16 summarizes the reactions involved in the hexokinase procedure.

The hexokinase procedure can be carried out with the use of reagents which are supplied from various companies. From Table I it can be seen that these reagents vary in their specificity depending whether or not they have removed fructose hexokinase. However, as long as one is dealing with serum and not with a fructosuria, the procedure is specific.

Many use the hexokinase procedure without protein precipitation. That this is a procedure which is not acceptable is illustrated in Table II where it is shown that unless hemoglobin is removed there will be interference in the results obtained. In severely hemolyzed blood, errors as high as 25% are not uncommon.

If the fluorometric procedure is used, with protein precipitation, then bilirubin will not interfere with the hexokinase procedure. Even if protein precipitation is not resorted to, the interference from bilirubin does not become significant until one is dealing with an infant in severe jaundice. This can be seen in Table III.

If the fluorometric method is used after protein precipitation then the glucose can be readily assayed on 1 µl of plasma with the hexokinase procedure.

A widely used procedure is the method which uses o-toluidine. This method may be used directly if 25 µl of serum is added to 2 ml of reagent(25). This suggests that if one wishes to go to smaller quantities then one needs to use an ultramicro cuvette. With the use of an ultramicro cuvette, one can readily perform this test on 5 µl of serum provided that the total volume at the end of the test is less than 400 µl in volume. This is a practical volume with some of the newer ultramicro cuvette systems used. Figure 17 illustrates the course of events during the heating of a solution with the o-toluidine reagent.

It will be noted that at 100°C that the color comes up rapidly, but then rapidly fades, and many have noticed that in the o-toluidine method unless one waits a substantial period of time, one is dealing with a fading color. However, it should be noted that when heated at 37°C that the color will not develop for at least 2 hours, but will yield a higher absorbence, because the color is more stable. A good compromise is to heat at temperatures of the order 55°C or 65°C in which case one can then conveniently read at the end of 10 or 15 minutes with adequate reading time for practical purposes. This is not done in most laboratories. Most laboratories continue to heat at 100°C, which is not the correct way to use this procedure.

$$\text{ATP + Glucose} \xrightarrow[\text{(E.C. 2.7.1.1)}]{\text{Hexokinase}} \text{Glucose-6-phosphate + ADP}$$

$$\text{NADP + Glucose-6-phosphate} \xrightarrow[\text{(E.C. 1.1.1.49)}]{\substack{\text{Glucose-6-phosphate} \\ \text{dehydrogenase}}} \text{6-phosphogluconate + NADPH}$$

Figure 16.   Glucose estimation by the hexokinase procedure

Table I

Comparison of the various hexokinase enzyme mixtures

for specificity in glucose analysis

Preparation	Sucrose, 200 mg/100 ml	Mannose, 100 mg/100 ml	Fructose, 100 mg/100 ml
Ref. #24	0	0.2	18.9
Sigma	0	0.1	4.7
Worthington	0	0	6.2
Calbiochem	0.5	0.8	15.5
Gen. Diagnostics	1.1	2.4	85.5

*Values are glucose equivalents in mg/100 ml.

Table II

Effect of hemolysis on the assay of glucose by the

fluorescence-hexokinase method without protein precipitation.

Added Hemolysate (Hb, mg/100 ml)	Glucose Found (glucose, mg/100 ml)
0	69.0
100	71.9
200	75.3
300	79.3
1000	87.9
2000	95.7

Table III

Effect of bilirubin on the glucose fluorometric hexokinase

procedure with and without protein precipitation.*

Bilirubin (mg/100 ml)	Glucose (mg/100 ml)	
	Pptd.	Nonpptd.
2.7	77	77
5.4	63	59
7.8	73	71
11.2	118	113
18.1	85	85
21.1	90	85
40.0	382	377

*Results are means of duplicate determinations. Serums are from the routine laboratory. Bilirubin levels are assayed values.

Exactly what is happening during the heating can be seen in Figure 18. In Figure 18 it will be noted that the color at the 635 nm maximum, fades with heat with the appearance of another color with a maximum at approximately 410 nm. As a result, on continued heating one observes a murky green solution as distinct from the clear green-blue solution observed when heated at lower temperatuers.

The use of the lower temperature permits the performance of this test in the presence of substantial amounts of hemoglobin. Since hemoglobin has very little absorbance at 635 nm, then as much as 2% hemoglobin in the solution will not significantly affect the   results   obtained   for glucose. This is shown in Figure 19. The reason for this is that hemoglobin is stable at 55°C or 65°C while it decomposes at 100°C. If a direct method of doing glucose is to be sought, then the toluidine method is probably the method of choice. Bilirubin and lipemia also do not interfere because if the method is done properly, the lipids will dissolve in the glacial acetic acid in which the test is being performed.

The use of aniline derivatives for the identification of sugars was originally used in connection with identification of sugars in general by thin layer chromatography. Table IV shows the response of various sugars to the toluidine reagent when the colors are being developed on the thin layer chromatogram. It will be noted that the use of this reagent at low temperatures can distinguish sugars from others which may have the same R_f values, but do not develop the color at the low temperature. Heating the chromatogram at low temperature and then at high temperature can distinguish these sugars. However, Table IV also points out the significant fact that the o-toluidine method is not specific for glucose determination.

In figure 7 a procedure was described for aspirating a sample from a capillary tube and simultaneously adding zinc sulfate and barium hydroxide solutions in order to produce a Somogyi filtrate. Aliquots of the supernatant are suitable for assay for glucose and urea by various procedures. The reason for this is the fact that zinc hydroxide precipitates uric acid, creatinine and other substances, such as low molecular polypeptides, along with the proteins, so that there results a solution which is clear with relatively few components.

Another procedure which has adequate sensitivity for determining the glucose in 1 microliter of serum of filtrate, is the method which uses copper reduction, and subsequently determination of the cuprous ion with a suitable reagent (15). However, one must be careful that one has obtained complete precipitation, for, if uric acid or any other impurities remain, false high values will be obtained. This would result in disaster for the hypoglycemic infant. To uncover this condition is often one of the major reasons for doing this test.

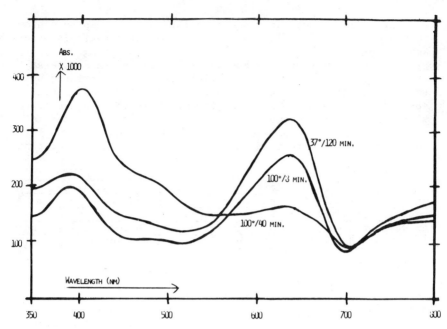

Figure 17.   Change in absorbance pattern of reaction product of glucose and toluidine with heating

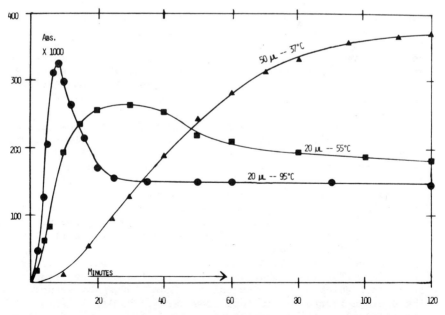

Figure 18.   Absorbance change with time of the toluidine glucose reaction product at various temperatures

This problem removes the cupreine method as an acceptable procedure for the Pediatric Laboratory for glucose analysis under
any circumstances.

In addition to the method described above, there are at
present, on the market, several glucose analyzers offered by
several commercial companies, wherein the individual injects
approximately 20 microliters of serum. This is then incubated
with glucose oxidase and the peroxide or oxygen generated is
measured with an oxygen sensing electrode. These instruments
cannot perform the test on 1 μl nor are they designed for that
purpose at the present time.

In view of the above discussion, it should be clear why
the author recommends that the laboratory of Neonatology precipitate proteins with a Somogyi filtrate, and then perform
the hexokinase procedure on the filtrate. Neither the glucose
oxidase procedure nor the toluidine method have adequate sensitivity without the use of special micro-equipment and special
techniques.

Urea. The diacetyl method continues as the most specific
method for urea at present (26). Addition of thiosemicarbazide,
antipyrine (15) or other additives remove the specificity of
this procedure for urea. Other substances including ammonium
and amines of various types begin to react, so that in uremia
a significantly elevated value is obtained which begins to
approach the nonprotein nitrogen level. This is extremely important because as the condition becomes worse, a greater and
greater disparity occurs between urea and nonprotein nitrogen.
If the urea is to be meaningful in this regard, it needs to
be a specific procedure and not react with other substances.
An example of this phenomenon in a patient is seen in Figure 20.

Recently, the old alkaline phenol method has been revived,
and is being widely used in clinical laboratories, without protein precipitation(27). In this procedure, the serum is added to an
alkaline phenol reagent, and the ammonia generated from urea
is determined either after the action of urease or after strong
alkaline treatment of the serum. The objection to this procedure is first, that all urease is rich in ammonia, and second,
the color produced with alkaline phenol is not specific for
ammonia. It will react with other compounds, especially for
those that liberate ammonia. By this procedure one obtains a
useful number from the point of view of determining whether
the patient has nitrogen retention, but a value which is some-
where between a urea and an N.P.N. determination.

In the Beckman instrument, change in conductivity is
used (28). The instrument uses 14 μl for the test but samples
from a cup which needs to contain at least 100 μl of serum.
The Beckman instrument suffers from certain faults. First,
the standard for urea must contain the proper amount of saline
or false values are obtained. Second, urine cannot be analyzed

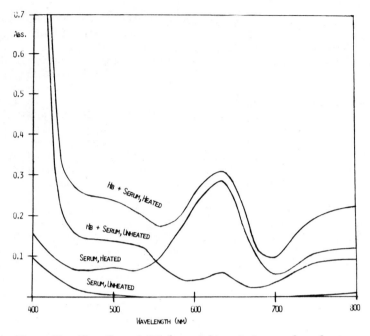

*Figure 19. The effect of 2% hemoglobin solution on the color pro-
duced with toluidine on glucose*

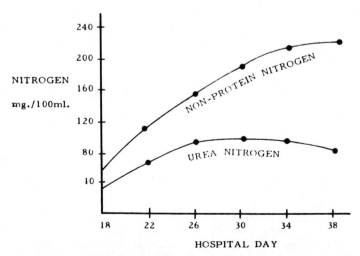

*Figure 20. Demonstration of disparity between nonprotein nitrogen
and urea levels in a patient with terminal kidney disease complicated
by liver involvement*

for urea, except under very special conditions. Third, fluoride
interferes, so that if blood is presented to the laboratory
with fluoride, the test cannot be done. This requires that
the laboratory convert to iodoacetate as a preservative. This,
of course, is very difficult in the main laboratory, but in
the Pediatric Laboratory, one can line the capillary in which
the blood is collected with iodacetate with very little difficulty, in order to preserve the sugar level, if the analysis
is not to be done promptly. On the other hand, since very
little time elapses in the Pediatric Laboratory between taking
the specimen, and analysis, no preservative at all need be
used, particularly for the urea determination, which is relatively stable. However, the fact that this instrument cannot
even perform the test on aqueous solutions of urea, and urine,
should eliminate it as an instrument to be recommended for any
laboratory. Any instrument used for urea analysis should be
able to perform the test under all conditions under which the
laboratory operates. This includes the analysis of blood which
has been taken in various ways, and the application to other
specimens, such as urine, gastric aspiration or amniotic fluid.

The above discussion does not mean that the use of urease
and subsequently the use of an ammonia electrode is not practicable for a urea determination. Unfortunately, the commercial
company that produced the urea analyzer, chose a conductivity
procedure, which happens to be unsuitable for the laboratory
of Neonatology. Had they chosen the ammonia electrode, which
happens to be a relatively good electrode, and is especially
specific, since only ammonia and not potassium can pass an air
space, then the instrument could have been made highly specific
for urea. In this case an ammonia determination would be done
initially and then subtracted by the computer, from the amount
which has been generated subsequently. In any case, with present technology, sensitivity is not adequate to use less than
approximately 15 µl of serum.

For the present, for reasons discussed above, the diacetyl
procedure is the method of choice for the Laboratory of Neonatology with equipment available at present. The importance
of the assay for urea in the blood of infants is emphasized
by the readiness with which the urea level responds to change
in diet in the infant (1). This is seen in Table V.

Sodium and Potassium. For the electrolytes, sodium and
potassium the flame photometer is the instrument of choice (29).
This instrument permits readily the dilution of the serum 200
fold, for analysis, using an internal lithium standard. Most
instruments require 1 ml for analysis. It is therefore practicable to measure out 5 µl and dilute it to 1 ml. This is best
done with a sampler-diluter of high precision. The tip of the
diluter needs to be a drawn out polyethylene tip, or the 5 µl
will not be measured with any degree of accuracy.

TABLE IV

Color developed at 37°C and 100°C for

several sugars with toluidine.

		Relative reading	
Sugars tested	Color	37°C	100°C
Glucose	Green	91	175
Galactose	Green	117	275
Mannose	Green	75	187
Fructose	Green	0	45
Sorbose	Green	0	64
Maltose	Green	0	15
Lactose	Green	0	70
Sucrose	Green	0	47
Trehalose	Green	0	10
Meliboise	Green	7	179
Raffinose	Green	0	35
Rhamnose	Yellow	35	29
Xylose	Red	205	377
Arabinose	Red	129	359
Rucose	Yellow	27	12

Table V

Urea nitrogen concentration in plasma of infants

after five days on breast or cow's milk.

	Breast	Cow
Mean	12.5	17.4
Range	8.7-15.4	9.4-23.9
Std. Dev.	± 1.9	± 3.9

Other methods for assaying for sodium and potassium such as with ion selective electrodes (30) or with the autoanalyzer, require much larger quantities of material. In addition, the ion selective electrodes, which have great potential, have not been developed at present to the point where they can be utilized in a practical way for micro sodium and potassium analysis. It is very important that one be able to distinguish between sodium concentration in specimens which differ by only 2 mEq/L. This requires that we have a reproducibility of 2 parts in 140, which is substantially less than 1%. This reproducibility can not be reached in an Autoanalyzer. It is practicable to reach this degree of precision however, in the routine laboratory of clinical chemistry with the commercially available flame photometers.

If one wishes to go to the nanoliter range there are instruments available such as one which operates with a glow discharge made by the American Instrument Company, which can determine sodium and potassium in a few nanoliters. In this procedure a glow discharge is set up between two electrodes with helium gas. On vaporization of the serum, the Na and K are excited by transfer of energy from excited He ions. At present, the inconvenience of this instrument makes it only of value in relationship to research in small animals. The design is seen in Figure 21.

Atomic absorption has not been effective for Na and K estimation for reasons discussed under Calcium Assay.

Chloride. Chloride analysis may be done in any one of 3 ways with adequate sensitivity for the Laboratory of Neonatology. It can be done amperometrically (31), by titration (32) or with the chloride electrode (33).

In the titrimetric procedure, the serum is diluted in 0.07 N nitric acid and titrated with a dilute mercuric nitrate solution in the presence of diphenylcarbazone (34). A purple color forms when excess mercury ions appear, over that needed to complex the chloride. Using an ultramicro buret this method has found wide use in the past. The microburets which are available such as the Rehburg buret are typified in Figure 22.

A second method which is now probably the most widely used method in the Pediatric Laboratory is to use amperometric titration. In this connection, a constant current flows through the solution. The silver dissolves and reacts stoichiometrically with chloride, precipitating silver chloride. When all of the chloride has reacted, there is a sharp increase in conductivity which is read as an end point. This instrument, therefore, measures the amount of time a current flows. Instruments are now available for which 5 microliters can be used routinely, rapidly, titration being of the order of about 20 seconds. More commonly 10 microliters is used with a longer time. This method is by far the most reproducible method available at

Figure 21.   Ultramicro instrument for Na and K estimation. Nanoliter specimen is placed on wire (inset) and is then vaporized in the
glow discharge with helium (American Instrument Co.).

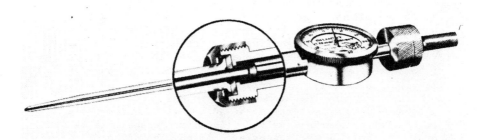

Figure 22.   A type of ultramicro buret where the liquid is expelled by displacement of
a plunger and readout on a dial indicator

present.

A third method for chloride estimation which is commonly employed is the silver-silver chloride electrode. In this method the solution is usually diluted in a buffer, and the voltage generated measured. The problem with this procedure is that the electrode needs to be carefully maintained or problems occur. With larger volumes the chloride electrode has been very successful.

Colorimetric methods, such as those which depend upon the measurement of the color developed when excess mercury salts are added to a chloride solution, are not reproducible enough for practical purposes. They are widely used in automatic equipment, but for the purpose of maintenance and treatment of newborns, this data does not have the adequate accuracy and reproducibility.

As a microanalytical tool the method of amperometric titration is the most reproducible and is the method of choice for the Laboratory of Neonatology, for the analysis of chloride.

Calcium and Magnesium. When it comes to the elements, it is theoretically most advantageous to excite the element, and read the emission as the element returns to the ground state. The flame photometer is an application of this principle. In the flame photometer, the temperature of the hydrocarbon flame supplies the exciting energy. In order to excite elements, such as calcium and magnesium, the temperature of the hydrocarbon flame is not high enough. For this reason, some have used flames generated by the reaction of, for example, nitric oxide and acetylene. These are inconvenient for the chemistry laboratory. Others have used the flame, and selected minor lines for identification of calcium and magnesium (35). This was the principle of the calcium and magnesium system used by Coleman Instrument Company for many years. Actually, these systems failed, mainly because they were theoretically unsound to begin with. The carbon arc will yield temperatures high enough for obtaining the spectra for calcium and magnesium, but are inconvenient for the routine laboratory. In this class of excitation sources, is the plasma jet. Figure 23 shows the use of the plasma jet in welding. This is an everyday procedure, where the gas, such as helium or argon, or a mixture of gases, is excited by high frequency excitation, and escapes from an orifice containing the energy which is high enough so as to serve for welding stainless steel and other substances.

It is necessary to supply a spray into the plasma jet, in order to excite the elements. This has presented some difficulty and it is a mystery to the author as to why the plasma jet has not been more widely applied for the analysis of sodium potassium, calcium and magnesium. It has the advantage of safety, in that one inert gas (argon) would be used, and high sensitivity. In addition, four elements, calcium, magnesium,

sodium and potassium could be assayed just as easily as we do
sodium, potassium today with a flame photometer.

At present, calcium and magnesium are estimated almost
exclusively by atomic absorption (36). Present instrumentation
permits the dilution of the specimen to approximately 1 - 100
for calcium and even higher for magnesium. For many instruments, the two elements are not read out simultaneously such
as is practicable for sodium and potassium with the flame photometer. The lower limit of serum volume at present, for the
practical assay for calcium and magnesium in the laboratory
of Neonatology, is approximately 10 µl . The instruments are
very readily automated, and it is not uncommon for results to
be available at the rate of 240 per hour in the routine laboratory, where a typical atomic absorption instrument such as
a Perkin-Elmer has been attached to an automatic feed system.
In the author's laboratory, an Autoanalyzer turntable is used
which rotates, at a speed, so that the 40 specimens can be
assayed in a 10 - 15 minute period. Figure 24 shows the principle of atomic absorption. Note that an elongated absorption
path is provided for higher sensitivity.

There are available also several kits for the assay of
calcium, in 10 or 20 microliter samples by chelate formation
colorimetrically or fluorimetrically. (Pierce Chem. Co.,
Rockford, Ill.). These are read either with the spectrophotometer or by spectrofluorometry. In our experience, while these
systems can be used for approximate results, the plot of concentration versus reading curves are rather flat and only an
approximation of the values can be obtained. This may be very
important late at night or at times when the atomic absorption
machine is down, but if the atomic absorption instrument is
available it should be used in preference to these procedures.

Assay of calcium and magnesium by specific ion electrodes
(37) is not practicable on micro quantities today, although
it is quite possible that these may become available in the
near future, especially with the developments that are taking
place in foreign countries in this area.

It must be pointed out that the atomic absorption system
as used today, cannot accurately determine the calcium level
of a solution. The reason for this is that results will vary
depending upon the other elements present and the composition
of the solution. Since it is impossible to duplicate every
feature of the particular serum being analyzed, results have
to be compared to standards which have been made up in serum
dialysates. Such standards are available in the form of the
Versatols where the calcium has been dialyzed out and then
weighed back. This is distinct from substances such as
Validate, which are used as controls and which values are results of analysis. The variability of serum composition
has significantly widened what is now considered the "normal
range" for serum Ca assay when done by atomic absorption (37a).

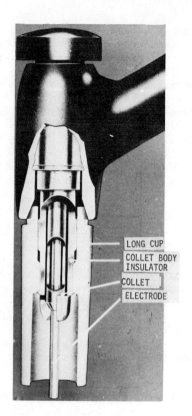

Figure 23. Heliarc torch used in welding as an example of the plasma jet

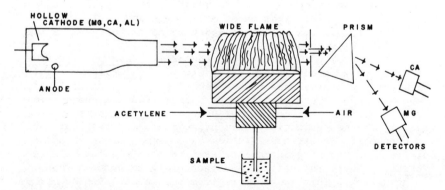

Figure 24. The basic principle used in atomic absorption. The sample is sprayed into the flame, and the calcium and magnesium emission from the lamp is absorbed. The extent of absorption is measured on the detector and translated in terms of concentration.

We have found that the use of serum standards for standardizing the instrument in the laboratory is useful. However,
the serum standards cannot be used for urines. In urines, one
runs into other problems and needs to use aqueous standards.
Therefore, at present, while atomic absorption is the instrument of choice, there is much to be desired for the determination of calcium and magnesium in the routine laboratory of
clinical chemistry.

Bilirubin. The most widely used method for bilirubin continues to be the method which couples bilirubin with the diazo
reagent and reads the color formed (38). Unfortunately the
sensitivity of this procedure is such that a lower limit of
approximately 10 microliters of specimen is a limitation on
the use of this procedure.

Recently, this problem has been approached by reverting
to reading the color of the bilirubin directly. This used to
be called an "Icterus Index", in which the color of the serum
was compared to a dilute dichromate solution (39). However,
the new approach has been to use two wavelengths. This can
be used in either of two different procedures. In one procedure the reading is made at the peak for bilirubin which is
at 453 nm and at an isosbestic point for hemoglobin (40). The
effect on the reading due to hemoglobin is subtracted from the
bilirubin value. Commercial instruments based on this principle have not been successful.

In another approach a reading is taken at 453 nm and also
at 572 nm. The reason 572 nm is chosen is because, at this
point, hemoglobin has the same molar absorbance as it has at
453 nm. Therefore, subtracting the reading at 572 nm is equivalent to subtracting the hemoglobin reading directly under the
bilirubin peak. This system has another advantage in that the
wavelengths at 453 and 572 are not far apart, and some correction is being made for lipemia and turbidity which might be
present in the sample being tested (41).

Unfortunately, Perkin-Elmer who has produced this instrument has built the instrument for the purpose of measuring
bilirubin in amniotic fluid. As a result, the instrument does
not read above a level of approximately 2 mg/100 ml. Therefore,
it is necessary to dilute the serum from newborns in order to
be read in this instrument. However, if one standardizes by
making a 1 to 5 dilution of all newborn serum, one can use
this method for screening purposes. One looks forward to the
further development of this instrument so that readings can
be made over a wide range.

Still widely used is the method of scanning for bilirubin
in amniotic fluid. A scan is run for some distance before and
after 450 nm. From the baseline drawn between 2 points (e.g.
350 nm and 550 nm), one examines the height of the peak.
Normally, no peak will be present. Where the bilirubin is

elevated, a peak will form with a maximum at approximately
450 nm. The rise above this baseline is called the O.D. 450
value which is the measure of the bilirubin concentration in
amniotic fluid. Where one is dealing with amniotic fluid and
therefore with a single specimen, this method is practicable,
since it takes approximately 15 - 20 minutes per scan. This is
too slow for the routine laboratory of Neonatology. In addition, the method is not sensitive enough to be utilized for
small quantities such as 5 microliters unless special attach-
ments are made to the spectrophotometer. Figure 25 shows a
typical O.D. 450 scan for bilirubin (42,43).

   Protein. In listing those procedures which have been used
in the past for analysis of protein in serum using volumes of
the order of 10 µl of serum, one may include the Kjeldahl procedure, the color obtained with phosphotungsic acid on reduction
by tyrosine in the protein (also commonly called the Folin-
Ciocalteu reagent) and the biuret method. Of these, the
Kjeldahl procedure has adequate sensitivity but is too time
consuming (44). The Folin-Ciocalteu procedure, commonly referred to as the Lowry method in its micro version, is not
specific for protein (45). Any phenol will react with this
reagent, and high values will be obtained if the patient is
being treated with salicylates. The biuret procedure is
specific for protein, and can be made to react with small
amounts of serum, suitable for use in a routine Laboratory of
Neonatology (15,46). However, certain facts must be brought
out when the biuret method is used.
   The biuret method has been known since the turn of the
century but was never used because of the interference of other
substances in the serum, particularly turbidity, caused by
lipids. This was corrected by Kingsley (46), when he introduced the idea of extracting the lipids with ether before applying the biuret reagent. The author has, for over 30 years,
used a method which precipitates the proteins with Bloor's
reagent (5). Bloor's reagent is made up of 1 part of ether
and 3 parts of alcohol. The lipid extract and extract of bilirubin and heme are discarded by decantation after centrifugation and the biuret reagent is added to the residue. In this
way, accurate values are obtained (15).
   Recently, in a study of the various methods for doing proteins in amniotic fluid it was noted that values ranging up
to 12% have been reported in literature. What was being measured in these cases was the turbidity and the presence of
hemolysis in amniotic fluid. When the Bloor's reagent extract
is applied, substantially lower and more consistant values were
obtained (47).
   The same is true for specimens of serum from the newborn.
Those who attempt to apply the biuret method to newborn sera,
end up with values in the normal infant, resembling those for

adult serum, namely of the order of 6.5 - 7.5%. Actually,
serum protein levels in the newborn are at approximately 5.5%
when the test is accurately performed (48). The effect of
extracting of serum with Bloor's reagent before applying the
biuret reaction is shown in Table VI. In Table VI, it will
be noted that even with serum, when the lipids are not substantially elevated, there is an error of at least 10% in the
direction of an overestimate. It is a fact that in many labor-
tories in this country, the protein determination has become
of little value in the Pediatric Laboratory because of the fact
that the determination is being performed by merely adding
biuret reagent directly to serum and reading the hemolysis,
bilirubin, lipemia and incidentally the protein and interpret-
ing this as a protein determination.
     It is recommended that the protein be precipitated and
extracted by Bloor's reagent before adding the biuret reagent.

     Blood Gases and Blood PH. For measurement of pCO_2, pO_2,
and pH there are 3 instruments on the market. One is marketed
by Corning, another by Instrumentation Laboratories (IL) and
the third by the Radiometer Corporation. The performance of
each of these instruments is fairly good. However, only the
Corning instrument is able to perform simultaneous pCO_2, pO_2,
and pH levels on samples of less than 150 µl in size. The IL
and the Radiometer instrument, require 0.5 ml of whole blood
for the assays. In the case of the IL instrument, it is
possible by maneuvering to utilize 250 microliters. In the
case of the Corning instrument, the instrument is set to read
the three parameters on 250 µl and by special use of the instrument to do the determination on 125 microliters. Unfortunately,
this creates a problem for the Pediatric Laboratory, since it
requires that one obtain substantial amounts of capillary blood.
This may be very difficult in the particular infant who is in
most severe distress. At the present time there is a need for
an instrument that can read all three parameters simultaneously
on a maximum of 25 microliters of whole blood. This is not
beyond the realm of modern technology.
     The principle of the pH electrode has been discussed
thoroughly in various treatises (49). The pCO_2 electrode
is the glass electrode separated from the blood by a thin Teflon
membrane. The CO_2 diffuses through the membrane changing the
pH of the bicarbonate buffer, which is sensed with the pH electrode and then read out in terms of pCO_2. The pO_2 is read by
allowing the oxygen to diffuse through a polyethylene membrane
(50, 51). A constant current flows in an acid buffer, so as to
deposit hydrogen gas and polarize the surface of a platinum
electrode. As the oxygen diffuses to the platinum electrode
the hydrogen reacts with oxygen to form water, depolarizing
the electrode and increasing the current. The greater the rate
at which the oxygen diffuses into the electrode, the higher

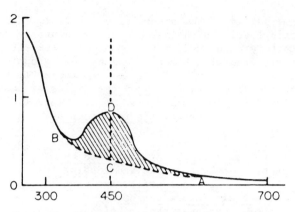

*Figure 25.   Typical scan, plotting absorbance vs. wave-
length for amniotic fluid for bilirubin assay*

Table VI

Effect of turbidity on the % protein found
in serum as determined with and without
eluting with Bloors Reagent.   Results are in g/100 ml.

Total Lipids mg/100 ml	Replicates Washed with Bloors Rgt.			Replicates (not washed)			Difference of Means
592	5.0	5.0	5.0	5.8	5.7	5.8	0.8
630	6.2	6.3	6.2	7.1	7.1	7.1	0.9
855	7.9	7.9	8.0	8.5	8.6	8.5	0.6
1080	5.9	6.0	5.9	9.2	9.2	9.4	3.3
1350	7.8	7.9	7.9	10.0	9.9	10.0	2.1
1755	7.5	7.5	7.4	11.8	11.8	11.7	4.3

the current, and therefore, the higher the pO_2.

The difficulty with pO_2 measurement is the fact that when measuring pO_2 from blood, the blood is constantly being depleted of oxygen and low values are obtained. When standardizing the blood with gases, one is dealing with a constantly changing supply of gas through the electrode, and this source is not being depleted. As a result, the pO_2 of blood oxygen tends to be underestimated in these systems. In some of the instruments, a correction factor is built in, to compensate for the effect, and in others, it is recommended that the blood be placed into the electrode, allowed to come to approximately equilibrium, and then a fresh specimen is put in to obtain the final result. The more often this is done, the closer one comes to the correct value. Unfortunately, this requires substantial amounts of blood. If one has approximately 1 ml blood, one can obtain a fairly reasonable reading.

Recently, interest has been aroused in obtaining P_{50} values on infants blood, especially in screening for genetic abnormalities (51). The P_{50} value is the pO_2 value when the blood is half saturated. This is usually done by equilibrating the blood with oxygen at two known pO_2 values. The blood is then taken and the oxygen content is measured at these two values. By interpolation on a chart, the pO_2 value at half saturation is determined. In order to do this, a useful instrument is the Lex-O_2-Con (Lexington Instrument Company, Waltham, Mass.). This is an instrument into which 20 µl of whole blood is injected. The blood is then carried by means of a gas containing hydrogen and no oxygen to a cadmium electrode.

The oxidation of the electrode generates a current. The current is integrated and the total amount of current is then printed out in terms of oxygen content (52). In effect, this is a system of amperometric titration for oxygen. This instrument uses only 20 µl of whole blood. It takes approximately nine minutes for each assay and this is a serious disadvantage.

The determination of total carbon dioxide is still being done where accuracy and precision are required by the use of a micro gasometer. This is shown in Figure 26. In this instrument the gas is liberated and the pressure produced by the carbon dioxide measured before and after it is reabsorbed into alkali. Attempts to measure carbon dioxide content by other means have not been particularly successful. In the autoanalyzer, the blood is acidified and the CO_2 is then absorbed into a buffer, and the change in color of a phenolphthalein solution is moderated. This correlates rather poorly, with the actual CO_2 content of the blood. Attempts to calculate total CO_2 from pCO_2 values and pH result in huge errors because of the fact that the pCO_2 is related to the total CO_2 by a logarithmic function, and a very small change in pCO_2 results in a large change in total CO_2. Since the pCO_2 is measured at present with much less accuracy than total CO_2 can be measured in a gasometer (53,

54), this method is not to be accepted.

It is recommended for the present that in the Pediatric Laboratory the total CO_2 always be measured with a micro gasometer. (See Figure 26).

If CO_2 is removed from blood and passed through a one meter cuvette of an infrared spectrophotometer, and the absorption characteristic peak integrated, the CO_2 can be very accurately measured. Alternatively, CO_2 can be liberated from a solution and then collected in a weak buffer. The pH of this buffer can be brought back to its original value by electrometric titration, using a hydrogen electrode as a means of measurement. If this system is set up, carbon dioxide can be measured in extremely minute quantities. Unfortunately, in neither of the above cases have commercial companies taken the initiative and placed such instruments on the market. This is true in spite of the fact that the instrument for measuring carbon dioxide by amperometric titration is at present being used in the determination of carbon in organic specimens after combustion. The introduction of such instrumentation into the Pediatric Laboratory awaits development by a manufacturer.

Miscellaneous Serum Components. The discussion of the tests most commonly done in the Laboratory of Neonatology, above, illustrates the various types of instrumentation used. Here, various other procedures will be discussed at random in order to illustrate some basic principles, which have many applications.

Molecular diffusion (55) has been used in various ways in micro analysis. In Figure 27, is seen the Conway diffusion dish, in which the substance to be tested is placed on the outside, and the reagent is placed in the central cup. The cup is covered, and after a time, the substance being analyzed diffuses into the central cup where it produces an effect which can then be interpreted in various ways. In the Figure, carbon monoxide is being determined. This same method is very useful for alcohol determination, where dichromate oxidizes the alcohol after it diffuses into the dichromate from the blood.

A variation of this system is the rotator (Figure 28), which has come into importance in recent times, in the determination of ammonia in Reyes Syndrome (56). In this system, the blood is placed into a bottle, a stopper containing a glass rod, which has been dipped in dilute sulfuric acid is fit into the bottle. When the test is being performed, potassium carbonate is added quickly to the bottle, and the bottle is corked. On rotation, the ammonia diffuses from the blood to the sulfuric acid held on the glass tip. After a fixed period of time, the rubber stopper is removed, and the glass tip is dipped into an aqeous solution. Subsequently, reagents, such as Nessler's reagent, or the alkaline phenol reagent, are added to the solution, in order to generate a color in order to be read.

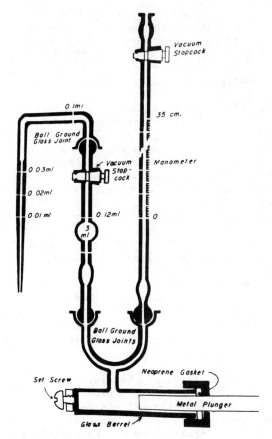

Figure 26. The microgasometer for CO₂ assay

Figure 27. Estimation of CO in blood with a Conway diffusion dish. Palladium chloride is reduced to black palladium powder in the center compartment by the diffused CO.

Amino Acids. Thin-layer chromatography has found wide
application in the clinical chemistry laboratory. An application that is practicable in the Laboratory of Neonatology
is the screening of serum and urine for the amino acidopathies.
In order to do this we use a micro ultrafiltering apparatus
which has been designed in our laboratory (57). This is seen
in Figure 29.

A 20 microliter sample is placed in a narrow tube which
comprises the other part of an assembly. A Millipore filter
is then placed in the lower part of the assembly. An instrument is then put together by screwing the upper part into the
lower part and sealing the bottom of the lower part with an
Allen screw. The assembly is now centrifuged as shown in
Figure 30, where the operator is placing one of the micro ultrafiltering devices into the cup of the high-speed centrifuge.

It is centrifuged at 12000 r.p.m. for between 10 and 20
minutes. The instrument is removed from the centrifuge and
disassembled, removing the Allen screw. A capillary is inserted
into the lower tube and the filtrate is then spotted on thin-
layer chromatography. The results, comparing serum which has
been filtered, and serum which has not been filtered, is shown
in Figure 31. It can be readily seen that a smoother pattern
with less trailing, and especially with very little material
left at the origin is obtained after ultrafiltration.

Figure 32 shows typical abnormal patterns that are obtained
in the Laboratory of Neonatology.

Sampling With Capillaries. Earlier it was pointed out
that with the aid of a constriction pipette a sample can be
measured accurately. A similar effect can be obtained by allowing the serum to enter a capillary open at both ends. The
serum will reach the opposite end of the capillary if it is
held at an angle and then stoppered, and if the capillary has
been carefully calibrated an accurate volume can be measured
out. Such capillaries are now available commercially, and have
been in use in automated equipment in the authors laboratory
for at least 10 years. It is now possible to take the capillary
and empty its contents into a container for analysis, or into
a stream for the purpose of determining any of the materials
which can be determined with the autoanalyzer. Figure 33 shows
an instrument which is used for this purpose (58).

With the instrument of Figure 33, the capillary is picked
up, moved over, and emptied into a cup. The cup is shown in
Figure 34. A diluting solution from the autoanalyzer pump
drips into the cup continuously, creating the bubble pattern,
since the solution is being removed more rapidly than it is
being added. The capillary dispenser then presents the
capillary to the flowing stream and blows out the specimen.
In this way, the usual procedure for analysis can now proceed.

In our laboratory, we use this procedure routinely for

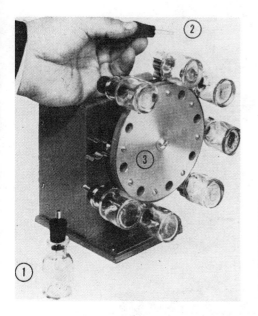

Figure 28. Modification of the Conway technique using rotated bottles in place of the Conway diffusion dish. 1, bottle with a rubber stopper and glass plug containing an edged end which has been dipped in sulfuric acid; 2, roughed end of the glass plug; 3, rotator with clips holding the bottles in place.

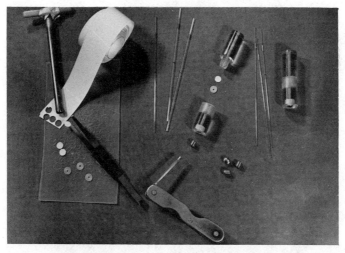

Figure 29. Assembly for micro-ultrafiltration. The tweezers hold the Millipore filter, cut from the strip. The washers are shown below the tweezers. In the center, the top and bottom portion of the filter and washer are shown aligned with the Allen screw. An Allen wrench is used to tighten the screw in place. When assembled, it looks like the assembly on the right. The capillaries are used for measuring out the specimen and placing them in the upper chamber of the assembly.

*Figure 30. Placing the assembly in the
12,000 r.p.m. micro centrifuge*

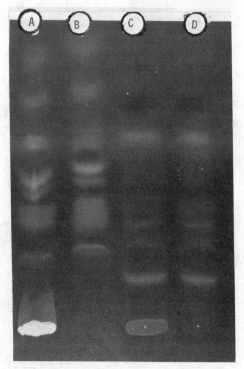

*Figure 31. Demonstrating the advantage of
ultrafiltration before TLC. A, serum unfiltered; B, serum filtered; C, urine unfiltered;
D, urine filtered.*

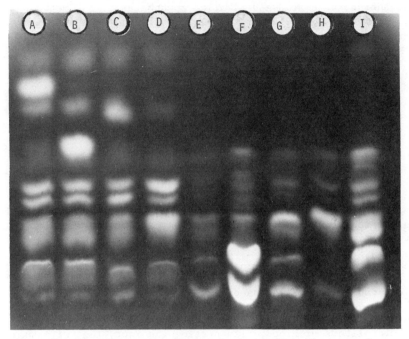

Figure 32.   Chromatograms of plasma and urine samples with various abnormalities. A, Phenylalaninemia; B, tyrosinemia; C, elevated plasma methionine seen in homocystinuria; D, glycinemia; E, normal urine; F, argininosuccinic aciduria; G, homocystinuria; H, hyperglycinuria; I, hyperlysinuria.

Figure 33.   The micro sampler dispenser. The capillaries are shown on the turntable, and one capillary is in position, ready to be lifted to the vertical position to be emptied into the cup.

phosphorus, uric acid and alkaline phosphatase. The method
is particularly applicable to enzyme analysis, because as little
as 25 microliters can be added. This can be followed by 5 or
6 ml of wash solution, so that there is no question about transfer of material from one specimen to another. This is particularly important with alkaline phosphatase, where values over
50 can be obtained in juxta position, to values as low as 2.
This is a 25 to 1 differential. Figure 35 shows one of our
technicians in our laboratory setting up and performing the
test with a capillary dispenser.

Recently, we have developed a new version of this system,
and this is shown in Figure 36. In this system, instead of
the capillary being used as a blow-out pipette, the capillaries
are used as wash-out pipettes. The capillaries are dispensed
in a block, and the solution flows through the capillaries
sequentially as they are presented to 2 press plates which
apply pressure to the side of the block and maintain contact
at all time. This done with O-rings and has an effect similar
to a suction cup sliding along the block. In Figure 36, it
shows how 3 capillaries can be simultaneously emptied into three
different channels of an autoanalyzer so that three determinations can be done simultaneously.

We do not use this procedure for glucose, but Figure 37
shows a series of glucose determinations being performed on
25 microliters of blood, illustrating the fact, that with this
system, there may be no wash-out from specimen to specimen.
In the procedure, determinations are done at 72 per hour.

Figure 37 illustrates the type of pattern one can obtain
with the capillary system. Note complete return to baseline
so that the area under the curve may be calculated by a computer
for evaluation.

Lipid Screening. The problems of lipid analysis in the
newborn is difficult because of the fact that most methods for
analysis for lipids require substantial amounts of serum, yet
a total lipid determination is very important in various types
of disease. This problem can be solved by thin-layer chromatography (59). Figure 38 shows a typical pattern obtained when
an extract from 10 microliters of serum is subjected to thin-
layer chromatography. If these specimens are scanned, and an
internal standard is run, one can obtain a rough approximation
of the distribution of the various lipids in the serum. This
is shown in Figure 39, in which a normal specimen is run in
an adult.

In Figure 40, one can see the effect on the ratio of total
to free cholesterol in a patient with alcoholic cirrhosis.
Note that the cholesterol esters are markedly depressed in
this patients serum and the free cholesterol band represents
most of the cholesterol in the serum.

Another example is a case of acute pancreatitis. The low

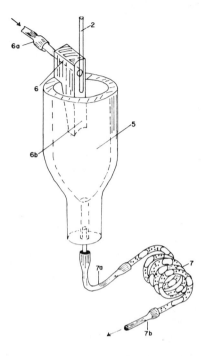

Figure 34. Cup for receiving the specimen from the micro sample dispenser. 2, capillary; 5, cup; 6 and 6A, assembly for leading the diluting fluid from the pump to be mixed with the contents of the capillary; 7, 7A, and 7B, assembly for mixing the sample with the diluting fluid before going into the autoanalyzer.

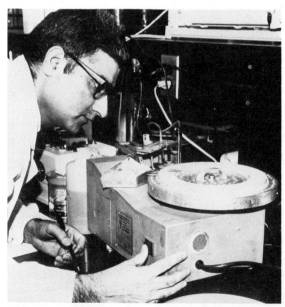

Figure 35. Technician adjusting the capillary dispenser for analysis

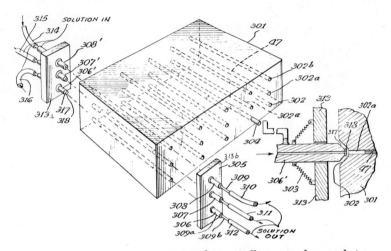

Figure 36. *Instrument for emptying three capillaries simultaneously into three channels. 302 represents the various holes in the block. 304, capillary as it is being placed in the block; 306, 307, and 308, connections which are made each with a separate capillary so as to move the specimen from the capillary into the analyzing system. The inset on the right shows how the connector 306 moves into the depression in the block to make contact with the capillary holder. Number 47, capillary in this inset.*

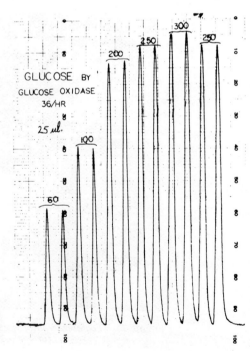

GLUCOSE BY
GLUCOSE OXIDASE
36/HR

25 µl.

Figure 37. *Pattern obtained for glucose by the glucose oxidase procedure using 25 ml in a capillary. Note the return to baseline between specimens.*

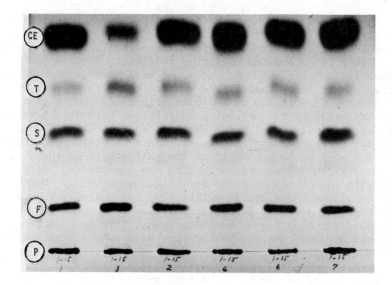

Figure 38. *Patterns obtained from the extract of 10 μl of serum for lipid fraction by thin-layer chromatography. In sequence, starting from the bottom, phospholipids, free cholesterol, cholesterol aniline as an internal standard, triglycerides, and cholesterol esters. The free fatty acids occur between cholesterol and the internal standard and are only barely visible in the print, on the extreme right. They are readily visible, normally, to the eye.*

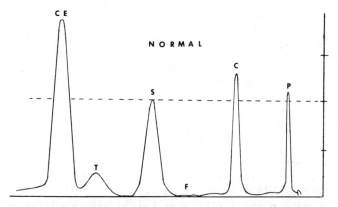

Figure 39. *A lipid pattern from normal serum which has been scanned for density of the thin-layer chromatograph, showing the various peaks. P, phospholipids; C, cholesterol; F, free fatty acids; S, internal standard, T, triglycerides; CE, cholesterol esters.*

free cholesterol shows that the patient has liver involvement
since it cannot be esterified.

The difficulty with this procedure is the method of staining. There is no problem obtaining resolution between the
various lipid fractions. Recently, we have been exploring this
system, and it seems that if one resorts to dyes in place of
phosphotungstic acid, as we had done originally, there is a
better opportunity for obtaining correlation between the values
obtained chemically, and those obtained by thin-layer chromatography. We have found some improvements in staining characteristics when we have esterified the cholesterol by spraying
with butyryl chloride, and iodinating the unsaturated fatty
acids with iodine monochloride or iodine monobromide. Under
these conditions, the lipids will take a basic stain, such as
basic fuchsin, and hold it against elution procedures so as
to produce a reasonably clear background. This is true, provided the dye is protected by spraying with some covering agent,
such as mineral oil.

Tape System of Analysis. A tape system which is used
widely for analysis in the Pediatric Laboratory is a system
whose principle was developed by the author. A reagent is
placed on a paper tape. The paper is covered with a membrane,
such as cellophane, cellulose nitrate or cellulose acetate,
porous to low molecular weight substances. Finally, the serum
is placed above the porous membrane, so that diffusion of the
components of serum take place and a stain is produced on the
paper (60). This principle has been incorporated for example,
with glucose oxidase, in the commercially available Dextro-
Sticks. In addition, a similar principle is being applied by
some for the analysis of components in urine (Ames Co., South
Bend, Indiana).

The author has developed several variations of this system,
but the general principle of this system is outlined in Figure
43. In this system a specimen is placed on a sample tape,
which comprises Mylar carrying small discs of paper. The tape
turns over and meets a porous tape, which in this case is cellophane, and the reagent tape which may be a toluidine succinate
deposit on the lower tape, as an example. When the filtrate
reaches the toluidine succinate pressure and heat is applied.
A characteristic color is then formed, which is then ready by
reflection on a densitometer (60). The principle of this system
is shown in Figure 41.

This system potentially, has value for the Pediatric Laboratory. It needs further development, however. For example,
a small drop of blood from a fingertip can be placed on an IBM
card containing a small circle of filter paper. After air drying, this could then be brought down to the laboratory and
placed on an assembly of cellophane covering a paper, moistened
with a suitable reagent. When pressure is applied, the color

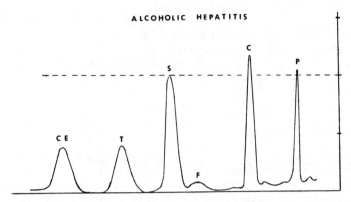

Figure 40. *Scan of the lipid pattern from a patient with alcoholic hepatitis. Note the decrease in the percentage of free cholesterol which has been esterified.*

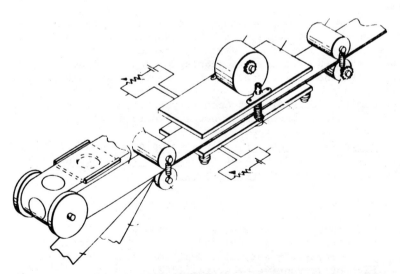

Figure 41. *The principle of the tape system of analysis. The three tapes are the reagent tape on the bottom, cellophane in the center, and sample tape on top. The sample placed on the top tape folds over and is pressed by the press plate and warmed so that the material dialyses through the membrane. The stain is then formed and is read by reflecting densitometry on the reagent tape.*

is produced on the lower moist paper, which can then be removed
and read in a densitometer. In this case, there is perfect
identification of the specimen, since the IBM card on which
the patients blood was placed originally, can have its information transferred to the reagent card.

Future Developments

Long Range Trends. Long range, the trend in the laboratory
of Neonatology is to move toward the use of smaller volumes
of blood for greater amounts of information. A typical example
would be the development of the specific ion electrodes, which
have the potential for the estimation of the concentration of
the components Na, K, Cl, Mg, Ca, pO_2, pCO_2, and pH on minute
quantities of whole blood directly on a single sample of the
order of 10
Screening for the numerous disease of genetic origin on
newborns will be expanded so that eventually a battery of tests
will be utilized for the determination of the erythrocyte
abnormalities and abnormalities of intermediate metabolism.
It is predicted that a compulsory program will be directed by
governmental agencies in this direction.
The problems of the Laboratory of Neonatology are unique
and distinct in many details from those of the general clinical
chemistry laboratory. This requires a separate operation co-
ordinated with the operation of the Pediatric Department of
the hospital. It requires a highly sophisticated Chemist at
the doctorate level as supervisor, trained in this area to
insure that the results are meaningful and to supervise and
accelerate the development of the techniques in this area.
Developments in this direction are already taking place rapidly.
The Committee on Pediatric Chemistry of the American Association of Clinical Chemists is now active in developing the list
of normal values for the infant.
Probably, the most rapidly developing science in medicine
today is the Science of Neonatology. It is important that the
development of the laboratory keep pace.

Literature Cited

1. Natelson, S.; Crawford, W. L.; and Munsey, F. A.;
    Correlation of Clinical and Chemical Observations in
    the Immature Infant. Ill. Dept. of Public Health Pub.
    Div. of Preventive Medicine (1952).
2. Heird, W. C.; Driscoll, J. M. Jr.; Schullinger, J. N.;
    Grebin, B; and Winters, R. W.; Intravenous alimentation
    in pediatric patients, J. Ped. (1972), 80, 351 - 372.
3. Dudrick, S. J.; Wilmore, D. W.; Vars, H. M.; and

Rhoads, J.E.; Can intravenous feeding as the sole means of nutrition support growth in the child and restore weight loss in an adult. An affirmative answer. Ann. Surg. (1969), 169, 974 - 984.

4. Bellingham, A. J.; Detter, J. C.; and Lenfant, C.; Regulator mechanisms of hemoglobin oxygen affinity in acidosis and alkalosis. J. Clin. Invest (1971), 50, 700 - 706.

5. Natelson, S.; Techniques in Clinical Chemistry, 3rd Edition. Chas. C. Thomas, Springfield, Ill., 1971.

6. Huijing, F.; A rapid enzymic method for glycogen estimation in very small tissue samples. Clin. Chim. Acta (1970), 30, 567 - 572.

7. Brady, R.O.; Cerebral lipidoses. Ann. Rev. Med. (1970), 21, 317 - 334.

8. Constantopoulos, G.; and Dekaban, A. S.; Chemical definition of the mucopolysaccharidoses. Clin. Chim. Acta (1975), 59, 321 - 336.

9. Beutler, E.; Red Cell Metabolism: A Manual of Biochemical Methods. Grune & Stratton, N.Y. (1971).

10. Chu, T. C.; and Chu, E. J. H.; Porphyrin patterns in different types of porphyrins. Clin. Chem (1967), 13, 371 - 387.

11. Vincke, H.; Hereditary hypophosphatasia. Acta Paediat. Belg. (1970), 24, 131 - 138.

12. Wallace, J. E.; Microdetermination of diphenyl hydantoin in biological specimens by ultraviolet spectrometry. Anal. Chem. (1968), 40, 978 - 980.

13. Natelson, S.; Routine use of ultramicro methods in the clinical laboratory. Am. J. Clin. Path. (1951), 21, 1153 - 1172.

14. Bessey, O. A.; Lowry, O. H.; and Brock, M. J.; A method for the rapid determination of alkaline phosphatase with five cubic millimeters of serum. J. Biol. Chem. (1946), 164, 321 - 329.

15. Natelson, S.; and Pochopien, D. J.; Novel approach to the design of a Pediatric microanalytical laboratory. Microchem. (1973), 18, 475 - 485.

16. Sanz, M. C.; Brechbuhler, T.; and Green, I. J.; The ultramicro-determination of total and protein-bound iodine. Clin. Chem. (1956), 1, 570 - 576.

17. Kaiser, E.; Kunstadter, R. H.; and Mendelsohn, R. J.; Electrolyte concentrations in sweat and saliva; comparison in patients with cysticfibrosis of pancreas and other conditions. Amer. J. Dis. Child. (1956), 92, 369 - 373.

18. Natelson, S.; and Clark, M. K.; Estimation of bromide on fingertip blood in bromide intoxication. Proc. Soc. Expt. Biol. Med. (1955), 90, 723 - 725.

19. Fischl, J.; Serum iron determination using direct color

extraction. Clin. Chim. Acta (1960), 5, 164 - 170.

20. Moody, G. J.; and Thomas, J. D. R.; Selective Ion Sensitive Electrodes. Merrow Pub. Co., 276 Hempstead Rd., Watford Herts, England.

21. Bittner, D. L.; U. S. Patent #3,282,649 (1966).

22. Saifer, A.; and Gerstenfeld, S.; The photometric microdetermination of blood glucose with glucose oxidase. J. Lab. Clin. Med. (1958), 51, 448 - 460.

23. Kapuscinski, V.; and Zak, B.; Use of perchloric acid filtrate and stabilized anthrone for determination of serum glucose. Am. J. Clin. Path. (1953), 23, 784 - 788.

24. Tomisek, A. J.; and Natelson, S.; Fluorometric assay of ultramicro quantities of glucose with Somogyi filtrate and hexokinase. Micro-chem. J. (1974), 19, 54 - 62.

25. Takahara, K.; Sasaki, M.; Tomisek. A. J.; and Natelson, S.; Sensitive o-Toluidine reagent for glucose assay at moderately elevated temperatures. Microchem. J. (1974), 19, 319 - 329.

26. Natelson, S.; A rapid method for the estimation of urea in biological fluids as the urea diacetyl complex. Am. J. Clin. Path (1951), 21, 275 - 281.

27. Chaney, A. L.; and Marbach, E. P.; Modified reagents for determination of urea and ammonia. Clin. Chem. (1962), 8, 130 - 132.

28. Accord, W.; and Feldman, F. J.; Design consideration for a fully automated rate electrochemical glucose and urea nitrogen analyzer. Clin. Chem. (1974), 20, 903.

29. Natelson, S.; The routine use of the Perkin-Elmer flame photometer in the clinical laboratory. Am. J. Clin. Path. (1950), 20, 463 - 472.

30. Frant, M. S.; and Ross, J. W., Jr.; Potassium ion specific electrode with high selectivity for potassium over sodium. Science (1970), 167, 987 - 988.

31. Cotlove, E.; and Nishi, H. H.; Automatic titration with direct read-out of chloride concentration. Clin. Chem. (1961), 7, 285 - 291.

32. Gindler, E. M.; Mercurimetric determination of chloride in biologic fluids using 2-(8-Hydroxyquinoly-5-azo)-benzoic acid (QBA). Clin. Chem. (1968), 14, 1172 - 1175.

33. Seligson, S.; McCormick. G. J.; and Sleeman, K.; Electrometric method for the determination of chloride in serum and other biological fluids. Clin. Chem. (1958), 4, 159 -169.

34. Driscoll, J. L.; and Martin, H. F.; Detection of brominism by an automated chloride method. Clin. Chem. (1966), 12, 314 - 318.

35. Teloh, H. A.; Estimation of serum calcium by flame

photometry. Archives of Pathol. (1958), 66, 474 - 481.

36. Pybus, J.; Feldman, F. J.; and Bowers, G. N., Jr.;
    Measurement of total calcium in serum by atomic
    absorption spectrophotmetry with use of a strontium
    internal reference. Clin. Chem. (1970), 16, 998 - 1007.

37. Arnold. D. E.; Stansell, M. J.; and Malvin, H. H.;
    Measurement of serum ionic calcium using a specific ion
    electrode. Am. J. Clin. Path. (1968), 49, 627 - 634.

37a. Natelson, S.; Richelson, M. R.; Sheid, B.; and
    Bender, S. L.; X-ray spectroscopy in the clinical
    laboratory. Clin. Chem. (1959), 5, 519 - 531.

38. Doumas, B. T.; Perry, B. W.; Sasse, E. A.; and
    Straumfjord, J. V., Jr.; Standardization in bilirubin
    solutions. Clin. Chem. (1973), 19, 984 - 993.

39. Henry, R. J.; Golub, O. J.; Berkman, S.; and
    Segalove, M.; Critique on the icterus index determin-
    ation. Am. J. Clin. Path (1953), 23, 841 - 853.

40. Bilirubinometer, Model 10200 - American Optical Co.,
    Buffalo, N. Y., 14215. Also the Sherwood Medical
    Industries, Bridgton, Missouri.

41. Dubin, A.; Application of multi-wavelength spectroscopy
    to analysis of amniotic fluid bilirubin, in Amniotic
    Fluid. Natelson, S.; Scommegna, A.; and Epstein, M. D.,
    ed.; John Wiley, N. Y. (1974) pp. 191 - 197.

42. Alvey, J. P.; Obstetrical management of Rh incompata-
    bility based on liquor amnii studies. Amer. J. Obstet.
    Gynecol. (1964), 90, 769 - 775.

43. Liley, A. W.; Liquor amnii analysis in the management
    of the pregnancy complicated by rhesus sensitazation.
    Am. J. Obstet. Gynecol. (1961), 82, 1359 - 1370.

44. Dambacher, M.; Gubler, A.; and Haas, H. G.; A new time-
    saving method for determining nitrogen in biological
    material. Clin. Chem. (1969), 14, 615 - 622.

45. Daughaday, W. H.; Lowry, O. H.; Rosenbrough, N. J.;
    and Fields, W. S.; Determination of cerebrospinal fluid
    protein with the Folin phenol reagent. J. Lab. Clin.
    Med. (1953), 39, 663 - 665.

46. Kingsley, G. R.; Direct biuret method for determination
    of serum proteins as applied to photoelectric and
    visual colorimetry. J. Lab. Clin. Med. (1942), 27,
    840 - 845.

47. Blumenfeld, T. A.; et al., eds.; Normal values for
    Pediatric Clinical Chemistry. Am. Assoc. of Clin. Chem.
    Publication (1974).

48. Natelson, S.; Penniall, R.; Crawford, W. L.; and
    Munsey, F. A.; Noncasein protein to casein ration of
    feeding formulas. Effect on blood component levels in
    normal infants. Am. J. Dis. Child. (1955), 89,
    656 - 668.

49. Bates, R. G.; Determination of pH, Theory and Practice,

        2nd Ed. Wiley, New York (1973).
50.   Astrup, P.; and Rorth, M., eds.; Oxygen Affinity of
      Hemoglobin and Red Cell Acid Base Status. Academic
      Press, New York (1972).
51.   Natelson, S.; and Natelson, E. A.; Applied Clinical
      Chemistry, pp. 42 - 49. Plenum Press, New York (1974).
52.   Natelson, S.; Routine use of ultra-micro methods in
      the clinical laboratory. Am. J. Clin. Path. (1951),
      21, 1153 - 1172.
53.   Menning, C. M.; and Natelson, S.; Improved methods of
      analysis for oxygen, carbon monoxide and iron on
      fingertip blood. Clin. Chem. (1955), 1, 165 - 179.
54.   Natelson, S.; and Barbour, J. H.; Equation and nomogram
      for approximation of alkali requirements in acidosis.
      Am. J. Clin. Path. (1952), 22, 426 - 439.
55.   Conway, E. J.; and O'Malley, E.; Microdiffusion methods.
      Ammonia and urea using buffered absorbance (revised
      methods for ranges greater than 10 mu/g N). Biochem.
      J. (1942), 36, 655 - 661.
56.   Seligson, D.; and Seligson, H.; A microdiffusion
      method for the determination of nitrogen liberated as
      ammonia. J. Lab. Clin. Med. (1961), 38, 324 - 330.
57.   Century, B.; Vorkink, W. P.; and Natelson, S.; Thin
      layer chromatographic screening of aminoacids in plasma
      and urine of newborns. Clin. Chem. (1974), 20,
      1446 - 1450.
58.   Natelson, S.; Automatic analysis of microsamples
      contained in capillaries with a microsample dispenser.
      Microchem. J. (1968), 13, 433 - 458.
59.   Chedid, A.; Haux, P.; and Natelson, S.; Use of thin
      layer chromatography on silica gel for serum lipid
      fractionation and measurement in the routine clinical
      laboratory. Clin. Chem. (1972), 18, 384 - 390.
60.   Natelson, S.; Analysis of components in biological
      fluids in a gravity-free environment emphasizing
      procedures suitable for use in an orbiting laboratory.
      Progress report to National Aeronautics Space Agency,
      Contract #NAS 9-7934, NASA Headquarters, Washington,
      D.C., 20546 1966, 1967, 1968, 1969.

Blood Gas Abnormalities

HARRY F. WEISBERG

Division of Biochemistry, Department of Pathology, Mount Sinai Medical Center, Milwaukee, Wis. 53201

The term "blood gases" has different meanings; the most accurate refers to the gases in the blood -- carbon dioxide, oxygen, and nitrogen -- whereas the most expedient refers to the data obtained from present-day laboratory instruments -- pH, Pco_2, and Po_2. Some confusion results since the data overlap two major areas of diagnosis. Diagnosis of "acid-base imbalance" is accomplished using values for pH and Pco_2 (though arterial blood samples are touted as the best, venous blood can also be used). The diagnosis of "hypoxia" requires arterial blood Po_2 values; however, three types of hypoxia have normal arterial values (vida infra).

Acid-base imbalance can easily be diagnosed by use of a diagram (Figure 1) or a flowchart (Figure 2) in which 13 diagnostic areas are identified. Knowledge of the pH and Pco_2 values can distinguish areas or diagnoses 1-7. The CO_2 content or actual bicarbonate value is used to distinguish a "mixed" metabolic and respiratory abnormality from a "pure respiratory" abnormality -- area 8 from 9 or 10 and area 11 from 12 or 13. Base excess/deficit (previous base excess $\pm$) or the ΔCT (delta CO_2 content) is necessary only to distinguish between an "acute" or "chronic" respiratory condition -- 9 vs 10 and 12 vs 13 (Figures 1 and 2). Figure 2 has many sets of data in parentheses; these are not necessary for the differential diagnosis of an acid-base imbalance. In similar fashion, the Po_2 values are not needed in the diagnosis of an abnormal condition of acid-base. Table 1 summarizes the data of Figures 1 and 2 and, in addition, gives the physio-pathological basis for the alterations of the (arterial) Po_2.

A classification of the causes of hypoxia is presented in Table II. Only anoxic anoxia (due to decreased ambient oxygen or to respiratory disease) has arterial Po_2 values decreased (with accompanying decreased venous Po_2 values). However, hemic, ischemic, and histoxic hypoxia may be present (termed non-ventilatory hypoxia) with normal arterial Po_2 values. Thus the best evaluation of hypoxia is an analysis of both arterial and venous

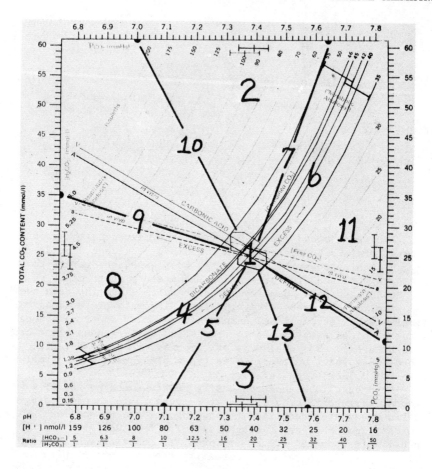

Interpretation of Electrolyte, Acid–Base, and Oxygen Imbalance

Figure 1. Acid–base balance evaluation diagram with 13 diagnostic areas (1)

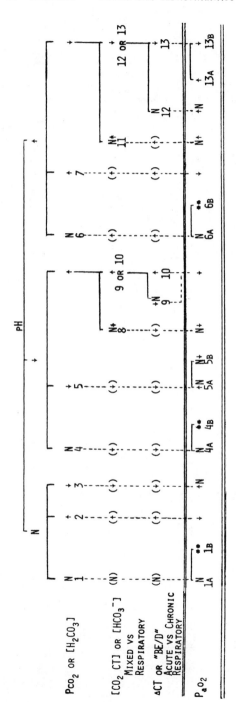

Figure 2. *Flow-chart for differential diagnoses of acid–base imbalance* (1)

TABLE I

Differential Diagnosis of Acid-Base Equilibrium.
PO$_2$ values are arterial. From Weisberg ($\underline{1}$).

#	pH	Pco$_2$ or [H$_2$CO$_3$]	[CO$_2$ CT] or [HCO$_3^-$]	ΔCT or BE/D	Po$_2$**	COMMENTS
1	EupHemia					
1a	N	N	N	N	N	Normal *blood* "gases" (Hemic hypoxia) (Ischemic hypoxia) (Histotoxic hypoxia)
1b	N	N	N	N	↓	V̇/Q̇ inequality Shunts
2	N	↑	↑	↑	↓	Respiratory Acidosis, Compensated; see #8, #9, and #10 Hypoventilation[†] (Shunts)[¶] (V̇/Q̇ inequality)[¶] (Metabolic Alkalosis, Compensated)[Δ]; see #6, #7, and #11
3	N	↓	↓	↓	↑N	Respiratory Alkalosis, Compensated; see #11, #12, and #13 Hyperventilation (Metabolic Acidosis, Compensated); see #4, #5, and #8
	HypopHemia					
4a	↓	N	↓	↓	N	Metabolic Acidosis, Uncompensated (Hemic hypoxia) (Ischemic hypoxia) (Histotoxic hypoxia)
4b	↓	N	↓	↓	↓	V̇/Q̇ inequality Shunts
5a	↓	↓	↓	↓	↑N	Metabolic Acidosis, Partial compensation (by Hyperventilation)
5b	↓	↓	↓	↓	N↓	Metabolic Acidosis & Shock; see #13b
8	↓	↑	N	↓	N↓	Mixed Respiratory Acidosis & Metabolic Acidosis
9	↓	↑	↑	↓N	↓	Respiratory Acidosis, Acute
10	↓	↑	↑	↑	↓	Respiratory Acidosis, Chronic (Partial compensation)

TABLE I (CONTINUED)

Differential Diagnosis of Acid-Base Equilibrium. PO_2 values are arterial. From Weisberg (1).

	HyperpHemia					
6a	↑	N	↑	↑	N	Metabolic Alkalosis, Uncompensated (Hemic hypoxia) (Ischemic hypoxia) (Histotoxic hypoxia)
6b	↑	N	↑	↑	↓	$\dot{V}/\dot{Q}$ inequality Shunts
7	↑	↑	↑	↑	↓	Metabolic Alkalosis, Partial compensation (by Hypoventilation)
11	↑	↓	N	↑	N↑	Mixed Respiratory Alkalosis & Metabolic Alkalosis
12	↑	↓	↓	N	↑N	Respiratory Alkalosis, Acute°
13a	↑	↓	↓	↓	↑	Respiratory Alkalosis, Chronic (Partial compensation) Impaired diffusion
13b	↑	↓	↓	↓	↓	Decreased ambient O_2 (Impaired diffusion) (Shunt) ($\dot{V}/\dot{Q}$ inequality) "Inappropriate pulmonary ventilation in acutely ill patient" eg, Myocardial infarct Pulmonary embolus Shock Later pH↓; see #5b

* Arrows show direction and not extent of change; N = normal.
** A "low" Po_2 may become "normal" or "increased" due to:
    Hyperventilation
    O_2 Therapy
      Increased Concentration (100% should produce P_aO_2 >600)
      Increased pressure [hyperbaric chamber, respiratory ventilators (eg, PEEP or CPPB)]
    Po_2 polarographic electrode "error" due to halogenated hydrocarbons (eg, Halothane)
† Po_2 usually <50
¶ If present in addition to hypoventilation, Po_2 will be lowered further.
Δ Po_2 usually >50
° Also transient hyperventilation in response to arterial puncture.

TABLE II

Classification of Hypoxia. Modified from Weisberg (1).

I. ANOXIC:
    A. AMBIENT ($F_I O_2$ ↓)
        1. Altitude
        2. O_2 Dilution ("Fire damp", "Black Damp")
        3. Anesthetic or O_2 Therapy mishaps

    B. RESPIRATORY:
        1. ALVEOLAR HYPOVENTILATION
            ("Ventilatory insufficiency")
        2. DIFFUSION DEFECT
            ("Alveolar-capillary block")
        3. VENTILATION/CIRCULATION ($\dot{V}/\dot{Q}$) INEQUALITY
            ("Physiologic" shunt)
        4. VENOUS-ARTERIAL SHUNT
            ("Anatomic" shunt)

II. HEMIC:
    A. ANEMIC
        1. Hemorrhage
        2. Depressed marrow, etc.
            a. X-ray
            b. Phenylhydrazine

    B. TOXIC
        1. "Abnormal" Hemoglobin
            a. CO-
            b. Met-
            c. Sulf-

TABLE II (CONTINUED)

Classification of Hypoxia.   Modified from Weisberg (1).

III.   ISCHEMIC ("Stagnant", "Circulatory", "Hypokinetic"):
       A.   ISCHEMIA
            1.   Hypovolemia
            2.   Congenital defects
            3.   Peripheral stasis

       B.   MINUTE-FLOW DISCREPANCY
            1.   Decreased cardiac output
            2.   Increased tissue demand for O_2

IV.   HISTOTOXIC:
       A.   ENZYMATIC
            1.   Cyanide
            2.   Narcotics
            3.   Alcohol

       B.   OXYGEN

       C.   "WATER & ELECTROLYTES"
            e.g., Na↓

blood specimens (Table III).

A footnote in Table I (and Table VI) states that Po_2 values may be erroneously elevated due to the effect of halogenated hydrocarbons on the polarographic electrode. Severinghaus et al (2) reported that Halothane, a brominehydrocarbon anesthetic, can be polarographically reduced by the Clark-type oxygen electrode at polarizing voltages greater than 0.4 volt and also increases the sensitivity of the electrode to oxygen, resulting in as much as 10-fold spuriously elevated Po_2 values. This was confirmed for a different type of oxygen electrode which uses a polarizing voltage of 0.7 volt (3). However, the consensus of conversations with various anesthesiologists does not agree with these reports (4). Halothane does not affect the affinity of hemoglobin for oxygen (5).

A more common cause for "altered" Po_2 values is the age of the individual. Normal Po_2 values decrease with age; in addition, surgical procedures cause a temporary (post-operative period) decrease of the individual's Po_2 values. Various regression formulas have been presented describing the decrease of Po_2 with increasing age under normal conditions (6-12), after surgery (10, 13-17), and with oxygen therapy (10, 16).

I have used the following "rule-of-thumb" formulas to predict the expected Po_2 values under room air conditions in normal (equation 1) and post-operative (equation 2) patients; the "variation" of the prediction formulas is $\pm$ 5.

$$P_aO_2 \quad = \quad 105 - \frac{age}{3} \tag{1}$$

$$\overline{p}\text{-op } P_aO_2 \quad = \quad 100 - \frac{age}{2} \tag{2}$$

Equations 3 and 4 are used when 100% oxygen is given to normal and post-operative patients, respectively; in this case the "variation" is ± 25.

$$P_aO_2 \quad = \quad 575 - age \tag{3}$$

$$\overline{p}\text{-op } P_aO_2 \quad = \quad 500 - \frac{5}{4} age \tag{4}$$

Dry air at sea level and 20° has partial pressures of 159, 0.3, and 601 mmHg, respectively, for the three gases, oxygen, carbon dioxide, and nitrogen. In ambient air (contains water vapor of 17 mmHg at 20°), the partial pressures of the gases

TABLE III

Blood Gas Values Under Various Conditions

CONDITION	PaO$_2$	PaCO$_2$	PaO$_2$ >600 on 100% O$_2$	P$_v$O$_2$	P$_v$CO$_2$
NORMAL VALUES	95 (75–100)	40 (35–45)M 37 (32–42)F		40 (30–50)	46 (42–55)M 43 (39–52)F
AMBIENT O$_2$ ↓	↓	↓	YES	AS "ARTERIAL"	
HYPOXIA:					
HYPOVENTILATION	↓	↑(N)	YES	AS "ARTERIAL"	
DIFFUSION DEFECT	↓	↓(N)	YES	AS "ARTERIAL"	
V̇/Q̇ INEQUALITY	↓	↑N(↓)	YES	AS "ARTERIAL"	
SHUNTS	↓	N(↑↓)	NO	AS "ARTERIAL"	
NON-VENTILATORY HYPOXIA:					
HEMIC	N	N		↓	N
ISCHEMIC	N	N		→	↑
HISTOTOXIC	N	↓(N)		↑	↓(N)
HYPERVENTILATION	↑(N)	↓		AS "ARTERIAL"	
O$_2$ THERAPY	↑N	(↑N↓)		AS "ARTERIAL"	

are 156, 0.3, and 587, respectively; upon <u>humidification at 37°</u> (47 mmHg water vapor), the partial pressures are 150, 0.3, and 563. <u>Alveolar air</u> (end-pulmonary capillaries) has the same water vapor of 47 mmHg but the partial pressures of the gases are 104, 40, and 569 mmHg whereas the values for <u>arterial</u> blood (same 47 mmHg for water vapor) are 100, 40, and 573 mmHg. Note that because of differences in gas characteristics the carbon dioxide partial pressure is the <u>"same"</u> for arterial blood and alveolar air whereas alveolar P_{O_2} is higher but alveolar P_{N_2} is lower than in arterial blood. <u>Expired air</u> (at 37° with 47 mmHg water vapor) is a mixture of alveolar and humidified ambient air so that the partial pressures are 120, 27, and 566 mmHg for oxygen, carbon dioxide, and nitrogen. <u>Venous blood</u> values are 47, 40, 46, and 573 mmHg for the partial pressures of water, oxygen, carbon dioxide, and nitrogen.

In order to evaluate the ventilatory status of a patient the alveolar oxygen tension ($P_{A}O_2$) must be known. It can be determined from the "alveolar gas equation" (equation 5),

$$P_{A}O_2 \;=\; F_{I}O_2\,(P_B - 47) - P_{A}CO_2\left(F_{I}O_2 + \frac{1 - F_{I}O_2}{R}\right) \quad (5)$$

in which P_A is the partial pressure of a gas in the alveoli, F_I is the fraction of the gas in the inspired air, P_B is the barometric pressure, 47 is the water vapor pressure at 37° at sea level, and R is the respiratory quotient (normal of 0.8, which may drop to below 0.5 in asphyxia). Substituting room air conditions at sea level results in

$$P_{A}O_2 \;=\; 0.209\,(760 - 47) - 40\left(0.209 + \frac{1 - 0.209}{0.8}\right)$$

$$= \; 149 - 48$$

$$= \; 101$$

For most clinical purposes, using room air and considering arterial PCO_2 ($P_{a}CO_2$) the "same" as alveolar PCO_2 ($P_{A}CO_2$), equation 5 can be "simplified" to equation 6.

$$P_{A}O_2 \;=\; 150 - \frac{5}{4}\,P_{a}CO_2 \quad (6)$$

$$= \; 150 - 50$$

$$= \; 100$$

It may not be well known that the weather bureau reports of barometric pressure are corrected to sea level even though describing conditions in the mountains, etc. Table IV gives the barometric pressure at various altitudes; these should be used when applicable in equations 5 and 6. Representative cities and the variations in their respective altitudes are given in Table V.

The difference between alveolar and arterial Po_2 values is called the oxygen A-a gradient (also $P_{(A-a)}o_2$ or $D_{(A-a)}o_2$ or $AaDo_2$) and is normally about 10 mmHg. It is used to evaluate ventilation/perfusion ($\dot{V}/\dot{Q}$) inequalities. With increasing age, the gradient rises so that "normal" values for 70-80 year old individuals are 20-25 mmHg. Upon breathing 100% oxygen for 20 minutes the gradient is increased ("normal") up to 100 mmHg. Breathing room air, a simplification is given in equation 7; however, for patients on oxygen therapy, the P_ao_2 should be subtracted from equation 5.

$$P_{(A-a)}o_2 \quad = \quad 150 - \frac{4}{5} P_aco_2 - P_ao_2 \qquad (7)$$

In early pulmonary disease, a patient may be hyperventilating while breathing room air so that the P_aco_2 is decreased, yet the P_ao_2 may be relatively normal; with such pulmonary pathology the $P_{(A-a)}o_2$ will be increased. With frank pulmonary disease, oxygen therapy may mask the expected hypoxia so that the P_ao_2 is normal or elevated; again the $P_{(A-a)}o_2$ will be increased. On the other hand, in a patient with an elevated P_aco_2 (hypoventilation), if the $P_{(A-a)}o_2$ is not elevated then the hypoventilation is probably due to extra-pulmonary factors such as narcosis, muscle weakness, paralysis, etc. For room air conditions, an increase of the $\dot{V}/\dot{Q}$ ratio will show low Pco_2 and elevated Po_2 values with the "ultimate" being a point equal to the inspired room air, P_ao_2 150 and P_aco_2 0 mmHg. A decrease of the $\dot{V}/\dot{Q}$ ratio will show a fall of the Po_2 but a rather constant Pco_2; again the "ultimate" would be a point equal to mixed venous blood, P_ao_2 40 and P_aco_2 46 mmHg. The oxygen gradient, $AaDo_2$, with the patient breathing 100% oxygen for 20 minutes, is used as a criterion for weaning a patient from a mechanical ventilator (19). An abnormally high $AaDo_2$ gradient (above 350 mmHg) is an indication that the patient will need continued ventilatory support with high inspired fractions of oxygen.

The $P_{(A-a)}o_2$ is also used in calculating the amount of shunt present (equation 8)

$$\% \text{ shunt} \quad = \quad \frac{0.03 \times P_{(A-a)}o_2}{0.03 \times P_{(A-a)}o_2 + av}$$

TABLE IV

Conversions for Barometric Pressure and Altitude in Terms of mmHg per each 100 ft. Modified from Consolazio et al. (18).

ALTITUDE	0	100	200	300	400	500	600	700	800	900
0	760	757	754	752	749	746	744	741	738	736
1000	733	730	728	725	722	720	717	714	712	709
2000	706	704	701	699	696	694	691	688	686	684
3000	681	678	676	674	671	668	666	664	661	659
4000	656	654	651	649	646	644	642	639	637	634
5000	632	630	628	626	623	621	618	616	613	611
6000	609	607	604	602	600	598	596	594	591	589
7000	586	584	582	580	578	576	573	571	569	567
8000	564	562	560	558	556	554	552	550	547	545
9000	543	541	539	537	535	533	530	528	526	524
10000	522	521	519	517	514	512	510	508	506	504
11000	502	501	499	497	495	493	491	489	487	485
12000	483	481	479	477	475	474	472	470	468	466

in which av is the difference in oxygen <u>content</u> of arterial and
mixed venous blood or the oxygen uptake related to cardiac output.
An approximation useful clinically is given in equation 9.

$$\% \text{ shunt} = \frac{P_I O_2 - P_a O_2}{25} \tag{9}$$

Normally the shunt is 2-6%; for room air conditions equation 9
becomes

$$\frac{150 - 90}{25} = 2.4\%$$

To properly calculate the extent of a shunt, however, requires
the patient to breathe 100% oxygen for 15-20 minutes. Table
III illustrates that the low $P_a O_2$ in hypoventilation, diffusion
defect, and $\dot{V}/\dot{Q}$ inequality is corrected by breathing 100% oxygen
whereas in a true veno-arterial shunt it is not.
    Table VI summarizes the material presented in the previous
discussion. It correlates the changes in oxygen and carbon dioxide partial pressures, showing the pathological causes for the
imbalances. In addition, it contains the various diagnoses of
acid-base abnormality (using same numbers as in Figures 1 and 2
and Table I). Considering the format of Table VI as a tic-tac-
toe set-up, we can label the nine portions by the letters A-I
for identification in Table VII which gives examples of various
conditions associated with such blood gas abnormalities (20-30).

Po_2

	↓	N	↑
↑	A	B	C
Pco_2 N	D	E	F
↓	G	H	I

TABLE V

ALTITUDE VARIATIONS OF REPRESENTATIVE CITIES

CITY	ALTITUDE	COMMENTS
Buffalo	572→650	Lake Erie
Chicago	580→600	Lake Michigan
Cleveland	572→800	Lake Erie
Dead Sea	-1300	Lowest Spot; 23-25% Salt (vs 4-6% for Ocean)
Death Valley, Calif.	-282	$T^o > 120^o F$; Max $134.6^o F$
Denver	5280	
Detroit	580→581	Lake Huron
Duluth	602→1200	Lake Superior
Lake Erie	572	
Huron	580	
Michigan	580	
Ontario	246	
Superior	602	

TABLE V (CONTINUED)

ALTITUDE VARIATIONS OF REPRESENTATIVE CITIES

CITY	ALTITUDE	COMMENTS
Leadville, Col.	10,200	
Mexico City	7347→8000	Volcanoes →14,000
Milwaukee	580→705	Lake Michigan Mitchell Field 693
Minneapolis	838→"1100"?	Mid-Point Equator & N. Pole at Falls of St. Anthony
Philadelphia	150	
Phoenix	1100	
Pittsburgh	710→1365	
Rochester, NY	500→697	"Along" Lake Ontario
Salt Lake City	4255	Salt Lake 27% Salt
San Francisco	0→938	
Toronto	246→250	Lake Ontario
Tucson	2400	

Table VI. Blood Gas Imbalance. Presented in part at ASCP-CAP Annual Meeting, San Francisco, Oct. 1972 (1); based on material from 20 and 21.

$P_{a_{O_2}}$

HYPOXEMIA   N   HYPEROXEMIA

$P_{a_{CO_2}}$

HYPOVENTILATION   N

O₂ Therapy°

V̇/Q̇ maldistribution – severe

Hypothermia△
O₂ Therapy°

[Met alk - (2, 7), Comp or Partial]

[Resp Acid - (9, 10, 2) Acute, Chronic, or Comp]   [Resp Acid & Met Acid (8)]

{General Net}

{"Local" "Nonuniform" "Regional" "Uneven"}

HYPOVENTILATION Shunts

V̇/Q̇ maldistribution

Pulmonary disease - poor compensation

"NORMAL" BLOOD GASES

[(1b) Normal "Acid-Base" (1a)]
[(4b) Met Acid - Acute (4a)]
[(6b) Met Alk - Acute (6a)]

O₂ Therapy°

NON-VENTILATORY HYPOXIA		
(1a, 4a, 6a)	$P_{v_{O_2}}$	$P_{v_{CO_2}}$
Hemic	↓	N
Ischemic	↓	↑
Histotoxic	↑	↓N ¶

¶Also $P_{a_{CO_2}}$; pH↑

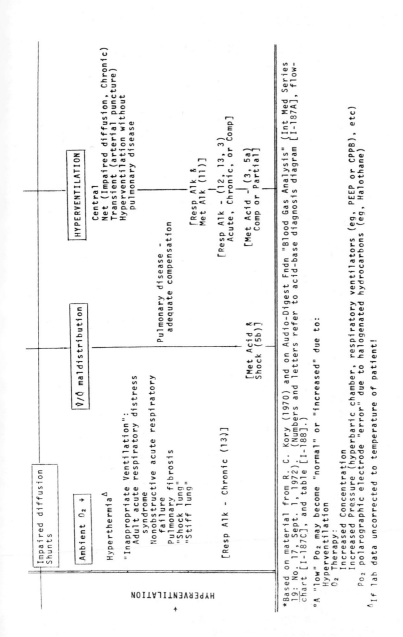

Impaired diffusion
Shunts

Ambient O_2 ↓

Hyperthermia △

"Inappropriate Ventilation":
  Adult acute respiratory distress
    syndrome
  Nonobstructive acute respiratory
    failure
  Pulmonary fibrosis
  "Shock lung"
  "Stiff lung"

[Resp Alk - Chronic (13)]

HYPERVENTILATION
↓

V/Q maldistribution

[Met Acid &
Shock (5b)]

HYPERVENTILATION

Central
Net (Impaired diffusion, Chronic)
Transient (arterial puncture)
Hyperventilation without
  pulmonary disease

Pulmonary disease -
  adequate compensation

[Resp Alk &
Met Alk (11)]

[Resp Alk - (12, 13, 3)]
  Acute, Chronic, or Comp]

[Met Acid - (3, 5a)]
  Comp or Partial]

*Based on material from R. C. Kory (1970) and on Audio-Digest Fndn "Blood Gas Analysis" [Int Med Series
19: No. 17, Sept. 1, 1972]. (Numbers and letters refer to acid-base diagnosis diagram [I-187A], flow-
chart [I-187C], and table [I-188].)

°A "low" PO_2 may become "normal" or "increased" due to:
  Hyperventilation
  O_2 Therapy:
    Increased Concentration
    Increased Pressure (hyperbaric chamber, respiratory ventilators (eg, PEEP or CPPB), etc)
  PO_2 polarographic electrode "error" due to halogenated hydrocarbons (eg, Halothane)

△If lab data uncorrected to temperature of patient!

TABLE VII

Conditions Associated with Blood Gas Imbalance

Modified from Weisberg (1)

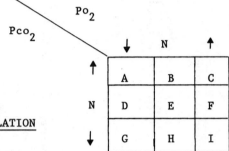

(A) $Po_2 \downarrow$; $Pco_2 \uparrow$
ALVEOLAR HYPOVENTILATION
   1. General
       a. Physiological
           (1) Sleep
           (2) CO_2 Retention
           (3) Metabolic Alkalosis

       b. Impaired Movement of Respiratory Cage & Diaphragm
           (1) Abdominal Distension
           (2) Ankylosing Spondylitis
           (3) Ascites
           (4) Chest Injury
           (5) Kyphoscoliosis
           (6) Myxedema
           (7) Obesity
           (8) Pleural Disease

       c. Neurological Impairment of Respiratory Drive &
           Cage
           (1) CNS Lesions of Respiratory Center
           (2) Muscular Dystrophy
           (3) Myasthenia Gravis
           (4) Narcotics & Drugs
           (5) Pickwickian Syndrome
           (6) Poliomyelitis

   2. Net (Secondary to Pulmonary Disease)
       a. Obstruction to Airways
           (1) Asthma, Severe
           (2) Bronchitis, Chronic
           (3) Cystic Fibrosis
           (4) Emphysema
           (5) Laryngeal Spasm

TABLE VII (Continued)

Conditions Associated with Blood Gas Imbalance

Modified from Weisberg (1)

      b. Distortion of Pulmonary Parenchyma

(B) Po_2 N; Pco_2 ↑
     O_2 Therapy

(C) Po_2↑ ; Pco_2↑
     O_2 Therapy

(A)-(D) Po_2↓ ; Pco_2 N↑
     Collapse of Lung
     Pneumonia

(D) Po_2↓ ; Pco_2 N
     "Age"
     Atelectasis
     Bronchitis, Early
     Cardiac Failure
     Congenital Heart Disease with R-L Shunt
     Pneumonia
     "Prematurity"

(E) Po_2 N; Pco_2 N
     Normal
     "Non-Ventilatory Hypoxia"
         Hemic Anoxia
         Ischemic Anoxia
         Histotoxic Anoxia

(F) Po_2↑ ; Pco_2 N
     O_2 Therapy

(D)-(G) Po_2↓ ; Pco_2 N↓
     Asbestosis
     Idiopathic Fibrosis
     Pulmonary Edema
     Sarcoidosis

(G) PO_2↓ ; PCO_2 ↓
     Acute Pulmonary Inflammation
     Alkylating Agents
         Busulfan
         Cyclophosphamide

TABLE VII

Conditions Associated with Blood Gas Imbalance

Modified from Weisberg (1)

Drug Overdose
"Interstial Pulmonary Fibrosis"
Myocardial Infarct
Post-Op
Pulmonary Oxygen Toxicity
Radiation Pneumonitis
"Shock Lung"
    Hemorrhage
    Thermal Injury
Trauma (e.g., Thoracic)
Viral Pneumonitis

(G)-(H) $Po_2\downarrow$ N; $Pco_2\downarrow$
Asthma, Early
Pulmonary Embolus
Shock, Late

(I) $Po_2\uparrow$; $Pco_2\downarrow$
Anxiety
Dehydration
Diabetic Acidosis
Hyperventilation Syndrome
Neurologic Disease
Shock, Early
Uremia

Literature Cited

1. Weisberg, H. F.; Interpretation of Electrolyte, Acid-Base,
    and Oxygen Imbalance, Private mimeographed printing,
    4th ed., 1974.
2. Severinghaus, J. W.; Weiskopf, R. B.; Nishimura, M.;
    and Bradley, A. F.; Oxygen Electrode Errors Due to
    Polarographic Reduction of Halothane. J. Appl. Physiol.
    (1971), 31, 640-642.
3. Bates, M. L.; Feingold, A.; and Gold, M. I.; The Effects
    of Anesthesia on an In-vivo Oxygen Electrode. Am. J.
    Clin. Path. (1975), 64, 448 - 451.
4. Laver, M. B.; Personal Communication (1975).
5. Weiskopf, R. B.; Nishimura, M.; and Severinghaus, J. W.;
    The Absence of an Effect of Halothane on Blood Hemoglobin
    O_2 Equilibrium in Vitro. Anesthesiology (1971), 35,
    579 - 581.
6. Raine, J.; and Bishop, J. M.; A-a Difference in O_2 Tension
    and Physiological Dead Space in Normal Man. J. Appl.
    Physiol. (1963), 18, 284 - 288.
7. Stephen, C. R.; and Talton, I.; Immediate Postoperative
    Care, with Particular Reference to Blood-gas Studies.
    Can. Anesth. Soc. J. (1964), 11, 586- 597.
8. Conway, C. M.; Payne, J. P.; and Tomlin, P. J.; Arterial
    Oxygen Tension of Patients Awaiting Surgery. Br. J.
    Anaesth. (1965), 37, 405 - 408.
9. Sorbini, C. A.; Grassi, V.; Solinas, E.; et al; Arterial
    Oxygen Tension in Relation to Age in Healthy Subjects.
    Respiration (1968), 25, 3 - 13.
10. Kitamura, H.; Sawa, T.; and Ikezono, E.; Postoperative
    Hypoxemia: The Contribution of Age to the Maldistribution
    of Ventilation. Anesthesiology (1972), 36, 244 - 252.
11. Neufeld, O.; Smith, J. R.; and Goldman, S. L.; Arterial
    Oxygen Tension in Relation to Age in Hospital Patients.
    J. Am. Geriatr. Soc. (1973), 21, 4 - 9.
12. Wahba, W. M.; Body Build and Preoperative Arterial Oxygen
    Tension. Can. Anesth. Soc. J. (1975), 22, 653 - 658.
13. Gordh, T.; Linderholm, H.; and Norlander, O.; Pulmonary
    Function in Relation to Anaesthesia and Surgery Evaluated
    by Analysis of Oxygen Tension of Arterial Blood. Acta
    Anaesth. Scand. (1958), 2, 15 - 26.
14. Palmer, K. N. V.; and Gardiner, A. J. S.; Effect of
    Partial Gastrectomy on Pulmonary Physiology. Br. Med. J.
    (1964), 1, 347 - 349.
15. Nunn, J. F.; Influence of Age and Other Factors on Hypoxia
    in the Postoperative Period. Lancet (1965), 2, 466 - 468.
16. Davis, A. G.; and Spence, A. A.; Postoperative Hypoxemia
    and Age. Anesthesiology (1972), 37, 663 - 664.
17. Marshall, B. E.; and Wyche, M. Q.; Hypoxaemia During and
    After Anesthesia. Anesthesiology (1972), 37, 178 - 209.

18. Consolazio, C. F.; Johnson, R. E.; and Pecora, L. J.;
    Physiological Measurements of Metabolic Functions in Man,
    McGraw-Hill, New York 1963.
19. Sahn, S. A.; Lakshminarayan, S.; and Petty, T. L.; Weaning
    from Mechanical Ventilation. J.A.M.A. (1976), 235,
    2208 - 2212.
20. Kory, R. C.; Personal Communication (1970).
21. Audio Digest Fndn., Blood Gas Analysis, Int. Med. Series
    19 (17), Sept. 1, 1972.
22. Comroe, J. H.; Forster, R. E.; DuBois, A. B.; et al.;
    The Lung: Clinical Physiology and Pulmonary Function
    Tests, Year Book, Chicago, 2nd ed., 1962.
23. Van Liere, E. J.; and Stickney, J. C.; Hypoxia,
    University Chicago Press, Chicago, 1963.
24. Dejours, P.; Respiration, Oxford, New York 1966.
25. Fishman, A. P.; Goldring, R. M.; and Turino, G. M.;
    General Alveolar Hypoventilation; A Syndrome of Respira-
    tory and Cardiac Failure in Patients with Normal Lungs.
    Quart. J. Med. (1966), 35, 261 - 275.
26. Zilva, J. F.; and Pannall, P. R.; Clinical Chemistry in
    Diagnosis and Treatment, Year Book, Chicago 1972.
27. Snider, G. L.; Interpretation of the Arterial Oxygen
    and Carbon Dioxide Partial Pressures; A Simplified
    Approach for Bedside Use. Chest (1973), 63, 801 - 806.
28. Mays, E. E.; An Arterial Blood Gas Diagram for Clinical
    Use. Chest (1973) 63, 793 - 800.
29. West, J. B.; Respiratory Physiology - The Essentials,
    Williams & Wilkins, Baltimore, 1974.
30. Davis, H. L.; Acute Respiratory Insufficency, in
    Stollerman, G. H. (ed), Adv. Int. Med. (1974), 19,
    213 - 238.

Analytical Aspects of Clinical Enzymology

ELIAS AMADOR and ALI ANSARI

Departments of Pathology, Charles R. Drew Postgraduate Medical School, University of Southern California School of Medicine and Los Angeles County/Martin Luther King, Jr. General Hospital, Los Angeles, Calif. 90059

Clinical enzymology, born early this century with the demonstration that body fluids contain amylase and lipase, progressed slowly until the end of World War II by the addition of a few diagnostic tests such as the measurements of serum acid and alkaline phosphatase activity (1,2,3). Then as a result of the rapid growth during the past 30 years of protein biochemistry and genetics, the study of human enzymes has provided powerful insights into the etiology of a large number of diseases, has provided many new and useful diagnostic tests, and is now being exploited in the development of new analytical tools for the specific measurement of organic molecules. The development of enzyme measurements for the understanding, detection, diagnosis, and management of disease rests on a solid foundation of analytical validity provided by the pure reagents and solid-state electronic instruments now available.

Nature of Enzymes

Enzymes are exceptionally efficient catalytic proteins which increase the speed of a chemical reaction without themselves undergoing a permanent change. Under optimal conditions, most enzymatic reactions proceed from 10^8 to 10^{14} times more rapidly than the corresponding non-enzymatic reactions. For example, one molecule of catalase, the enzyme which converts hydrogen peroxide into water and atomic oxygen, is able to deal with approximately 5 million molecules of H_2O_2 per minute. This represents an acceleration of at least 10^{10} over the rate of the spontaneous reaction (4). Another striking and biochemically important aspect of enzyme catalyzed reactions is their specificity for the reaction catalyzed and the structure of the substrate utilized.

Urease, for instance, posseses exceptionally high
specificity. It is very active in catalyzing the breakdown
of urea to carbon dioxide and ammonia, but inactive when sub-
stituents such as methyl and other alkyl groups are attached
to the NH_2 groups of urea, or if the oxygen is replaced by
sulfur. Virtually all intracellular processes essential to
life including the biosynthesis of the enzyme themselves, are
enzyme catalyzed. Structurally all enzymes are proteins, often
with integral glycosidic moities or attached metals, lipids,
or a vitamin derived coenzyme essential for enzymatic activity.
The environment is also critical, for enzymes are sensitive
to heavy metals, detergents, changes of pH and ionic strength.
It is important to keep in mind that enzymes are recognized
by their catalytic activity, and that this activity can be and
often is shared by a number of closely related proteins, the
isoenzymes. Isoenzymes can be differentiated by small physico-
chemical differences in electrophoretic mobility, degree of
inhibition by certain chemicals, resistance to thermal denaturation, etc. Isoenzymes differ from each other in their subunit composition when the enzyme molecule is an aggregate of
different subunits. Biologically, the small differences in
substrate specificity, product inhibition and regulator respon-
siveness between each "family" of isoenzymes may allow the body
to modulate enzymatic activity according to local biochemical
needs (5). Clinically, these differences are quite useful in
locating the tissue which is releasing a particular isoenzyme
in response to disease.

Classification of Enzymes. A systematic classification and
nomenclature has been established by the Commission on Enzymes
of the International Union of Biochemistry (6), which divides
enzymes into six general groups:

1. Oxidoreductases - catalyzing oxidation-
   reduction reactions.
2. Transferases - catalyzing group transfer
   reactions.
3. Hydrolases - catalyzing hydrolytic reactions.
4. Lyases - catalyzing the addition of groups
   at the site of a double bond or vice versa.
5. Isomerases - catalyzing isomerization.
6. Ligases (synthetases) - catalyzing the condensation of 2 molecules coupled with the
   cleavage of a pyrophosphate bond of ATP or
   similar triphosphate.
To the above we may add:
   Transcriptases - catalyzing the translation
   of information from one linear macromolecule
   into the structure of the nascent linear
   macromole.

Instrumentation
         Instruments that follow the conversion of a substrate into
a product, must be capable of taking two or more readings
during an accurate time base. Since the rate of enzyme
catalysis may vary with time as a function of substrate or product concentration, an instrumental analog output (i.e., a
recorder tracing) is highly useful. Modern digital electronic
circuits enable instruments to print digital results – a
highly convenient feature. Many enzyme assays require ultraviolet light for the measurement of the reaction (i.e., the
change of NAD into NADH) catalyzed by the enzyme being measured or by additional enzyme reactions coupled to it. Consequently, the instrument should be equipped with a light source,
monochromator and detector suitable for measurements in the
near UV range (7).

         Light Sources. The tungsten lamp is commonly used as a
source of visible and near UV light. Other lamps used are
hydrogen, quartz or glass–halogen and hollow cathode lamps. Miniature lamps of the last two types are now being used in some
newer instruments to provide high intensity near – UV light.

         Monochromators. Replica gratings and narrow band-pass
filters are used commonly, more so than quartz prisms. Computer control of the monochromator is available in some instruments, so that optimum intensity at the desired wavelength or
maximum absorption by the examined substance can be obtained.
The recent availability of low cost microprocessors has brought
the possibility of on-line control of all elements of the spectrophotometer, plus on-line data reduction into the realm of
practicality.
         Current instruments use complex and refined optical sys-
tems in order to radiate the cuvette with monochromatic light
selected from the radiant spectrum of the light source. A
radically different approach may be practical when tunable
lasers become available at reasonable prices.
         The photodetectors in current use, such as photomulti-
plier tubes, can respond to only one signal at a time, and
hence the spectrum of light absorption or fluorescent emission
by the sample can only be scanned by manipulating the monochromator. A complete spectrum of both emission and absorption can be obtained, however, by using a vidicon tube to
monitor the entire light spectrum passing through the cuvette,
without this light having been diffracted by a monochromator.
The dramatic increase in information yield and in optical simplification should greatly enhance the power of spectrophotometric methods.

         Time Base. Until recently, the only available way of
measuring the duration of an enzyme reaction was through the

use of conventional mechanical escapement watches, with which
the operator visually correlated the elapsed time with the instrumental readings or determined when to add a reaction-
stopping reagent. This approach was obviously fraught with
errors due to lapses in the operator's attention, lack of
visual correlation of the time base with the instrumental readings, etc. An analog time base can monitor the speed of movement of a chart paper strip by an electric motor. While the
analog time base still is highly useful, it is being comple-
mented by the digital time base using oscillating quartz crys-
tals. These digital clocks in turn can automatically control
the digital printout of the instrumental reading at accurately
predetermined time intervals, thereby eliminating errors due
to operator-instrument interaction. Digital timers are also
incorporated into computers or into microprocessors which in
turn can control the entire instrument.

Cuvets. The cuvet in which an enzyme reaction proceeds
can be of any size or shape, as long as it has optical surfaces
for the entry and exit of light. The conventional 3 ml rectang-
ular Beckman cuvet has been gradually replaced by cuvets which
require only a small volume, at most 1 ml of reaction mixture,
and even by cuvets which require only a few microliters. These
cuvets may have glass, quartz, or sapphire optical surfaces,
with the other walls being made of any inert material, including Kel-F. Flow-through cuvets maintain the light path constant and eliminate cuvet transport devices and optical variations between cuvets (8). Flow-through cuvets are now reliable and quite popular. For multiple cuvets, manual transport
devices are available for the accurate positioning of micro-
cuvets, and mechanized transport devices include mechanical
dwell-cams, the manual transport employed in some spectrophotometers, and the rapidly spinning cuvets used in the centrifugal
fast analyzer (9) (Fig.1).

Specimen Transport. For many years the market was dom-
inated by the continuous flow, bubble-interrupted, system of
Skeggs (10). While this system has been invaluable to most
clinical laboratories and was the first widely accepted
mechanized system for handling large numbers of enzyme assays,
it is now recognized that in its widely used Auto-Analyzer-I
form it suffers from several limitations which include carry
over from sample to sample, low sensitivity read-out instruments, and especially the single point read-outs. The miniature flow-through cuvets used in the Auto-Analyzer-II and in
the computer operated SMAC have reduced these defects to a
negligible level. Of the many alternatives available, the two
which at present appear to be the leading contenders are:
a) the centrifugal fast analyzer, in which a rotor containing
many samples spins rapidly past a single photometric station

(Fig. 2) and b) discrete sample processing using small test tubes, in order to ensure the physical separation of each enzyme assay (i.e., the LKB-8600) (Table I).

Temperature Control. While it was well known that enzyme catalysis is a direct function of temperature, little attention was paid to its control in kinetic enzyme assays until the pioneer work of Schneider and Willis (11). These workers showed that the temperature compartment of the Beckman DU spectrophotometer varied widely as a function of room temperature and of the number of times the cuvet compartment was opened. Thus, while most authors have assumed that they were conducting their assay at room temperature (i.e., a nominal 25°) direct measurements showed that the cuvette temperature was closer to 32° C. Schneider and Willis suggested that thermospacers, hollow plates adjacent to each side of the cuvette compartment through which water at a constant temperature is circulated, be used in order to standardize clinical enzyme assay temperatures. This arrangement works well if the room temperature can be kept reasonably close to that of the water bath. Otherwise, each time the cuvet compartment is opened a significant temperature fluctuation occurs. A better approach was introduced by R. J. Emary, who designed for the Gilford spectrophotometers a flow-through microcuvet which contains in its walls a temperature microsensor and an electric heater, all controlled by solid state electronic circuitry. This cuvette can be calibrated by removing one of its windows, and inserting a miniature thermistor into its cavity, in order to check the accuracy of the settings in the electronic circuitry. This arrangement is said to yield temperatures stable to within 0.1°C. The cuvet temperature fluctuations which occur in the centrifugal fast analyzers can be controlled by similar devices built into the rotor.

Kinetic Read Out. Of the many instruments dedicated to enzyme analyses only those which provide a continous strip-chart recording of the enzyme kinetics or continuous monitoring with several digital print-outs of each enzyme reaction can be considered to be true kinetic analyzers. Equally acceptable is the fast centrifugal analyzer, in which each of the multiple cuvettes in the rotor is monitored several hundred times per minute by the stationary photodetector (Fig. 2). The remaining automated instruments rely on either one point or two point measurements, and hence cannot detect variations from zero-order kinetics (Table I).

Instrument Productivity. The number of samples that can be processed by one instrument in a given period of time is determined by the length of time each sample has to be read by the photodetector or other read-out device, or by the number of cuvets per unit time which pass the detector. For example,

TABLE I

SOME AUTOMATED INSTRUMENTS FOR ENZYME ANALYSES

INSTRUMENT	1	2	3	4	5	6	7	8	COST
BECKMAN SYSTEM TR	M	45	MK	F340+	HAB25,30,37	FQ	D	+	$ 15,000
PERKIN ELMER	M	150	MK	F340		FQ	D	+	---
GILFORD 300N	M	60	MPK	M340-700	E25,30,37	FTQ	D+A	+	$ 8,000
GILFORD 3500	M	60	MPK	M340-700	E25,30,37	FTQ	D	+	$ 25,000
DUPONT ACA	M	60	3PK	FB340	HAB 37	PD	D	+	$ 80,000
LKB 8600+8200 PRINTER	M	80	MK	F340	HAB30,35,37	PD	D+A	+	$ 22,000
HYCEL MARK X	100	40	EP	F340	WB37	FQ	D+A	+	$ 90,000
HYCEL MARK XVII.	100	40	EP	F340	WB37	FG	D+A	+	$120,000
ABBOTT BICHROMATIC A100	M	90	3PK	F34	WB30,37	PD	D+A	+	$ 24,000
VICKERS 300	M	300	2PKTS	F340	HBL	F	D	+	$250,000
ORTHO DIAG. ACCUCHEM	M		2PKTS	F340	OB37	FTQ	D	+	$180,000
TECHNICON AAII	250	60	SP	F340	OB37	FT	D+A	+	$ 18,000
TECHNICON SMAC	M	150	3PK	F340	OB37	FT	D+A	+	$224,000
U.CARBIDE CENTRIFICHEM	M	200	MPK	F340	HAB25,30,37	FQ	D+A	+	$ 32,000
ELECTRONUCLEONIC GEMSAEC	M	200	MPK	M340-700	WB UP TO 50	FQ	D+A	+	$ 40,000
AMINCO ROTOCHEM	M		MPK						

COLUMN NO. 1 = SAMPLE VOLUME, M=MICRO LESS THAN 100 MICRO LITERS
COLUMN NO. 2 = MAXIMUM NO. OF SAMPLES PER HOUR
COLUMN NO. 3 = PRINCIPLE OF MEASUREMENT, M=MULTIPLE, S=SINGLE, P=POINT, K=KINETIC
COLUMN NO. 4 = WAVE LENGTH, F=FILTER, M=MONOCHROMETER, G=GRATING
COLUMN NO. 5 = TEMPERATURE CONTROL, WB=WATER, OB=OIL BATH, HAB=HOT AIR BATH, E=ELECTRIC
COLUMN NO. 6 = CUVETTE, P=PLASTIC, D=DISPOSABLE, FT=FLOW THROUGH
COLUMN NO. 7 = DISPLAY, D=DIGITAL, A=ANALOG
COLUMN NO. 8 = COMPUTER AND DATA REDUCTION, +=YES
COST=APPROXIMATE PRICE FOR COMPLETE SYSTEM

Figure 1. Front view of the miniature centrifugal analyzer. The mechanical, analytical, and optico-electronic components are in one compact unit. Digital data reduction is in another unit, not shown. (Courtesy of Dr. Carl A. Burtis, of the former Oak Ridge National Laboratory).

Figure 2. Top view of the miniature centrifugal analyzer. The sample disc, not shown, fits on the rotor holder and can process 16 samples and 1 reference simultaneously. (Courtesy of Dr. Carl A. Burtis).

the miniature centrifugal fast analyzer can process 16 samples plus one reference cell past the photodetector several hundred times a minute, and reactions can be monitored in one or two minutes for all 16 samples. The rotor can be brought to full speed within a fraction of a second and can be stopped within an equally short period of time by a built-in clutch. Automatic mixing of sample and reagents occurs within one second. The remainder of the minute or two can then be used for monitoring the enzyme kinetics in the multiple cuvets. Since all cuvets are surveyed within the same time, the instrument yields truly comparable results. The fact that the instrument is controlled by a small computer or by a microprocessor allows for true automation. The centrifugal fast analyzer is in the authors' opinion the ideal instrument for monitoring enzyme kinetics. The rotors can be preloaded with lyophilized reagents, which can be dynamically dissolved by the addition of buffer to the spinning rotor. Multiple samples can then be introduced into each of the radial cuvettes, or a single sample can be dynamically apportioned between the multiple cuvettes, each of which contain reagents for a different enzyme reaction. Consequently, multiple samples can be monitored for the same enzyme activity, or several different enzyme activities can be measured for the same sample. The very fast data reduction offered by the on-line computer provides the operator with printed results as soon as the analysis is complete. This approach provides highly precise data (Table II).

Other analyzers such as the Gilford Automated Enzyme Analyzer and the LKB-8600 Reaction Rate Analyzer analyze discrete samples one at a time. These instruments provide kinetic analyses, digital data reduction at the time each sample is analyzed, and excellent electronic and optical characteristics. Recently, Atwood has developed kinetic enzyme analyzers which require only 9 seconds for measuring an enzyme activity, using highly stable and sensitive electronic circuits (12). This short read out time allows a large number of samples to be processed by one instrument in an automated mode.

The continuous flow methods used by the Auto Analyzer have traditionally relied on the single point measurement of a dialysate of the incubated mixture (10). More recently, the computerized sequential multiple analyzer (SMAC) provides two point analysis by electronically eliminating the bubble signal and by passing the same bubble segmented stream through two cuvets separated by a time delay coil. Critical evaluations of this system are not available at this time. Other automated analyzers such as those produced by Hycel rely upon single point assays using colorimetric methods, and hence the results may be dubious.

An entirely different breed of instruments has been introduced by Beckman for measuring substrate concentrations using enzymes as the reagent and specific potentiometric electrodes

TABLE II

WITHIN-ROTOR VARIATION OF TWO MINIATURE ANALYTICAL SYSTEMS

		ANALYTICAL RESULTS[a]		
LABORATORY	N	MEAN	STANDARD DEVIATION	RELATIVE STANDARD DEVIATION
A	16	59.30	0.4	0.63
B	16	60.10	0.4	0.63

[a]Data obtained from 16 replicate alkaline phosphatase assays that were measured within a single rotor. Results are given in I.U., 30° C.

Data courtesy of Dr. C. A. Burtis, Molecular Anatomy Program, Oak Ridge National Laboratory of the former Atomic Energy Commission.

as the detectors. Instruments for measuring glucose and urea
with highly specific methods are currently available. This
approach relies on the measurement of reaction rate as first
described and recently reviewed by Malmstadt (13).

Analytical Considerations

Available methods provide measurements of enzyme activity
rather than of enzyme concentration. In order that the measured
activity be proportional to enzyme concentration, the reaction
conditions which include pH, temperature, initial substrate
concentration, sample and total volume and reaction time
must be held constant and be carefully controlled.
Under optimum conditions when substrate and coenzyme concentrations are at saturating levels, i.e., the concentration
of substrates far exceeds the concentration of the enzyme, and
other variables are optimized and maintained constant, the initial rate of an enzymatic reaction is directly proportional to
the amount of enzyme present. If one of the reactants absorbs
monochromatic light, a given enzymatic activity can often be
monitored in a spectrophotometer by following the negative rate
of change in absorbance of the substrate as it is consumed, or
positive rate of change in absorbance of the product as it is
formed. Methods based on rate of the reaction-kinetic methods -
offer many advantages over single or end-point (usually
colorimetric) techniques (14-18).

Advantages of Kinetic Methods
1. Visual proof of linear kinetics, making obvious
   the occurrence of undesirable conditions such as
   substrate depletion or lag phase non-linearity.
2. Visual display of changes in the reaction rate.
3. Maximum accuracy as the measurement can be made
   in the region of maximum linear velocity.
4. The method requires less time since the reaction
   velocity is measured directly.
5. Greater specificity since the rate of the reaction
   usually is not affected by interfering substances
   commonly found in serum, and since each sample
   serves as its own blank.
6. There is extensive clinical documentation of UV-
   kinetic enzyme results showing excellent correlation with confirmed diagnosis.
7. Measurements are feasable over a broad range of
   enzyme activities.
8. Kinetic methods are adaptable to most enzymes.

Disadvantages of End-Point Methods

1. The method of color development may be non-
   specific and therefore the reaction may be affected
   by many interfering factors commonly found in serum
   such as turbidity, hemoglobin and bilirubin.
2. Non-linearity during progession of enzyme reaction
   or an initial lag phase which is undetected and may
   result in significant error.
3. The chromogen is often not completely specific,
   and metabolites and drugs may give falsely elevated
   results.
4. End-point methods are often not based on kinetically optimum conditions. However, an end-point
   method is often the only convenient one available.
   In this case, the method should have been validated
   by showing that the catalysis of the substrate
   follows well defined kinetics, rate of reaction is
   proportional to enzyme concentration, blanks and
   interfering substances are corrected for, and that
   appropriate standards are available.

Analytical Criteria for Clinical Enzyme Methods. The great
variety of methods available for certain of the clinically
useful enzymes can be confusing in the absence of criteria for
assessing these methods. These criteria should be similar to
those used to judge other quantitative clinical chemistry
methods, and should also take into account the kinetic nature
of the reaction. Some years ago, Amador and Wacker (17)
suggested the following criteria, which are now widely used:

1. The kinetics should be zero-order during the
   initial portion of the reaction, over a practical working range that includes the usually
   encountered enzyme activities.
2. The measured activity should be directly proportional to enzyme concentration over a
   practical working range.
3. The reaction mixture should be as simple as
   possible, preferably consisting of premixed
   reagents of known stability. Lyophilized reagents or the single premixed reagent for LD
   assays are good examples.
4. The concentrations of substrate, coenzyme,
   buffer, activators, pH, etc., should provide
   maximum enzyme activities.
5. Inhibitors should be removed from sample. An
   example is urinary phosphate, which can be removed by dialysis prior to measuring the urinary
   alkaline phosphatase activity (18).
6. Inhibitors should not be present in the reagent
   solution. Examples are the dehydrogenase inhib-

itors which form from NADH when it is stored
improperly, and the use of glycine as a buffer
for alkaline phosphatase.

7. The rate measurement should be standardized with
the purified substrate or product of the enzyme.
For example, glutamic-oxalacetic transaminase
activity can be standardized with oxalacetate
but not with "convenient" substances such as
pyruvate (17). When reference serums are used,
the label value should be confirmed at frequent
intervals by the actual method being used routinely,
as label values can be in error (19). Conversion
factors to convert the results obtained by one
method into those obtained by another can give
erroneous results and should not be used.

Clinical Criteria for Clinical Enzyme Methods. While it
is possible to measure the activity of several thousand enzymes
in body samples, in most cases it is practical to measure only
a few while obtaining clinically useful results. In order to
select the enzyme measurements which will be most useful, the
following guidelines are suggested:

1. Increases or decreases in enzyme activity produced
by disease should be sufficiently large so that
confusion with the normal range does not result.
For example, the elevated serum GPT seen in acute
viral hepatitis is useful because it is many times
greater than the normal range.

2. The normal range should be established with samples
obtained from an adequate sample of healthy persons
of specified age and sex. The effect of physiological variables such as activity, eating, menstru-
ation and pregnancy should be known. The confidence
limits should be determined with the appropriate
statistical tools. Normal ranges determined with
hospital patients should be rejected (20, 21).

3. The correlation between altered enzyme activities
and a given disease, i.e., the diagnostic accuracy
should be based on accepted symptoms, and
laboratory changes. Tissue diagnoses should be
used whenever possible as a standard of reference
(22).

4. The diagnostic specificity for a given disease should
be determined by examining patients with other
diseases of the same organ, and diseases of
several organs known to contain that enzyme.
Ideally, the proposed test should clearly differentiate either between diseases of the same organ
or between affected organs. For instance, the CK

isoenzyme pattern may be useful in distinguishing
heart from other organ damage, but the alkaline
phosphatase isoenzymes yield ambiguous data when
biliary versus liver versus other tissue damage is
being differentiated (23).

5. The diagnostic usefulness should be established by
   appropriate retrospective or prospective studies
   to see if the test in fact improves the diagnostic
   accuracy. For inherited enzyme diseases, the measurement of the enzyme activity can be diagnosti-
   cally specific and highly useful. For otherwise
   obvious diseases such as metastatic prostatic carcinoma, enzyme tests may be of little value (24).

Reagents. The measurement of enzyme activities requires
rigid control of the analytical conditions, including accurate
measurement of reagent and sample volumes, and careful control
of temperature, pH and reagent stability.

Buffers. pH is usually maintained within a range of 0.1
pH unit through the use of commonly available buffers with a
pK close to the pH desired. The commonly employed buffers and
some of their characteristics are listed in Table III. The "good"
buffers described by Cleland have not improved the clinical
assay of enzymes, while the commonly available relatively simple
buffers have (25). Barbital is a commonly used buffer, but has
little to offer because it is quite weak and therefore does not
maintain pH adequately. Other than serving as a buffer for
electrophoresis, barbital should probably be abandoned. Glycine
is also a commonly used buffer, but has the disadvantage
of being a chelating agent, and is a well known and strong
inhibitor of alkaline phosphatase. Surprisingly, glycine is
still commonly used to buffer alkaline phosphatase activity
assays, but its use should definitely be discontinued (25).
Tris (THAM) buffer is also commonly used, but it should be recognized that the pH of its solution is significantly affected by
variations in temperature. Sodium or potassium phosphate and
pyrophosphate have excellent buffering capacities. Phosphate
tends to interact with NADH and slowly degrades it over a period
of weeks (14). Pyrophosphate has good buffering capacity over
the broad pH range used for most clinical enzyme assays, is inexpensive, and accordingly is an excellent buffer for the enzyme
reaction or for color developer solutions which when added to
the reaction abruptly change the pH to stop the enzyme reaction
and develop color. The organic acids such as lactic, acetic,
and citric acids are also excellent buffers in the lower pH
ranges (26), but citrate is a chelating agent of the divalent
metals necessary for some enzyme activities.

Substrates. Many of the substrates used for enzyme reac-

TABLE III

SOME COMMON BUFFERS AND THEIR USEFUL PH RANGES

		PK	PH RANGE
GLYCINE	HYDROCHLORIC ACID	2.4	1.0 to 3.7
POTASSIUM PHTHALATE	HYDROCHLORIC ACID	2.9	2.2 to 3.8
ACONITIC ACID	SODIUM HYDROXIDE		2.5 to 5.7
CITRIC ACID	SODIUM CITRATE		3.0 to 6.2
ACETIC ACID	SODIUM ACETATE	4.75	3.6 to 5.6
CITRIC ACID	SODIUM HYDROXIDE		2.2 to 6.5
PHENYL ACETIC ACID	SODIUM PHENYL ACETATE	4.3	3.5 to 5.1
SUCCINIC ACID	SODIUM HYDROXIDE		3.8 to 6.0
POTASSIUM ACID PHTHALATE	SODIUM HYDROXIDE	5.4	4.2 to 6.0
DI-SODIUM HYDROGEN PHOSPHATE	POTASSIUM DI-HYDROGEN PHOSPHATE	6.7	6.5 to 7.5
SODIUM BARBITAL (VERONAL)	HYDROCHLORIC ACID	7.98	6.8 to 9.2
TRIS (HYDROXYMETHYL) AMINO-METHANE	HYDROCHLORIC ACID	8.07	6.8 to 8.5
BORIC ACID	SODIUM HYDROXIDE	9.23	7.9 to 9.2
GLYCINE	SODIUM HYDROXIDE	9.78	8.6 to 10.6
SODIUM BICARBONATE	SODIUM CARBONATE	9.9	9.2 to 10.7
DIETHANOLAMINE	HYDROCHLORIC ACID	8.7	8.5 to 10.5
ETHANOLAMINE	HYDROCHLORIC ACID	8.8	8.6 to 10.4
2-AMINO-2-METHYL-1-PROPANOL	HYDROCHLORIC ACID	9.3	9.0 to 10.5
3-AMINO-PROPANOL	HYDROCHLORIC ACID	9.4	9.0 to 10.8
TRI-ETHANOLAMINE	HYDROCHLORIC ACID	7.6	7.0 to 8.0
SODIUM PYROPHOSPHATE	SODIUM HYDROXIDE		8.0 to 9.0
2-ETHYL-AMINO-ETHANOL	HYDROCHLORIC ACID	9.9	8.0 to 11.0

tions are artificial, and accordingly the measured activity may
not necessarily be an accurate reflection of the physiological
activity found in the organism. This consideration becomes particularly important when it is necessary to know the activity
of a suspected mutant enzyme in order to detect an inherited
metabolic disease, such as Tay-Sachs disease. In these
instances, if an abnormally low activity is found with an artificial substrate, the measurement should be repeated using the
natural substrate whenever possible (27).

When the substrate is available in either the d- or
l-racemic form, it is preferable to use the appropriate isomer
rather than its mixture. In a case of transaminase assays for
GOT and GPT activity, for example, the initial assays used the
d-l amino acid as substrate, and a marked improvement in activity and linearity was found by Henry and co-workers when they
used l-aspartate or l-alanine, respectively (28).

Exogenous Coenzymes and Enzymes. Even when the coenzyme
is known to be tightly bound to the apoenzyme, it is desirable
to determine if addition of pure coenzyme will further activate
the reaction mixture. Prolonged incubation may be necessary
to obtain complete binding of the added coenzyme to the apoenzyme (29). Also, some of the commercial reference sera which
have been prepared by extensive dialysis may be coenzyme defi-
cient, and hence may show marked activation by added coenzyme,
as in the case of commercial sera containing GOT which is
markedly activated by added pyridoxal-pyridoxamine phosphates
(26) (Fig. 3). When linked enzyme assays are being used, the
exogenous enzymes and coenzymes must be present in large excess
in order to insure very fast turn-over of the products of the
primary enzyme reactions, and provide linearity over an adequate
working range with a minimal lag phase. While it is possible
to use two or even three or more linked enzyme reactions to
measure an initial enzymatic reaction, it is now recognized that
at most two exogenous enzymes should be used, as otherwise
marked limitations in working range and low primary enzyme activity will result (30). Some coenzymes, such as NAD, are prepared by the manufacturers using ethanol. The purified NAD may
therefore contain trace amounts of ethanol which may serve as
a substrate for serum alcohol dehydrogenase in the absence of
other substrates, leading to troublesome "blanks" sometimes
called "nothing" dehydrogenase.

When linked enzyme assays are used, the exogenous added
enzymes may also be contaminated with small traces of the primary enzyme whose activity is measured, thereby leading to
falsely high activities. In this instance it is also desirable
to make certain that the added enzymes are free of any undesirable activity, i.e., pig heart malic dehydrogenase should be
free of GOT activity when used for GOT assays (17).

Product Acceptors. Many enzyme assays use acceptors, as for
instance 2-ethylaminoethanol and other aminated alcohols which
act as acceptors for the phosphoryl product of the reaction
catalyzed by alkaline phosphatase (25) (Fig. 4). Hydroxylamine
can act as an acceptor for the hydroxyacetone produced by eno-
lase and semicarbazide can act as an acceptor for the pyruvate
produced by LD. It is necessary to optimize the concentration
of such an acceptor before using it routinely as often what may
be a theoretically desirable acceptor is in practice superfluous.

Enzyme Reference Serums. Several companies sell
lyophilized or stabilized reference serums for the calibration
of instruments and for quality control. The label values given
for the enzymatic activity of these serums should never be taken
at face value, as at times they may be quite erroneous (19,33).
Also, these values should only be used for the assay with which
they were standardized, as interconversion of activity from one
method to another for the same enzyme may often lead to marked
errors. For instance, it is not recommended that alkaline phosphatase expressed in Bodansky units be multiplied by a factor
to convert it to the units of the King-Armstrong method, or any
other method for that matter.

Optimization of Substrate Concentrations. Computer analyses
of enzyme kinetics may be very useful for the calculation of
enzyme constants, eliminating the tedium associated with manual
calculations. Recently, computer models for optimizing reagent
concentrations have been described but these models require so
many experimental points that the model rests on the experimental
data rather than having predictive usefulness (31).
     The experimental verification of published results with
newer buffers, more sensitive instruments or better reagents
has led to a significant improvement, and often simplification
of the method (32). Consequently, newly described methods
should always be checked out point by point before using them
routinely.

Sample Collection and Enzyme Stability. Serum samples are
collected with chemically clean, sterile glassware. Blood is
allowed to clot at room temperature, the clot is gently separated from the test tube with an applicator stick, and the blood
is centrifuged for 10 minutes at 1,000 g. If the red cells are
known to contain the enzymes whose activity is being measured,
as in the case of LD, even slightly hemolyzed serums must be
discarded. When acid phosphatase is to be measured, the serum
should be placed immediately in ice and processed as soon as
possible, or it should be acidified by the addition of a small
amount of sodium citrate. Anticoagulants such as EDTA, fluoride
and oxalate inhibit some serum enzymes. However, heparin activates serum lipoprotein lipase.

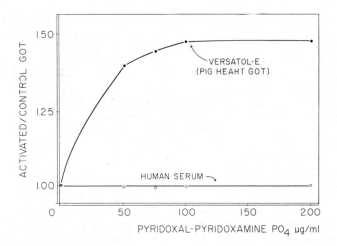

Figure 3. *Addition of the GOT coenzymes pyridoxal and pyridoxamine phosphates in concentrations up to 200 μg/ml has no effect on human serum GOT but activates by 45% the pig heart GOT activity of Versatol-E, a commercial reference serum*

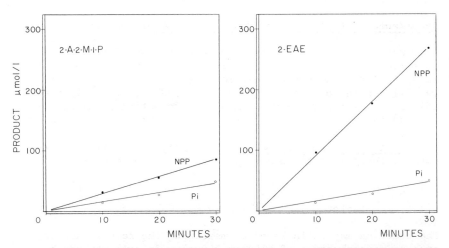

Figure 4. *The release of nitrophenol (NP) and inorganic phosphate (Pi) is zero order in 2-amino-2-methyl-1-propanol and in 2-ethylaminoethanol (2-A-2-M-1-P and 2-EAE). About as much Pi is released in both buffers, but the amount of NP released is 2.6 times greater in 2-EAE. The difference between the NP and Pi slopes represents the amount of transphosphorylation, which is also greater in 2-EAE.*

Urine may be collected for assays of enzyme activities following cleansing of the   genitalia with mild antiseptic soap followed by rinsing with water. The urine is collected in a chemically clean container with no preservative. As the activity of urinary enzymes is a function of the volume of the specimen it is important to time the collection accurately. A collection period of 8 hours is quite adequate, and the use of longer periods is not desirable because enzyme activities can rapidly decrease in the relatively hostile medium of the urine. The urine should be refrigerated and transferred promptly to the laboratory, where it should also be processed promptly. Delays of more than two hours after the collection is completed may lead to markedly erroneous results. Urines with bacterial overgrowth, hemolyzed blood, or those obtained following any type of instrumental examination of the urinary tract may also lead to erroneous results, and should not be used for assays of enzyme activities. The stability of some clinically important enzymes in the various body fluids is given in Table IV.

White blood cells, red blood cells and cultured fibroblasts are commonly used to measure enzyme activities, especially for the diagnosis of inherited enzyme abnormalities. Leukocytes may be collected by sedimentation in viscous media such as Fycol. The collection of red cells presents no problem following centrifugation of anticoagulated blood. The assay of enzymes and fibroblasts requires appropriate tissue culture facilities and extensive experience in dealing with cultured human cells.

Recommended Methods for Diagnostically Useful Enzymes

Many enzyme activities have been proposed for diagnosis, in serum, urine, cerebrospinal fluid and other body fluids, and the proposed methods have been reviewed elsewhere (17). Here we will confine ourselves to the tried and most commonly used enzyme activities which yield useful information in ambulatory or hospital patients.

Lactic Dehydrogenase (LD). LD catalyzes the reversible conversion of lactate to pyruvate in the presence of NAD:

$$\text{lactate} + \text{NAD}^+ \xrightleftharpoons{\text{LD}} \text{pyruvate} + \text{NADH} + \text{H}^+$$

The reaction may be followed by measuring the rate of appearance or disappearance of NADH at 340 nm. In some methods a coupled reaction using diaphorase or phenazine methosulfate plus an indicator dye are used. The amount of pyruvate formed can also be measured colorimetrically. With the general avail-

ability of UV spectrophotometers, the LD kinetic method (340
nm) is now widely used. The reaction employing pyruvate and
NADH requires preincubation to eliminate other substrates found
in serum which are consumed by endogenous serum enzymes in the
presence of NADH. While the lactate and NAD reaction does not
require this preincubation step, it is 2.5 times slower
than the pyruvate reaction. This drawback can easily be corrected by increasing the proportion of serum in the final reaction mixture. The precision of either method is excellent and
standardized methods are available (34). The colorimetric
methods for measuring LD activity are either cumbersome, require
expensive reagents such as phenazine methosulfate and nitro-
tetrazolium blue as indicator dye, or else are unreliable as
in the case of the dinitrophenylhydrazine colorimetric method
which suffers from large blanks, non-zero order kinetics, and
other significant systematic errors (15,16).
    LD is well known to be the combined activity of 5 isoen-
zymes (35) which in turn are thought to result from the combination in varying proportions of two basic subunits, heart (H)
and muscle (M) subunits, to form a tetramer (36). Additional
isoenzymes in skin and testicle have been described, and it may be
that the LD isoenzyme spectrum ultimately will turn out to be
complex.
    Myocardium is characterized by a predominance of LD-1 (H_4
tetramer) whereas LD-5 (M_4 tetramer) is the dominant species
in liver and skeletal muscle. The heart isoenzyme LD-1 is heat
stable whereas liver and skeletal muscle LD-5 is heat labile.
The LD-1 is less than 30% of total LD in normal serum, whereas
in patients with an acute myocardial infarction it is between
50-90% of total LD activity. The ratio of LD-1/LD-2 is usually
greater than one in acute myocardial infarction (37).
    Electrophoretic methods of separation of LD isoenzymes have
become routine in clinical laboratories. Efforts are now being
made to standardize the methodologies used for LD isoenzymes,
particularly by Rosalki (38). The preferred methods are based
on electrophoresis on a solid medium, so that the several bands
may be scanned instrumentally. Differential isoenzyme inhibition with urea or other inhibitors is based on the fact that
the heart LD isoenzyme is more resistant to inhibition than
other isoenzymes. However, the analyst then has the problem
of allocating the observed degree of inhibition between the different isoenzymes of a given sample, a problem that has not been
resolved satisfactorily thus far. Hence, differential inhibition is not as reliable for isoenzyme separation as is electrophoresis.

    α-Hydroxy-butyric Dehydrogenase (HBD). HBD reflects the
activity of LD-1 (heart) towards α-hydroxy-butyrate which it
oxidizes to oxo-butyrate in the presence of NADH. Measurement
of this serum activity has been found to correlate well with

TABLE IV

STABILITY OF SOME CLINICAL ENZYMES IN HUMAN BODY FLUIDS

EC NO.	TRIVIAL NAME	ABBREVIATION	SPEC	25°C	4°C	-10°C
OXIDOREDUCTASES--CATALYZING OXIDATION-REDUCTION REACTIONS						
1.1.1.1	ALCOHOL DEHYDROGENASE	AD	S	7D	7D	1M
1.1.1.27	LACTATE DEHYDROGENASE	LD	S	24H	24H	UN-S
			U-D	6H	12H	UN-S
			U			
			CSF	4H	14H	
1.1.1.27	HYDROXYBUTYRATE DEHYDROGENASE	HBD	S	5D	5D	10D
1.1.1.42	ISOCITRATE DEHYROGENASE	ICD	S	5H	15D	21D
1.1.1.49	GLUCOSE-6-PHOSPHATE DEHYDROGENASE	GPD	RBC	7D	7D	7D
1.6.4.2	GLUTATHIONE REDUCTASE	GTD	S	7D	7D	8D
TRANSFERASES--CATALYZING GROUP- TRANSFER REACTIONS						
2.1.3.3.	ORNITHINE CARBAMYL TRANSFERASE	OCT	S	3D	1W	1Y
2.3.2.1.	GLUTAMYLTRANSFERASE (GGT)	GMT	S	2D	30D	1Y
			U			UN-S
			U-D			5W
2.6.1.1.	ASPARTATE TRANSAMINASE (GOT)	AST	S	2D	14D	1M
			U	5H		2D
			CSF	6H		
2.6.1.2.	ALANINE TRANSAMINASE (GPT)	ALT	S	2D	1W	UN-S
2.7.7.12	HEXOSE-1-PHOSPHATE URIDYL TRANSFERASE	HUT	RBC	14D	14D	1W
2.7.3.2	CREATINE KINASE	CK	S	2D	1W	1M

TABLE IV (CONTINUED)
STABILITY OF SOME CLINICAL ENZYMES IN HUMAN BODY FLUIDS

EC NO.	TRIVIAL NAME	ABBREVIATION	SPEC	25°C	4°C	-10°C
HYDROLASES CATALYZING HYDROLYTIC REACTIONS						
3.1.1.3	LIPASE	LPS	S	7D	21D	
3.1.1.8	CHOLINESTERASE	CHS	S	10D	7D	S-M
			RBC		3D	
3.1.3.1.	ALKALINE PHOSPHATASE	ALP	S	2D	3D	1M
			U	6H	6H	UN-S
			U-D	1D	1D	UN-S
3.1.3.2.	ACID PHOSPHATASE	ACP	S	4H	14D	115D
			U	7D	15D	UN-S
3.1.3.5	5-NUCLEOTIDASE	NTP	S	4D	4D	5M
3.2.1.1	AMYLASE	AMS	S	27D	7M	2M
3.2.1.31	B-GLUCURONIDASE	GRS	S	1D	7D	7D
3.4.1.1	LEUCINE AMINOPEPTIDASE	LAS	S	7D	7D	7D
3.4.4.1	PEPSIN	PPS	S		21D	
3.4.4.4	TRYPSIN	TPS	DF	V-UN-STABLE		
			FEC		8D	
3.5.4.3	GUANINE DEAMINASE	GDS	S	3D	2W	10M
3.5.4.4	ADENINE DEAMINASE	ADS	S	3D	2W	6M
LYASES CATALYZING THE ADDITION OF GROUPS TO DOUBLE BONDS OR VICE VERSA						
4.1.2.13	ALDOLASE	ALS	S	5H	5D	15D
ISOMERASES CATALYZING ISOMERIZATIONS						
5.3.1.1	TRIOSEPHOSPHATE ISOMERASE	TPI	RBC	2D	6D	3.5W
5.3.1.9	GLUCOSE PHOSPHATE ISOMERASE	GPI				

SPEC=SPECIMEN, S=SERUM, U=URINE, U-D=URINE DIALYZED, CSF=CEREBROSPINAL FLUID, DF=DUODENAL FLUID, RBC=ERYTHROCYTES, H=HOUR, D=DAY, W=WEEK, M=MONTH, UN-S=UNSTABLE.

measurements of the activity of the heart LD isoenzyme in serum.
The method of Wilkinson as modified by Rosalki appears to be
the method of choice (39).

HBD is a biochemical rather than electrophoretic assessment of the LD isoenzyme which is associated with heart. All
five isoenzymes of LD exhibit some activity toward α-hydroxy-
butyrate as substrate, but heart LD shows the greatest activity.
Serum HBD measurement is not as valuable as the electrophoretic
determination of heart LD isoenzyme. High HBD activity has also
been found in diseases of the liver. Rises associated with the
hepatic effects of congestive heart failure can be disconcert-
ing in the differential diagnosis of myocardial infarction.
Wilkinson has used the serum HBD/LD ratio for the differentiation of myocardial disease from other disorders in which HBD
activity is elevated, whereas Rosalki has not found the ratio
to be helpful (39).

Creatine Kinase (CK)

CK catalyzes the reversible phosphorylation of creatine
in the presence of ATP and magnesium. When creatine phosphate
is the substrate, the resulting creatine can be measured as the
ninhydrin fluorescent compound, as in the continuous flow Auto
Analyzer method. Kinetic methods based on coupled enzymatic
reactions are also popular. Tanzer and Gilvarg (40) developed
a kinetic method using the two exogenous enzymes pyruvate
kinase and lactate dehydrogenase to measure the CK rate by following the oxidation of NADH. In this procedure the main reaction is run in a less favorable direction.

$$\text{creatine} + \text{ATP} \overset{\text{CK}}{\underset{\longleftarrow}{\longrightarrow}} \text{creatine phosphate} + \text{ADP}$$

$$\text{phosphoenolpyruvate} + \text{ADP} \overset{\text{PK}}{\underset{\longleftarrow}{\longrightarrow}} \text{pyruvate} + \text{ATP}$$

$$\text{H}^+ + \text{pyruvate} + \text{NADH} \overset{\text{LD}}{\underset{\longleftarrow}{\longrightarrow}} \text{lactate} + \text{NAD}^+$$

A kinetic procedure employing the reverse reaction is
coupled to the enzymes hexokinase and glucose-6-phosphate dehydrogenase, as used by Nielson and Ludvigson after the method of
Oliver (41). This procedure was later modified and optimized
by Rosalki (38).

$$\text{creatine phosphate} + \text{ADP} \xrightarrow[\text{Mg}^{2+}]{\text{CK}} \text{creatine} + \text{ATP}$$

$$\text{ATP} + \text{glucose} \xrightarrow[\text{Mg}^{2+}]{\text{HK}} \text{ADP} + \text{glucose-6-phosphate}$$

$$\text{glucose-6-phosphate} + \text{NAD}^+ \xrightarrow{\text{G-6-PDH}} \text{6-phosphogluconate} + \text{NADH} + \text{H}^+$$

The ATP formed by CK is used by exogenous hexokinase to phosphorylate glucose. The resulting glucose-6-phosphate is then oxidized by exogenous glucose-6-phosphate dehydrogenase and NADP to 6-phosphogluconic acid and NADPH, a reaction measured kinetically at 340 nm. Several refinements of this procedure have been reported which include optimization of pH, substrate and exogenous enzyme concentrations, and CK activators such as sulfhydryl compounds (cysteine, glutathione, etc.). Adenosine monophosphate is included in order to inhibit any myokinase in the sample, as this enzyme also has CK-like activity. An interesting alternative is Worthington Biochemical's method, using an NADH dependent G-6-PD obtained from microbial sources. These coupled enzyme methods must employ a large excess of the exogenous enzymes, substrates and coenzymes in order to keep pace with the initial CK reaction, as otherwise spuriously low CK activities will be recorded. For this reason, the use of ninhydrin to monitor fluorimetrically the appearance of creatine appears to be the simplest and most accurate method (30).

CK has a dimeric structure composed of two subunits designated M and B (43), M for muscle and B for brain, with the isoenzymes being designated MM, MB and BB. The MM dimer is found in skeletal muscle and minimally in smooth and cardiac muscle. The BB dimer is found in brain and minimally in lung and smooth muscle (42). The MB isoenzyme of intermediate electrophoretic mobility is found chiefly in myocardium (43) and very little in skeletal muscle and smooth muscle.

The isoenzymes can be separated by electrophoresis on cellulose acetate, and Roberts, et al (44) have described a method whereby the separated isoenzymes are eluted and then assayed kinetically.

CK isoenzymes have been separated by electrophoresis on cellulose acetate, agar gel, agarose and polyacrylamide gel. Often these methods are not sensitive enough for quantitation of different CK isoenzymes. Konttinen and Somer (45) used electrophoresis on agarose to obtain sharper bands and increased sensitivity. Staining with nitro-blue tetrazolium was found to

be superior to other tetrazolium salts. Nerenberg et. al used
electrophoresis on agar gel, and quantitated the separated bands
by measuring the UV fluorescence of NADPH. This method has been
slightly modified by Roe et. al (43) and Wagner et. al (46),
who found it to be reproducible and easy but required a densitometer, fluorometer and one hour incubation time. Takahashi
(47) developed a method for separating CK isoenzymes using a
DEAE-Sephadex A-50 ion exchange column and a gradient elution
buffer system. Mercer (48) modified this column procedure using
a stepwise gradient elution. Worthington Corp. has packaged a
method based on a minicolumn so that it is simple enough for
routine use. The elution time (2-4 hours) usually associated
with column chromatography has been shortened by the use of
minicolumns and stepwise elution techniques. Need for pretreat-
ment of sample (usually dialysis) has also been eliminated by
equating the column's exchangeable chloride concentration to
the chloride concentration of the serum. Results using these
techniques are comparable to the results obtained with electrophoretic techniques. Henry, Roberts and Sobel (49) used batch
absorption on "DEAE glycophase" glass beads instead of minicolumns, in order to use very small samples of serum. All separa-
tive steps are performed in a single test tube and can be completed in a few minutes. This method has been compared to their
previously reported electrophoretic method and found to be comparable. Jockers-Wreton and Pfleiderer (50) have described
another technique for the quantitation of CK isoenzymes based
on specific antisera against the pure CK-MM and CK-BB isoenzymes
from human tissue. They report the method is highly specific
and sensitive and comparatively less time consuming, but these
antisera are not available commercially.

Rao et. al recently published another method for the quantitation of the MB fraction. The method is based on the selective activating capacity of dithiothreitol on CK isoenzyme MB,
after isoenzyme MM is activated by glutathione (51). Apparently
the MB isoenzyme is not activated by glutathione but is activated by dithiothreitol. The difference between CK activities
obtained in the presence of glutathione alone and those obtained
with both glutathione and dithiothreitol represent MB activity.
The correlation is excellent (r = 0.998) between the activity
of MB in the isoenzyme mixture determined by this method, and
the activity of isolated MB.

CK is distributed in various organs with highest concentrations in skeletal muscle, myocardium, and brain and lesser
amounts in the gastrointestinal tract, uterus, urinary bladder,
and kidney (42). The CK content of liver and red blood cells
is negligible so that diseases of these tissues are unlikely
to increase the serum CK activity. The serum CK level begins
to increase in 2-4 hours after myocardial infarction and reaches
a peak in 24-36 hours and returns to normal in about 3 days.
The maximum average elevation is about 7 times the upper limit

of normal. Compared to serum GOT, LD, and HBD, CK activity
rises sooner, achieves a higher peak and returns to normal more
rapidly. The degree of elevation is related to the magnitude
of tissue necrosis and correlates well with the clinical course
and prognosis. This makes the serum CK one of the most sensitive tests for myocardial infarction. The sensitivity and early
elevation of serum CK following myocardial infarction may be
helpful in the prompt selection of the patients with chest distress requiring the services of an intensive care unit. The
transient nature of the CK elevation following infarction is
a disadvantage and thus the timing of the blood samples is important. Although elevated serum CK activity is a sensitive
indicator of myocardial necrosis, abnormal values may occur
in a variety of extracardiac disorders such as muscle disorders,
neurologic and psychiatric disorders, hypokalemia, pulmonary
disease, hypothyroidism, prolonged coma, eclampsia, hemorrhagic
pancreatitis, gangrene of the gallbaldder, pancreatic carcinoma,
diabetic ketoacidosis, electric countershock, urologic procedures,
radiotherapy, sleep deprivation, and dissecting aneurysm. Increased physical activity and intramuscular injections should
be considered as potential etiologic factors of abnormal CK levels
in patients with chest pain, particularly when the ECG and other
serum enzymes are not confirmatory. Galen et. al (52) studied
the serum levels of GOT, HBD, CK and LD as well as isoenzymes
of LD and CK in a large number of patients with and without myocardial infarction. They concluded that total GOT, HBD and CK
activity in serum did not discriminate between two groups of
patients with and without myocardial infarction well enough to
be of diagnostic value in problem cases. On the other hand, the
separation and identification of CK and LD isoenzymes provided
the best discrimination between the two groups. Isoenzyme studies
provide the only laboratory method currently available to predict
accurately the presence or absence of an acute myocardial infarction. Combined CK and LD isoenzyme studies permit identification
of the tissue source of an elevated total enzyme level, and in
acute myocardial infarction it is possible to identify the myocardium as the specific source.

The only other condition which causes (MB) to appear in
serum is muscular dystrophy. The MB isoenzyme appears in the
serum of the patient with acute myocardial infarction within
6 hours and remains elevated for approximately 48-60 hours.
As the acute episode resolves, the MB fraction decreases
rapidly and is usually undetectable after 72 hours. Although
(MM) remains elevated and the total CK activity may be above the
normal range, it is important to recognize that the majority of
the MM is also derived from myocardium. The LD and CK total
activities and isoenzyme patterns are frequently normal up to
six hours after onset of symptoms. Between 6 and 12 hours
postinfarction there is usually an increased LD activity but
normal isoenzyme pattern, while (MB) has already appeared. An

LD isoenzyme abnormality does not precede the appearance of the (MB) in the serum following myocardial infarction. The reappearance of (MB) is interpreted as diagnostic of reinfarction, and correlates with new electrocardiographic changes and an altered clinical course.

Wagner et. al (46) studied 376 patients to evaluate the importance of identification of the myocardial-specific MB isoenzyme in the diagnosis of acute myocardial infarction. An attempt was made to determine the incidence of falsely positive (MB). No acute infarction was diagnosed in all patients in whom neither total CK nor the isoenzymes of LD indicated myocardial necrosis. Incidence of falsely negative (MB) was zero in 55 patients. They concluded that determination of the isoenzymes of CK provides both a sensitive and specific indication of acute myocardial infarction.

Glutamic-oxalacetic Transaminase (GOT).

GOT (AST is the more recent abbreviation) catalyzes the transamination of l-aspartic acid in the presence of α-ketoglutaric acid, with pyridoxal phosphate being a required co-enzyme. The reaction is:

$$\text{l-asparate} + \alpha\text{-ketoglutarate} \xrightarrow[\text{pH 7.8}]{\text{GOT}} \text{l-glutamate} + \text{oxalacetate}$$

$$\text{oxalacetate} + \text{NADH} + \text{H}^+ \xrightarrow{\text{MDH}} \text{malate} + \text{NAD}^+$$

The product of oxalacetic acid was first measured by Karmen using a coupled enzyme method, with exogenous malic dehydrogenase and NADH. The decrease in absorbance at 340 nm is a measurement of the GOT activity when the exogenous enzyme and co-factor are present in large excess. This method, with some technical revisions (14,28) is still the method of choice. Colorimetric measurements of the product oxalacetate have been made using dinitrophenylhydrazine, but these methods have been shown to suffer from numerous systematic drawbacks which can markedly effect accuracy (14). For example, there are variable serum blanks, the substrate concentrations employed are far from optimal, the method is standardized with pyruvate, a substance which has no role in the transamination reaction, the kinetics are not zero order, and the measured absorbances are not proportional to increasing enzyme activity. Consequently, the dinitrophenylhydrazine methods cannot be recommended for general use. Methods

based on the azoene dyes Ponceau Fast L and Violet B have been
described by Babson and co-workers and Klein and co-workers.
The methods have been modified by Sax and co-workers and by Amador and Salvatore, who stabilized the final color by the addition
of appropriate buffers at pH 3, optimized the substrate concentrations, and showed that acceptable correlation existed with the
revised kinetic method (26). Automated continuous flow methods
for these dyes, as well as for the kinetic method are now available (26).

Glutamic-pyruvic Transaminase (GPT)

GPT (or ALT) catalyzes the following reaction:

$$\text{l-alanine} + \alpha\text{-ketoglutarate} \xrightarrow[\text{pH 7.8}]{\text{GPT}} \text{l-glutamate} + \text{pyruvate}$$

$$\text{pyruvate} + \text{NADH} + \text{H}^+ \xrightarrow{\text{LDH}} \text{lactate} + \text{NAD}^+$$

The resulting pyruvate may be measured by coupling the reaction
with lactic dehydrogenase and NADH, or chemically by using dinitrophenylhydrazine. The kinetic method has been revised by
Henry and co-workers to optimize the analytical conditions, and
still is the method of choice (28).

Glutamyl Transferase (GMT)

This enzyme, also known as γ-glutamyl transpeptidase, catalyzes the transfer of the γ-glutamyl radical from a γ-glutamyl
donor to a variety of acceptors, which may be amino acids or peptides, or many compounds such as glutathione, S-pyruvoyl, S-
acetophenone and S-propanone. Derivatives of glutathione, din-
itropropionitrile, γ-glutamyl aniline, γ-glutamyl - α - naphthy-
lamide, and γ-glutamyl-β-naphthylamide, have been used as substrates. However, as some of these substrates are not sufficiently soluble to yield optimum substate concentration, are
carcinogenic (glutamyl aniline) or require long incubation time
and many procedural steps to convert the enzymatic product into
colored compound for colorimetric procedures, they have been
abandoned. Orlawski introduced γ-L-glutamyl-p-nitroanilide as
the substrate which is now widely used. It was also shown that
addition of glycyl-glycine as a co-substrate in the GMT test provided an activating and buffering agent in the system. In 1969
Szasz (53) published a kinetic photometric method for serum GMT

in which he used both γ-glutamyl-p-nitroanilide and glycylglycine.
The enzyme liberates p-nitroanilide with an absorption maximum
around 405 nm. The GMT activity is directly proportional to the
amount of p-nitroaniline liberated per unit time. This kinetic
method is said to be accurate, rapid and precise and seems to be
the method of choice.

The GMT in human serum reacts most rapidly with γ-glutamyl-
p-nitroanilide at pH 8.2. The same activity is found in 2-amino-
2-methylpropane-1:3 diol, diethanolamine, triethanolamine and
tris buffers. Magnesium ions have no effect on the activity but
favor the solubilization of the substrate. Bondar and Moss (54)
found that free glutamate, due to elevated serum glutamate concentrations or glutamate released by substrate breakdown, increases the apparent GMT activity. They concluded that the assay
should be performed in the presence of 1.0 mM/l glutamate in
order to reduce the possibility of falsely elevated results.
This was not observed by others. Rowe and co-workers have indicated that certain batches of p-nitroanilide substrate contain
impurities which may reduce GMT activity and increase the K_m
values (55). Huesby and Stromme (56) confirmed the presence of
such impurities and recommended pyridine extraction for substrate purification.

In automated instruments such as the LKB the reaction is
started by the addition of glycylglycine after preincubation of
enzyme with substrate. But the substrate may undergo hydrolysis
or internal transpeptidation during such preincubation, resulting in substrate concentration variation from sample to sample.
Seiffert and Chaves (57) incubated the sample and substrate at
pH 6.0, because at this pH the substrate is stable. When the
glycylglycine is added the pH becomes optimal and the reaction
starts. The substrate γ-glutamyl-nitroanilide is poorly soluble
in many buffers and solvents. This has caused difficulty
in attempts to adapt the enzyme reaction to automated or semiauto-
mated enzyme analyzers (such as the LKB 8600 reaction rate analyzer) in which enzyme reaction must be started by a small volume
of concentrated substrate solution. Such difficulties are more
pronounced at 37°C, for at this temperature the substrate K_m
is almost double that at 25° C and its optimal concentration is
significantly greater. Rosalki (58) observed that γ-glutamyl-
p-anilide is highly soluble in HCl. The enzyme reaction is
initiated using a concentrated substrate solution in 0.5 mM HCl,
after preincubation of samples at 37° with Tris-glycylglycine
buffer at a pH adjusted to yield optimal pH upon the addition
of the acid substrate solution. With this procedure, it is
possible to carry out the reaction at much higher substrate and
acceptor concentrations.

Alkaline Phosphatase (ALP)

Alkaline phosphatase catalyzes the dephosphorylation of a number of artificial substrates (2) including β-glycerophosphate, phenylphosphate, p-nitrophenylphosphate, thymolphthalein phosphate, and phenolphthalein phosphate. In addition, as shown recently for bacterial and human enzymes, alkaline phosphatase simultaneously catalyzes the transphosphorylation of a suitable substance which accepts the phosphoryl radical, thereby preventing the accumulation of phosphate in the reaction medium (25).

This acceptor is absent in most of the earlier assays, but commencing with the introduction for clinical use of the kinetic p-nitrophenylphosphate method buffered by 2-amino-2-methyl-1-propanol in 1963 (18), the use of a phosphoryl acceptor as the buffering agent has gained wide acceptance, leading to the introduction of diethylamine (DEA), and of 2-ethyl-amino-ethanol (EAE) (25) as the activating, phosphorylatable buffers. The degree of phosphorylation of the buffer correlates well with the degree of activation of the alkaline phosphatase activity (Table V). Relatively high concentrations of buffer (1-2M) and nonphysiological pH's (pH 10) are necessary (Fig. 5). In the human body, alkaline phosphatase must handle an unknown substrate, probably at a much lower turnover, and may transfer the liberated phosphoryl radical to another as yet unidentified physiological acceptor, possibly ethanolamine.

As in the case of acid phosphatase, the analyst may measure the liberated phosphate or the liberated organic radical. It is easier to measure the liberated organic radical, particularly if it is chromogenic, as in the case of p-nitrophenol, phenolphthalein, or thymolphthalein. These latter two substrates, while analytically valid, suffer from the defect of high cost and proprietary ownership. p-Nitrophenyl phosphate, the most chromogenic substrate, is widely available, and hence methods based on it are the methods of choice, particularly when an activating phosphorylatable buffer is employed. Magnesium ion has been said to activate alkaline phosphatase, but this reviewer has repeatedly observed no activation by this ion (Fig. 6). Surprisingly, the recently reported high concentrations of substrates which leads to maximum velocity, (20mM/1) of either phenylphosphate or nitrophenylphosphate are considerably higher than those initially reported (25). No ready explanation is available for this discrepancy, but it is possible that modern substrate preparations are free of impurities such as phosphate or phenol, which are known inhibitors of the enzyme.

When phenyl phosphate is the substrate, the released phenol is conveniently measured using the reaction described by Powell and Kind and King based on 4-amino antipyrine (4-AAP) and ferricyanide. It is possible to incorporate the 4-AAP directly into the buffered substrate mixture, so that color can be developed

TABLE V

BUFFER ACTIVATION OF SERUM ALKALINE PHOSPHATASE

BUFFER	RELATIVE ACTIVITY
	Phenyl Phosphate Substrate
Carbonate	1.0
2-Amino-2-Methyl-1-Propanol	2.51 ± 0.24
Diethanolamine	6.65 ± 0.41
2-Ethylaminoethanol	7.03 ± 0.41
	p-Nitrophenyl Phosphate Substrate
Glycine	1.0
2-Amino-2-Methyl-1-Propanol	3.13 ± 0.04
Diethanolamine	7.21 ± 0.17
2-Ethanolamine	9.37 ± 0.12

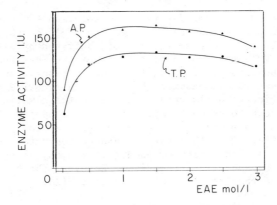

Figure 5.   *The increase in serum alkaline phosphatase activity (ALP) parallels the increase in trans-
phosphorylase activity (TP) produced by increasing
the molarity of 2-ethylaminoethanol (2-EAE).*

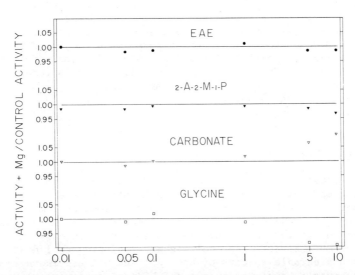

Figure 6.   *Magnesium in concentrations of 0.001–10 mM/l. produces
no significant activation of alkaline phosphatase in EAE, DEA, or
2A2M1P buffers. It activates the enzyme in carbonate buffer but
inhibits it in glycine buffer.*

by the simple addition of ferricyanide solution (Table VI).
Alkaline phosphatase assays based on β-glycerophosphate
now appears to be obsolete, and methods buffered by either glycine or barbital are also obsolete as these buffers inhibit ALP
or are poor buffers. Serum alkaline phosphatase is known to be
composed of several isoenzymes which presumably arise from bone,
liver, intestine, and placenta. The placental alkaline phosphatase is known to be much more resistant to heat denaturation
than the other isoenzymes, and this resistance provides a simple
test for it (5). The other enzymes can be separated through
the differential inhibition by phenylalanine, by electrophoresis and by specific antibodies. However, the clinical usefulness of the results obtained is in doubt (23).

Diseases of the Liver

     Serum enzymes have been used extensively in the detection
and differential diagnosis of diseases of the liver and biliary
tract as the latter are often curable by surgery, while diseases
of the liver usually are not, the differential diagnosis between
these two groups of diseases is of considerable clinical importance. The task is aided somewhat because the liver cells are
different in their enzymatic content from the cells lining the
bile duct. However, pathologic processes often involve both
type of cells, thereby obscuring the diagnostic boundaries.
     The enzymes found in liver cells (Group I enzymes) include
more than a dozen enzymes used in diagnostic laboratories, but
those used most commonly are the transaminases (GOT and GPT),
which continue to be the most widely used indicators of liver
cell integrity. Enzymes found in the biliary cells (Group II)
include alkaline phosphatase, glutamyl-transferase, leucine
amniopeptidase and 5-nucleotidase.

Liver Cell Enzymes

     In liver cells the activity of GOT is higher than that of
GPT, but most of the GPT activity is located in the cytoplasm
and therefore leaks more readily into the blood stream with minor
or reversible cell damage. Enzymes located in the mitochondria,
such as one of the GOT isoenzymes appear in serum only when there
has been more severe liver cell injury including cell death.
While considerable amounts of both GOT and GPT are found in
cardiac muscle, skeletal muscle and kidney, differential diagnosis is aided by the fact that the liver shows a much higher total
GPT activity. An important clinical application of measurements
of transaminase activity is the detection and diagnosis of viral

TABLE VI

EVOLUTION OF SERUM ALKALINE PHENYL PHOSPHATASE METHODS

STEP	KING-ARMSTRONG	KIND-KING	ROOS	HANSEN	AMADOR-URBAN
1.	ADD SERUM TO CARB BUFFERED SUBSTRATE	ADD SERUM TO CARB BUFFERED SUBSTRATE	ADD SERUM TO CARB BUFFERED SUBSTRATE	ADD SERUM TO CARB BUFFERED SUBSTRATE WITH 4-AAP	ADD 20uL SERUM TO EAE BUFFERED SUBSTRATE WITH 4-AAP
2.	INCUBATE 37° 30MIN	INCUBATE 15MIN	INCUBATE 22MIN	INCUBATE 15MIN	INCUBATE 10MIN
3.	ADD PHENOL REAGENT	ADD NaOH	ADD 4-AAP	ADD FERRICYANIDE	ADD BUFFERED FERRICYANIDE
4.	FILTER	ADD NaHCO$_3$	ADD FERRICYANIDE	READ ABSORBANCE	READ ABSORBANCE
5.	ADD FILTRATE TO SODIUM CARBONATE	ADD 4-AAP	READ ABSORBANCE		
6.	INCUBATE AT 37° FOR 5MIN	ADD FERRICYANIDE			
7.	READ ABSORBANCE	READ ABSORBANCE			
	REQUIRES A BLANK FOR EACH SERUM	REQUIRES A BLANK FOR EACH SERUM	REAGENT BLANK ONLY	REAGENT BLANK ONLY	REAGENT BLANK ONLY

4-AAP = 4-AMINO ANTIPYRINE, CARB = CARBONATE-BICARBONATE,
EAE = ETHYL-AMINO-ETHANOL (OR 2-DIETHANOLAMINE) AS PHOSPHORYLATABLE BUFFER
(BASED ON REFERENCES 2,25,32)

hepatitis, as the marked elevations of GOT and GPT activities reflect the clinical course of the disease. Persons with subclinical viral hepatitis often have mild elevations of the serum GPT activity.

Another common liver disease, alcoholic liver damage produced by moderate to heavy alcoholic intake, is also reflected by an elevation of the serum GOT and GPT activities. The serum glutamyl transferase activity is reported to be a sensitive index of alcoholic intake and can serve to monitor persons on alcoholic withdrawal programs (60). The LD-5 isoenzyme arises mainly from liver tissue, but has a short half-life (61), which is about 1/5 and 1/2 of the half life of the transaminases, GPT and GOT respectively. Some authors consider that a normal LD-5 isoenzyme activity in a jaundiced patient is sufficient evidence to exclude primary liver disease and that obstruction is probably responsible for the jaundice (62). In hemolytic jaundice the LDH-1 and 2 isoenzymes are elevated.

The Group II (biliary tract) enzymes are abnormal usually when the serum bilirubin concentration is also abnormal. Most commonly used is alkaline phosphatase which is a highly sensitive indicator of biliary tract obstruction, perhaps because the enzyme is synthesized as an induced response to obstruction of even small bile ducts. Most techniques used to identify the origin of an elevated serum alkaline phosphatase are not very useful from a clinical viewpoint (23). The simultaneous measurement of GMT activity has been found to be useful in differentiating between the hepatic and bony origin of alkaline phosphatase. An increased GMT activity in a patient with an increased ALP activity is a good indication that there is biliary biliary tract disease (62,63).

Solberg and co-workers have applied discriminate analysis of clinical laboratory tests combined with careful clinical and anatomic diagnoses of liver disease in order to determine which combinations of the many dozen liver diagnostic tests available are the best (64). These authors found that the measurement of GPT, GMT, GOT, ALP and ceruloplasmin were the most useful enzymatic tests, when combined with other non-enzymatic tests such as the measurement of bilirubin, cholesterol, hepatitis-B associated Australian antigen, etc. Another group of highly useful enzymes, not discussed in this review, are those clotting factors and the enzyme cholinesterase which are synthesized by the liver cells.

Reduction in liver cell mass or diffuse liver cell damage often results in a decreased activity of blood clotting enzymes in the blood plasma. The lack of quantitative methods resulting from the lack of chromogenic substrates and rate reaction methods for the measurement of the clotting factors, together with the lability of many of these clotting factors has restricted up to now the ready diagnostic application of the measurement of most clotting factor activities.

Amylase (AMS)

Amylase catalyzes the splitting of starch and similar polysaccharide macromolecules into smaller polysaccharides,
finally leading to maltose (65). It has the distinction of
being the first enzyme activity in body fluids used for the
diagnosis of disease, and its activity has been measured clinically during most of this century (1). All the traditional
methods use starch solubilized through heat and suspended in
a buffered solution. The iodometric method is classic for measuring the starch remaining after enzymatic attack. Starch solubilization is said to be enhanced by dimethylsulfoxide. In recent
years, a variety of other polysaccharide substrates coupled to
dyes have been used, thus as the amylase hydrolyses the substrates, dye is released into solution. The unhydrolyzed substrate is precipitated or separated by centrifugation, and the
amount of dye liberated into solution is then measured.

The voluminous literature concerning the assay of amylase
activity reflects general dissatisfaction with available methods.
The major problem associated with measuring amylase activity
is standardization of a substrate of known and reproducible composition and concentration. Starches are heterogenous in both
molecular weight and degree of branching, and both can profoundly
affect the susceptibility of the starches to amyloclastic attack.
Starches in water form a colloidal suspension whose micelles
vary in size and deteriorate rather rapidly with mold contamination. At lower temperatures starch in solution forms large
micelles which are less susceptible to amylase hydrolysis. A
wide variety of methods for the estimation of amylase has been
employed based mainly on the measurement of decrease in viscosity
of a starch solution, decrease in turbidity of a starch suspension, decrease in starch iodine color (amyloclastic), or increase in the reducing power of the starch solution (saccharogenic). Amyloclastic assays are reproducible and simple, but
some sera and urines contain material that inhibits formation
of the starch iodine color so that it is not always a true
estimate of the starch actually present.

The saccharogenic procedure of Somogyi modified by Henry
and Chiamori (65) still serve as the reference method, but
suffers from lack of standards, poor precision with normal
activities, poor sensitivity and inadequate substrate stability. Recently Shipe and Savory (66) have used a stable liquid
starch in which the optical brightener is absent. This suspension of oxidized corn starch contains antifoam (dimethylpoly-
siloxane) lubricant, sodium tetraborate as the preservative,
and Tris buffer. Shipe and Savory measured the light scattering with a fluorometer whose kinetic reading was recorded at
37° C for 12 minutes. The method was precise with day to day
variation of 3.4%. The method correlated well with the
Phadebas TM amylase test which will be discussed later. The

key to the nephelometric measurement of starch was the preparation of a stable colloidal suspension that does not settle out during the test run. Zinterhofer using a similar approach has used known formazan turbidity standards to establish the amount of light scattering thereby avoiding secondary enzyme standards (67). The rate of decrease in turbidity which is expressed in formazan turbidity units (FTU) per min. per ml of sample under specified conditions is proportional to the enzyme activity. The method measures amylase in serum or urine in 2 to 4 minutes using 50 ul of sample. The substrate is amylopectin dissolved in dimethylsulfoxide. Amylase activity expressed in FTU is approximately half that when expressed as Somogyi units per 100 ml. The method is linear up to 600 FTU. According to Seligson's group this is a fast method for emergency diagnoses.

In the late 1960's a new series of methods was introduced for the determination of amylase, involving the use of a starch-dye complex. Dyes such as Renazol brilliant blue (68) Reactive Red 2B (69) (used in the substrate Dy-Amyl, General Diagnostic Division, Warner-Chilcott Laboratories), Cibachrom Blue (70) (used in Amylochrome, Roche Diagnostic Division of Hoffman-La Roche Inc.) and other dyes (71) are bound to amylopectin or amylose. Most of these substrates are available commercially and many are being used on a routine basis.

In the Phadebas TM amylase test (72) (Pharmacia Labs) the substrate was a water insoluble cross-linked blue starch in tablet form which also contains some inert ingredients, sodium and potassium phosphate buffer salts and sodium chloride. This polymer was hydrolyzed by amylase into water soluble blue starch fragments. After centrifugation the absorbance of the blue supernatant was proportional to the activity of amylase present in the test samples. The day to day variation on a quality control serum had a coefficient of variation of 2.7% based on 30 days of data in our laboratory. The method is simple, reproducible and uses microquantities of serum.

Clinically, measurements of amylase in serum and urine, and measurements of lipase in serum, have been the most useful tests in the assessment of pancreatic disease, particularly in acute pancreatitis and in the recurrent attacks of chronic pancreatitis. The highest concentration of human amylase is found in the parotid (salivary) gland and pancreas. Liver, oviduct mucosa, skeletal muscle, gastric and small intestinal mucosa and red blood cells also have some amylase activity. The amylase in normal serum is of heterogeneous origin, and the major isoenzymes are from pancreas and parotid gland. Gamklon and Schersten (73) showed human liver tissue contains only traces of amylase activity. Hence the increased serum activity occasionally found in cases with liver or bile duct disease probably originates from other sites.

Since pancreatic and salivary isoamylases differ from one

another in electrophoretic mobility, determination of isoenzymes
of amylase in serum or urine may disclose the origin of
an elevated serum amylase activity. Electrophoretic separation
has been performed on agar, agarose, poly-acrylamide gel and
cellulose acetate and earlier also on paper. Skude (74) has
developed an electrophoretic separation technique on agarose
as a supporting media which he claimed to be the media of choice,
because of its high resolving power and ease of handling. The
method is claimed to be simple and can be performed routinely
in a clinical laboratory. Takeuchi et. al (75) separated
isoenzymes of amylase in human serum, urine, pancreatic juice
and saliva by electrofocusing. The amylases in serum were separated into two major isoenzymes with isoelectric points of pH
6.4-6.5 (saliva) and pH 6.9-7.0 (pancreas) respectively, and
one minor isoenzyme with an isoelectric point of pH 5.9 of unknown origin.

Amylase enters the blood largely via the lymphatics. An
increase in hydrostatic pressure in the pancreatic ducts leads
to a fairly prompt rise in the amylase concentration of the
blood. Neither an increase in volume flow of pancreatic juice
nor stimulation of pancreatic enzyme production will cause an
increase in serum enzyme concentration. Elevation of intra-
ductal pressure is the important determinant. Stimulation of
flow in the face of obstruction can, however, augment the entry
of amylase into the blood, as can disruption of acinar cells
and ducts. A functional pancreas must be present for the serum
amylase to rise. Serum amylase determination is indicated in
acute pancreatitis, in patients with acute abdominal pain where
the clinical findings are not typical of other diseases such
as appendicitis, cholecystitis, peptic ulcer, vascular disease
or intestinal obstruction. In acute pancreatitis, the serum
amylase starts to rise within a few hours simultaneously with
the onset of symptoms and remains elevated for 2 to 3 days after
which it returns to normal. The peak level is reached within
24 hours. Absence of increase in serum amylase in first 24
hours after the onset of symptoms is evidence against a diagnosis of acute pancreatitis (76).

Various conditions such as perforated peptic ulcer,
cholecystitis, common bile duct and intestinal obstruction,
trauma to the abdomen inducing pancreatitis and ruptured ectopic
pregnancy may cause an elevated serum amylase but the levels
are usually not as high as those found in acute pancreatitis.
Mumps and bacterial parotitis, which block the secretion of
salivary amylase are associated with mild elevations of serum
amylase.

Opiates and other narcotics and analgesic drugs may unpre-
dicatably elevate the serum amylase. The elevation may last up
to 24 hours. Therefore it is important that blood for amylase
determination be drawn before giving the patient analgesic drugs
for pain. Elevation of the enzyme in peritoneal fluid is strong

evidence of acute pancreatitis (77).

The rate of urine amylase excretion is a sensitive
reflection of the amylase released into the blood. The urine
amylase remains abnormal 1-2 weeks after the serum returns to
normal because the renal clearance of amylase rises 3-fold in
acute pancreatitis and takes 1-2 weeks to return to normal. In
pancreatitis, a number of investigators have reported a higher
percentage of urinary amylase elevations, as contrasted with
serum amylase elevations, particularly when the urinary amylase
output over an interval is measured. Random urine collections
for one, two and 24 hours are 792-4264 (2926±1074 S.D.) units
per 24 hours. However, the wide range of normals make interpretation of results difficult. Of 107 patients with elevated
serum or urine amylases, 16 were found to have a normal pancreas
at operation (78).

The study of the mechanism of urinary excretion of amylase
and the amylase clearance has been the subject of many studies
in recent years. Levitt et. al (79) studied the renal clearance of amylase in renal insufficiency, acute pancreatitis and
macro-amylasemia. In acute pancreatitis, the kidney cleared
amylase at a markedly increased rate. The ratio of the amylase
clearance rate to the creatinine clearance rate (C_{am}/C_{cr}) aver-
aged 3 times normal early in the course of acute pancreatitis,
and this elevation could persist after the serum amylase re-
turned to normal. Comparison of amylase clearance to creatinine
clearance was to minimize irrelevant changes due to variation
in renal function. The increased clearance of amylase makes the
urinary amylase a more sensitive indicator of pancreatitis.
The ratio of Cam/Ccr can be determined on a random urine sample
and thus avoids the time, labor, and errors involved in collecting the timed urine specimen required for the urinary amylase
determination.

Possible causes of increased ratio of C_{am}/C_{cr} in pancreatitis can be liberation of a more readily excretable form
of amylase, a protein with a molecular weight of 55,000 or less
which can be easily filtered via the glomerulus and undergoes
no appreciable tubular reabsorption.

Warshaw and Fuller (80) studied the specificty of increased
renal clearance of amylase in acute pancreatitis. They established 3.1% ± 1.1 S.D. for the C_{am}/C_{cr} ratio in normal persons.
In patients with acute pancreatitis this ratio rises regularly
and significantly to 9.8 ± 3.5 S.D. They suggested that renal
permeability to amylase is altered in acute pancreatitis and
provides the basis for using the C_{am}/C_{cr} ratio in the differential diagnosis of hyperamylasemia. Levine et. al (81) observed an increased clearance ratio in situations other than
acute pancreatitis both with and without elevated serum amylase
activity. They indicated that this ratio may be increased in
patients with diabetic ketoacidosis or extensive burns who also
present no clinical or other evidence of associated acute pan-

creatitis. Levitt and Cooperband (82) in an editorial suggested
that marked elevations of this ratio perhaps result from an
increase in glomerular permeability, and that small changes in
gluomerular permeability result in large changes in renal
amylase clearances.

Lipase (LPS)

Numerous workers have found that measurements of serum
lipase activity are useful in the diagnosis of pancreatitis (83,
84, 85). Despite this, serum lipase determinations are not
usually performed in clinical laboratories, probably due to inherent problems associated with the conventional methods, based
on an emulsified lipid substrate. The methods are also not
very suitable for manual batch analysis nor for automation due
to laborious post incubation procedures.
      Cherry and Crandall in 1932 (86) used olive oil as sub-
strate with gum acacia as the emulsifier. This method has
served as the basis for a number of modifications that increased
the stability of the emulsion, decreased incubation time and
gave better precision. When a serum sample is incubated with
a stabilized olive oil emulsion, lipase acts at the interface
of substrate and water to hydrolyze olive oil into fatty acid
plus diglycerides, and to a small extent to monoglycerides and
glycerol. The bile salt sodium deoxycholate activates the
reaction. These methods measure the liberated fatty acids by
titration with a standardized NaOH solution. An indicator such
as phenolphatalein, thymolphthalein or methyl red or a pH meter
are used to detect the end point.
      Lippi et. al (87) and Dirstine (88) circumvented titration
by converting the liberated fatty acids into copper salts, which
after extraction in chloroform are reacted with diethyldithio-
carbamate to form a colored complex which is measured photometri-
cally. While the end point appears to be more sensitive than
the pH end point determination, the advantages are outweighed
by the additional steps of solvent extraction, centrifugation
and incomplete extraction when low concentrations of copper salts
are present. Other substrates used for the measurement of lipase
activity have been tributyrin (89), phenyl laurate (90), p-nitro-
phenyl-stearate and β-naphthyl laurate (91). It has been shown
that these substrates are hydrolyzed by esterases and thus lack
specificity for lipase. Studies on patients with pancreatitis
indicate olive oil emulsion is definitely superior to water soluble esters as substrates for measuring serum lipase activity.
      Several tubidimetric methods (92, 93) have been described
specifically for the kinetic determination of lipase in serum
but these methods suffer from lack of linearity with increasing
enzyme concentration, and instability of emulsions.

Recently Shihabi and Bishop (93) described a refinement in the preparation of a stable substrate and demonstrated the feasibility monitoring the reaction kinetically. This procedure has been evaluated by Lifton et. al. (94), who found that this method correlated well (r = 0.914) with the copper soap-lipase method of Dirstine. They concluded that the method was rapid (less than 5 min. per sample), accurate, precise and linear over a clinically useful range. Its simplicity allows its application as an emergency procedure. Attempts to use this assay for urine lipase activity were unsuccessful.

Seligson's group (95) has published a similar turbidimetric procedure but used nephelometry to measure continuously the effect of lipase on the light scattering of an olive oil emulsion. The instrumentation and approach is the same as that described above for the nephelometric determination of amylase. The method according to the authors is fast and precise with good specificity and sensitivity. The short time required for analysis makes it suitable for emergency use. The technical simplicity permits this method to be easily automated, and it appears to be the lipase method of choice.

Acid Phosphatase (ACP)

Acid phosphatase catalyzes the dephosphorylation of an artificial organic substrate, such as B-glycerophosphate, phenylphosphate or thymolphthalein monophosphate. The analyst may measure either the phosphate or the organic radical liberated. In the older β-glycerophosphate method, phosphate was measured, but in all other methods the organic radical is measured. This has the advantage of considerably simplifying the methodology, increasing sensitivity and improving specificity. At present, the method which uses sodium thymolphthalein phosphate as a substrate, described by Roy and co-workers, appears to be the best documented and most specific for prostatic disease (96). After incubation of serum and substrate at a slightly acid pH, the reaction is stopped and the product color is brought out by the simple addition of an NaOH solution.

The adult male prostate contains abundant acid phosphatase which it secretes into the semen. The production of this enzyme is governed by the circulating levels of androgenic hormones. Castration or estrogen administration markedly reduces the prostatic urinary acid phosphatase of males. Other organs such as the liver, kidney, spleen, red cells and platelets also contain significant amounts of acid phosphatase.

Measurement of serum acid phosphatase activities as an aid in the diagnosis and treatment of advanced prostatic carcinoma is based on the observation by Gutman and Gutman that the activity is elevated by skeletal metastases (3). Many workers have

confirmed that the serum acid phosphatase activity is elevated
in 50 to 75% of patients with skeletal metastases, in about 30
to 40% of patients with soft tissue invasion, and in about 10
to 20% of patients with carcinoma localized within the prostatic
capsule. Remissions in metastatic growth, such as those produced by estrogen therapy, are usually but not always reflected
by a fall in this serum activity. Schwartz, Greenberg, and
Bodansky on the basis of studies of four patients over several
months suggested that elevated activities of serum isocitric
dehydrogenase and phosphohexose isomerase correlate better with
metastatic growth than those of serum acid or alkaline phosphatase (97).

Nodular hyperplasia of the prostate is usually associated
with a normal serum acid phosphatase activity. Complications
such as acute urinary obstruction or prostatic infarction will
elevate this serum activity for several days as will cystoscopy
and catheterization (98). Digital palpation of the prostate
may result in an elevation which subsides within a few hours.
The substrate phenyl phosphate, which is hydrolyzed by the serum
acid phosphatases originating from many tissues, has been used
in most of the published studies. Total serum acid phenylphosphatase is elevated in diseases of the liver, disease of bone
such as Paget's disease, and several blood dyscrasias,
especially those involving platelets (99,100).

Red blood cells also contain sufficient acid phenylphosphatase for mild hemolysis to cause false elevations. Therefore,
inhibitors such as ethanol, formaldehyde, copper sulfate, and
l-tartrate have been used to inhibit selectively the enzyme of
one or more tissues and enhance the specificity of the test
(101). Ethanol is unsuitable because it inhibits the enzyme
from erythrocytes and prostate simultaneously, and because it
yields serum activities which correlate poorly with prostatic
disease. Formaldehyde inhibits the erythrocytic enzyme and
has been said to yield clinically satisfactory results. The
copoper resistant acid phosphatase of serum is elevated by
metastatic carcinoma of the breast, as well as by other
metastatic cancers, and is also elevated by a wide variety of
non-cancerous diseases.

l-Tartrate is a most widely used inhibitor of prostatic
acid phenylphosphatase activity. With this inhibitor Bonner
and associates detected five cases of unsuspected carcinoma of
the prostate in 221 hospital patients and clarified the diagnoses in another four patients (98). Nonetheless, the
diagnostic specificity of an elevated l-tartrate inhibited
activity is not absolute, as Fishman et. al found it elevated
in 48 of 1,190 males without cancer. Whitmore and associates
also observed this activity to be elevated in 3 of 20 patients
with uncomplicated nodular hyperplasia (102). Hill compared
the total versus the "prostatic" serum activities in 20 patients
with localized untreated carcinoma of the prostate and observed

no significant difference in the incidence of elevated activities
as measured by two methods (103). Langley also observed a significant incidence of false positive activities (99).

β-glycerophosphate has been reported to be a specific substrate for an elevated serum acid phosphatase activity of prostatic origin. The diagnostic usefulness of this method had not
been examined critically until Marshall and Amador tested it
in 117 patients with carcinoma and in 63 patients with nodular
hyperplasia of the prostate (100). The β-glycerophosphatase
activity was elevated in 46% of patients with intracapsular
carcinoma and in 56% with extracapsular invasion or soft tissue
metastases. In 82% with skeletal metastases, the activity was
elevated. In all of the cases, the initial clinical diagnosis
of prostatic carcinoma had been made on the basis of rectal examination, x-ray findings or histologic examination of resected
prostatic tissue. Surprisingly, in no case was prostatic carcinoma first disclosed by elevated activity of serum acid phosphatase. Moreover, the normal activity in a significant proportion
of patients with skeletal metastases did not appear to hinder
the establishment of a correct diagnoses by other means.

An elevated activity of serum acid β-glycerophosphatase
was not specific for carcinoma, as Marshall and Amador found
it in 8% of patients with uncomplicated prostatic hyperplasia,
in some patients with bone fractures, carcinoma involving the
liver, and other diseases of bone and liver. This activity has
also been reported to be elevated in 3 of 12 patients with
Gaucher's disease.

Babson proposed α-naphthyl phosphate as an essentially
specific substrate for the activity of prostatic acid phosphatase
in serum (104). However Marshall, Price, and Amador found that
this substrate is not specific for the prostatic enzyme because
urine of human females contain 50 times more acid α-naphthyl
phosphatase than male serum and 50% as much activity as male
urine. Platelets have significant activity and the serum activity can increase to abnormal values following clotting. These
workers also observed elevated activities in females with skeletal metastases of the breast. In 50 hospitalized male patients
who had no evidence of prostatic cancer and 25 hospitalized
female patients, the incidence of false positive results was
12%, a magnitude sufficient to preclude meaningful clinical interpretation (105).

Renin

Renin is released by the juxta-glomerular cells when kidney
perfusion is impaired. Reduction of the blood volume markedly
stimulates release of this enzyme into the blood. The diuretic
drug furosemide also markedly stimulates the release of renin,

through unknown mechanisms, with the renin activity reaching a
peak in peripheral blood five hours after drug administration.
The adrenal hormone aldosterone markedly inhibits the release
of renin. Based on these observations, it has been proposed
that a standardized test for patients with arterial hypertension
be the measurement of serum renin activity 5 hours after
administration of furosemide. Initial studies have shown that
patients with aldosterone secreting tumors have extremely low
or zero stimulated renin activities; patients with other corti-
costeriod secreting adrenal tumors have low renin activities,
patients with idopathic hypertension have normal activities,
and patients with renal vascular hypertension have elevated
renin activities. The renin activities were measured using the
radio-immunoassay method of Haber, in which the amount of angiotensin I released from angiotensinogen is measured after a
suitable period of incubation. The converting enzyme is inhibited to prevent the conversion of angiotensin I into angiotensin II (106). This method is widely accepted and is commercially available.

Glucose-6-phosphate Dehydrogenase (GPD)

GPD in presence of NADP catalyzes oxidation of glucose-6-
phosphate to 6-phosphogluconolactone plus NADPH which is quickly
converted to 6-phosphogluconate. Human serum and RBC also
contain variable amounts of phosphogluconate dehydrogenase (PGD)
which in presence of NADP catalyzes the conversion of 6-phos-
phogluconate to ribulose-5-phosphate with the production of
another mole of NADPH. Therefore, with appropriate conditions
a single mole of glucose-6-phosphate may result in the production of 2 moles of NADPH. The activity of GPD, has been measured by three approaches:
1. Based on the difference in the rate of NADPH
   production with both glucose-6-phosphate and
   6-phosphogluconolactone as substrates and
   the rate of NADPH production with only 6-phos-
   phogluconolactone as its substrate (107).
2. Based on the inhibition of PGD by 2,3-diphos-
   phoglycerate (108).
3. An excess of PGD is added to the reaction
   mixture containing glucose 6-phosphate and
   NADP to assure that 2 moles of NADPH are
   produced per mole of glucose-6-phosphate
   oxidized (109). This method has been improved by Nicholson et. al (110) to make
   it micro, accurate and rapid. Catalano and
   co-workers (111) have compared the above
   three approaches and concluded that in terms

of relative reagent cost the third approach
is more economical.

The multiple human variants of G-6-PD and the relationship
of their kinetic properties to the presence of hemolytic anemia
under conditions which closely simulate the erythrocyte internal
environment have been elegantly studied by Yoshida (112). This
author found that those enzyme variants with significantly reduced physiological activity are those associated with hemolytic
anemia.

Literature Cited

1. Wohlgemuth, J.; Beitrag zur funktionellen Diagnostik des
   Pankreas. Berliner klin. Wschr. (1910), 47, 92-98.
2. King, E. J.; and Armstrong, A. R.; A convenient method for
   determing serum and bile phosphatase activity. Canad.
   Med. Ass. J. (1934), 31, 376-381.
3. Gutman, A. B.; and Gutman, E. B.; An "acid" phosphatase
   occurring in the serum of patients with metastasizing
   carcinoma of the prostate gland. J. Clin. Invest. (1938),
   17, 473-478.
4. Calvin M.; Chemical Evolution. Oxford University Press.
   New York, 1969.
5. Stadtman, E. R.; The role of multiple enzymes in the
   regulation of branched metabolic pathways. Ann. N.Y. Acad.
   Sci. (1968), 151, 516-530.
6. International Union of Biochemistry: Enzyme Nomenclature.
   Elsevier, Amsterdam. 1965, p.7.
7. Warburg, O.; Christian, W.; Giese, A.; Wasserstoffuber-
   tragendes co-ferment, seine zusammensetzung und wirkungs-
   weise. Biochem. Z. (1935), 282, 157-205.
8. Amador, E.; Pippert, J. A.; Emary, R. J.; Serum creatinine
   and glucose analyses by an automated rapid sampling digital
   system. Clin. Chem. (1971), 17, 655.
9. Scott, C. D.; Burtis, C. A.; A miniature fast analyzer
   system. Anal. Chem. (1973), 45 (3), 327A- 340A.
10. Skeggs, L. T.; New dimensions in medical diagnosis. Anal.
    Chem. (1966), 38 (5), 31A-44A.
11. Schneider, A. J.; Willis, M. J.; Sources of variation in
    a standardized and semi-micro procedure for serum glutamic
    oxalacetic transaminase. Clin. Chem. (1958), 4, 392-408.
12. Atwood, J. G.; DiCesare, J. L.; Making enzymatic methods
    optimum for measuring compounds with a kinetic analyzer.
    Clin. Chem. (1975), 21, 1263-1269.
13. Malmstadt, H. V.; Cordos, E. A.; Delaney, C. J.;
    Automated reaction rate methods of anaylsis. Anal. Chem.
    (1972), 44 (12), 26A- 41A.

14. Amador, E.; and Wacker, W. E. C.; Serum glutamic-
    oxaloacetic transaminase activity. A new modification
    and an analytical assessment of current assay technics.
    Clin. Chem. (1962), 8, 343-350.
15. Amador, E.; Dorfman, L. E.; and Wacker, W. E. C.; Serum
    lactic dehydrogenase activity. An analytical assessment
    of current assays. Clin. Chem. (1963), 9, 391-399.
16. Amador, E., Reinstein, H.; and Benotti, N.; Precision and
    accuracy of lactic dehydrogenase assays. Am. J. Clin.
    Path. (1965), 44, 62-69.
17. Amador, E.; and Wacker, W. E. C.; Enzymatic methods used
    for diagnosis, in Method Of Biochemical Analysis, vol. 13,
    edited by Glick, D. Interscience Publishers, New York,
    pp. 265 - 356, 1965.
18. Amador, E.; Zimmerman, T. S.; and Wacker, W. E. C.;
    Urinary alkaline phosphatase activity. II. An analytical
    validation of the assay method. JAMA (1963), 185, 953-957.
19. Dobrow, D. A.; and Amador, E.; The accuracy of commerical
    enzyme reference sera. Am. J. Clin. Path. (1970), 53
    60-67.
20. Amador, E.; and Hsi, B. P.; Indirect methods for estimating
    the normal range. Amer. J. Clin. Path. (1969), 52,
    538-546.
21. Amador, E.; and Masod, M. F.; Characterization of the
    normal serum glutamic-oxalacetic transaminase activity
    of healthy adults. Am. J. Clin. Path. (1967), 47,
    3-8.
22. Amador, E., Franey, R. J.; and Massod, M. F.; Serum
    glutamic-oxaloacetic transaminase activity; Diagnostic
    accuracy of the revised spectrophotometric and the
    dinitrophenylhydrazine methods. Clin. Chem. (1966),
    12, 475-481.
23. Winkelman, J.; Nadler, S.; Demetrio, J.; and
    Pileggi, V. J.; Clinical usefulness of alkaline
    phosphatase isoenzyme determinations. Am. J. Clin.
    Path. (1972), 57, 625-634.
24. Marshall, G.; and Amador, E.; Diagnostic usefulness of
    serum acid β-glycerophosphatase activities in prostatic
    disease. Am. J. Clin. Path (1969), 51, 551-554.
25. Amador, E.; and Urban, J.; Transphosphorylation by human
    alkaline phosphatases. Am. J. Clin. Path. (1972), 57
    167-172.
26. Amador, E.; Salvatore, A. C.; Serum gluatmic-oxalacetic
    transaminase activity. Revised manual and automated
    methods using diazonium dyes. Am. J. Clin. Path. (1971),
    55, 686-697.
27. Dreyfus, J. C.; Poenaru, L.; and Svennerholdm, L.;
    Absence of hexosaminidase A and B in a normal adult.
    New Engl. J. Med. (1975), 292 61-63.
28. Henry, R. J.; Chiamori, N.; Golub, O. J.; and Berkman, S.;

Revised spectrophotometric methods for the determination of glutamic-oxaloacetic transaminase, glutamic-pyruvic transaminase and lactic acid dehydrogenase. Am. J. Clin. Path. (1960), 34, 381-398.

29. Rej. R.; and Vanderlinde, R. E.; Effects of buffers on asparate aminotransferase activity and association of the enzyme with pyridoxal phosphate. Clin. Chem. (1975), 21, 1585-1591.

30. Dinovo, E. C.; Miyada, D. S.; and Nakamura, R. M.; Evaluation of direct and indirect compled enzyme assay systems for measurements of creatine kinase activity. Clin. Chem. (1973), 19, 994-997.

31. Russell, C. D.; Cotlove, E.; Serum glutamic-oxaloacetic transaminase: Evaluation of a coupled-reaction enzyme assay by means of kinetic theory. Clin. Chem. (1971), 17, 1114-1122.

32. Roos, K.; A simplified method for the determination of serum alkaline phosphatase activity. Scand. J. Clin. & Lab. Invest. 15, Suppl. (1963), 69, 233-243.

33. Bowers, G. N., Jr.; Kelley, M. L.; and McComb, R. B.; Precision estimates in clinical chemistry. I. Variability of analytic results in a survey reference sample related to the use of a non-human serum alkaline phosphatase. Clin. Chem. (1967), 14, 595-607.

34. Gay, R. J.; McComb, R. B.; and Bowers, G. N.; Optimum reaction conditions for human lactate dehydrogenase isoenzymes as they affect total lactate dehyrogenase activity. Clin. Chem. (1968), 14, 740-753.

35. Vessel, E. S., and Bearn, A. G.; Observations on the heterogeneity of malic and lactic dehydrogenase in human serum and red blood cells. J. Clin. Invest. (1958), 37, 672-677.

36. Cahn, R. D.; Kaplan, N. O.; and Levine, L.; et. al.: Nature and development of lactic dehydrogenase. Science (1962), 136, 962-969.

37. Wroblewski, F.; and Gregory, K. F.; Lactate dehydrogenase isoenzymes and their distribution in normal tissues and plasma and in disease states. Ann. N.Y., Acad. Sci. (1961), 94, 912-932.

38. Rosalki, S. B.; Standardization of isoenzyme assays with special reference to lactate dehydrogenase isoenzyme electrophoresis. Clin. Biochem. (1974), 7, 29-40.

39. Rosalki. S. B.; Serum hydroxybutyrate dehydrogenase. A new test for myocardial infarction. Brit. Heart J. (1963), 25, 795-802.

40. Tanzer, M. L.; and Gilvarg, C.; Creatine phosphokinase measurements. J. Biol. Chem. (1959), 234, 3201-3204.

41. Oliver, T. T.; A spectrophotometric method for the determination of creatine phosphokinase and myokinase. Biochem. J. (1955), 61, 116-122.

42. Dawson, D. M.; and Fine, I. H.;   Creatine Kinase in human tissues. Arch. Neurol. (1967), <u>16</u>, 175-180

43. Roe, C. R.; Limbird, L. E.; Wagner, G. S.; and Nerenberg, S. T.; Combined isoenzyme analysis in the diagnosis of myocardial injury: Application of electrophoretic methods for the detection and quantitation of the creatine phosphokinase MB isoenzyme. J. Lab. Clin. Med. (1972), <u>80</u>, 577-590.

44. Roberts. R.; Henry, P. D.; Witteeveen, S.A.G.J.; and Sobel, B. E.; Quantification of serum creatine phosphokinase isoenzyme activity. Am. J. Cardiol. (1974), <u>33</u>, 650-654.

45. Konttinen, A.; and Somer, H.; Specificity of serum creatine kinse isoenzymes in diagnosis of acute myocardial infarction. Br. Med. J. (1973), <u>1</u>, 386-389.

46. Wagner, G. S.; Roe, C. R.; Limbird, L. E.; Rosati, R.A.; and Wallace, A. G.; Importance of identification of the myocardial-specific isoenzyme of creatine phosphokinase (MB form) in the diagnosis of acute myocardial infarction. Circulation (1973), <u>47</u>, 263-269.

47. Takahashi, K.; Ushikubo, S.; Oimomi, M.; and Shinki, T.; Creatine phosphokinase isoenzymes of human heart muscle and skeletal muscle. Clin. Chim. Acta (1972), <u>38</u>, 285-290.

48. Mercer, D. W.; Separation of tissue and serum creatine kinase isoenzymes by ion-exchange column chromatography. Clin. Chem. (1974), <u>20</u>, 36-40.

49. Henry, P. D.; Roberts, R.; and Sobel, B. E.; Rapid separation of plasma creatine kinase isoenzymes by batch absorption on glass beads. Clin. Chem. (1975), <u>21</u>, 884-849.

50. Jockers, W.; Wretouy, E.; Pfleiderer, G.; Quantitation of creatine kinase isoenzymes in human tissues and sera by an immunological method. Clin. Chim. Acta. (1975), <u>58</u>, 223-232.

51. Rao, P. S.; Lukes. J. J.; Ayres, S. M.; and Mueller, H.; New manual and automated method for determining activity of creatine kinase isoenzyme MB by use of dithiothreitol: Clinical applications. Clin. Chem. (1975), <u>21</u>, 1612-1618.

52. Galen, R. S.; Reiffel, J. A.; and Gambino, S. R.; Diagnosis of acute myocardial infarction. JAMA (1975), <u>232</u>, 145-147.

53. Szasz, G.; A kinetic photometric method for serum γ-glutamyl transpeptidase. Clin. Chem. (1969), <u>15</u>, 124-136.

54. Bondar, R. J. L.; and Moss, G. A.; Enhancing effect of glutamate on apparent serum γ-glutamyl transpeptidase activity. Clin. Chem. (1974), <u>20</u>, 317-319.

55. Rowe, J. A.; Tarlow, D.; and Rosalki, S. B.; Impurity in γ-glutamyl p-nitroanilide used as substrate for

D-glutamyl transferase. Clin. Chem. (1973), 19, 435-436.

56. Huseby, N. E.; and Stromme, J. H.; Practical points
regarding routine determination of γ-glutamyl transferase (γ -GT) in serum with a kinetic method at 37° C.
Scand. J. Clin. Lab. Invest. (1974), 34, 357-363.

57. Seiffert, U. B.; and Chaves, M.; Zur messung der
aktivitat der γ-glutamyl-transpeptidase mit automaten.
Clin. Chim. Acta (1973), 48, 237-239.

58. Rosalki, S. B.; and Tarlow, D.; Optimized determination
of γ-glutamyltransferase by reaction-rate analysis.
Clin. Chem. (1974), 20, 1121-1124.

59. Posen, S.; Neale, F. C.; and Chubb, J. S.; Heat
inactivation in the study of human alkaline phosphatases.
Ann. Internal Med. (1965), 62, 1234-1243.

60. Rosalki. S. B.; Rau, D.; Serum γ-glutamyl-
transpeptidase activity in alcoholism. Clin. Chim. Acta
(1972), 39, 41-47.

61. Schmidt, E.; and Schmidt, F. W.; Clinical enzymology.
FEBS letters (1976), 62, E62-E79.

62. Batsakis, G.; Sodeman, T. A.; and Deegan, M. J.; Enzymatic
evaluation of hepatobiliary disease. Laboratory Med.
(1974), 5, 33-50.

63. Betro, M. G.; Oon, R. C. S.; and Edwards, J. B.;
Gammaglutamyl transpeptidase in diseases of liver and
bone. Am. J. Clin. Path. (1973), 60, 672-678.

64. Solberg, H. E.; Skrede, S.; and Blomhoff, J. P.:
Diagnosis of liver diseases by laboratory results and
discriminant analysis. Identification of best combinations of laboratory tests. Scand. J. Clin. Lab. Invest.
(1975), 35, 713-721.

65. Henry, R. J.; and Chiamori, N.; Study of the saccharogenic method for the determination of serum and urine
amylase. Clin. Chem. (1960), 6, 434-452.

66. Shipe, J. R.; and Savory, J.; Kinetic nephlometric
procedure for measurement of amylase activity in serum.
Clin. Chem. (1972), 18, 1323-1325.

67. Zinterhofer, L.; Wardlaw, S.; Jatlow, P.; and Seligson, D.;
Nephlometric determination of pancreatic enzymes I.
amylase. Clin. Chim. Acta (1973), 43, 5-12.

68. Rinderknecht, H.; Wilding, P.; and Haverback, B. J.;
A new method for the determination of α-amylase.
Experientia (1967), 23, 805.

69. Babson, A. L.; Kleinman, N. M.; and Megraw, R. E.; A
new substrate for serum amylase determination. Clin.
Chem. (1968), 14 802-803.

70. Klein, B.; Foreman, J. A.; and Searcy, R. L.; New
chromogenic substrate for determination of serum amylase
activity. Clin. Chem. (1970), 16, 32-38.

71. Sax, M. S.; Bridwater, A. B.; and Moore, J. J.;
Determination of serum and urine amylase with use of

Procion Brilliant Red M-2BS amylopectin. Clin. Chem (1971), 17, 311-315.

72. Ceska, M.; Birath, K.; and Brown, B.; A new and rapid method for the clinical determination of amylase activities in human serum and urine. Optimum conditions. Clin. Chim. Acta (1969), 26, 437-444.

73. Gamklon, R.; and Schersten, T.; Activity of α-amylase and α-1,4-glucosidase in human liver tissue. Scand. J. Clin. Lab. Invest. (1972), 30, 201-207.

74. Skude, G.; Electrophoretic separation, detection, and variation of amylase isoenzymes. Scand. J. Clin. Lab. Invest. (1975), 35, 41-47.

75. Takeucki, T.; Matsushima, T.; and Sugimura, T.; Separation of human α-amylase isoenzymes by electrofocusing and their immunological properties. Clin. Chim. Acta (1975), 60, 207-213.

76. Adams, J. T.; Libertino, J. A.; and Schwartz, S. I.; Significance of an elevated serum amylase. Surgery (1968), 63, 877-884.

77. Keith, L. M., Jr.; Zollinger, R. M.; and McCleary, R. S.; Peritoneal fluid amylase determinations as an aid in the diagnosis of acute pancreatitis. Arch. Surg. (1950), 61, 930-936.

78. Brooks, F. P.; Current Concepts: Testing pancreatic function. N. Eng. J. Med. (1972), 286, 300-303.

79. Levitt, M. D.; Rapoport, M.; and Cooperband, S. R.; The renal clearance of amylase in renal insufficiency, acute pancreatitis and macroamylase. Ann. Int. Med. (1969), 71, 919-925.

80. Warshaw, A. L.; and Fuller, J. A. F.; Specificity of increased renal clearance of amylase in diagnosis of acute pancreatitis. New Eng. J. Med. (1975), 292, 325-328.

81. Levine, R. I.; Glanser, F. L.; and Berk, J. E.; Enhancement of the amylase creatinine clearance ratio in disorders other than acute pancreatitis. New Eng. J. Med. (1975), 292, 329-332.

82. Levitt, M.; and Cooperband, S. R.; Increased renal clearance of amylase in pancreatitis. New Eng. J. Med. (1975), 292, 364-365.

83. Roe, J. H.; Ticktin, H. E.; and Schneider, M.; Determination and clinical significance of serum lipase. Enzymol. Biol. Clin. (1966), 7, 731.

84. Song, H.; Tietz, N. W.; and Tan, C.; Usefulness of serum lipase, esterase and amylase estimation in the diagnosis of pancreatitis - a comparison. Clin. Chem. (1970), 16, 264-268.

85. Ticktin, H. E.; Trujillo, N. P.; Evans, P. F.; and Roe, J. H.; Diagnostic value of a new serum lipase method. Gastroent. (1965), 48, 12-17.

86. Cherry, I. S.; and Crandall, L. A.; The specificity of
     pancreatic lipase: Its appearance in the blood after
     pancreatic injury. Am. J. Physiol. (1932), 100, 266-273.
87. Lippi, U.; Stevanato, G.; and Guidi, G.; A rapid
     photometric micromethod for serum lipase determination.
     Clin. Chim. Acta (1972), 37, 199-202.
88. Dirstine, P. H.; Sobel, C.; and Henry, R. J.; A new
     rapid method for the determination of serum lipase.
     Clin. Chem. (1968), 14, 1097-1106.
89. Goldstein, N. P.; Epstein, J. H.; and Roe, H. J.; Studies
     of pancreatic function IV. A simplified method for
     determination of pancreatic lipase using aqueous
     tributyrin as substrate, with one hundred normal values
     by this method. J. Lab. Clin. Med. (1948), 33, 1047-1051.
90. Saifer, A.; and Perle, G.; Photometric micro determina-
     tion of serum lipase with a phenyl laurate substrate.
     Clin. Chem. (1961), 7, 178-184.
91. Yang, J. S.; and Biggs, H. G.; Rapid, reliable method for
     measuring serum lipase activity. Clin. Chem. (1971),
     17, 512-518.
92. Vogel, W. C.; and Zieve, L.; A rapid and sensitive
     turbidimetric method for serum lipase based upon
     differences between lipases of normal and pancreatitis
     serum. Clin. Chem. (1963), 9, 168-181.
93. Shihabi, Z. K.; and Bishop, C.; Simplified turbidimetric
     assay for lipase activity. Clin. Chem. (1971), 17
     1150-1153.
94. Lifton, L. J.; Slicker, K. A.; Pragy, D. A. and Katz, L.A.;
     Pancreatitis and lipase, a re-evaluation with a five
     minute turbidimetric lipase determination. JAMA (1974),
     229, 47.
95. Zinterhofer, L.; Wardlaw, S.; Jatlow, P.; and
     Seligson, D.; Nephelometric determination of pancreatic
     enzymes. II lipase. Clin. Chim. Acta (1973), 44, 173-178.
96. Roy, A. V.; Brown, M. E.; and Hayden, J. E.; Sodium
     thymolphthalein monophosphate, a new acid phosphatase
     substrate with greater specificity for the prostatic
     enzyme in serum. Clin. Chem. (1971), 17, 1093-1102.
97. Schwartz, M. K.; Greenberg, E.; and Bodansky, O.;
     Comparative values of phosphatases and other serum
     enzymes in following patients with prostatic carcinoma.
     Cancer (1963), 16, 583-594.
98. Bonner, C. D.; Hamburger, F.; and Fishman, W. H.; Some
     factors other than neoplasms altering the prostatic
     fraction of acid phosphatase in the serum. Surg. Gyn.
     Obst. (1954), 99, 179-183.
99. Langley, J. R.; The deceptive acid phosphatases. Calif.
     Med. (1965), 103, 343-340.
100. Marshall, G.; and Amador, E.; Diagnostic usefulness of
     serum acid β-glycerophosphatase activities in prostatic

disease. Amer. J. Clin. Path. (1969), 51, 551-554.
101. Mathes, G.; Richmond, S. G.; and Sprunt, D. H.; Use of
l-tartrate in determining "prostatic" serum acid
phosphatase. Report of 514 cases. J. Urol. (1956), 75,
143-150.
102. Whitmore, W. F.; Bodansky, O.; Schwartz, M. K.;
Ying, S. H.; and Day, E.; Serum prostatic acid phosphatase levels in proved cases of carcinoma or benign
hypertrophy of the prostate. Cancer (1956), 9, 228-233.
103. Hill, J. H.; Prostatic serum acid phosphatase in
patients with localized prostatic cancer. Am. J. Clin.
Path. (1956), 26, 120-130.
104. Babson, A. L.; and Read, P. A.; A new assay for prostatic
acid phosphatase in serum. Am. J. Clin. Path. (1959),
32, 6-9.
105. Marshall, G.; Price, W. A.; and Amador, E.; Serum
α-naphthyl phosphatase activity. Am. J. Clin. Path.
(1969), 51, 202-206.
106. Latta, J.: Improved measurement of plasma renin activity
and concentration. Clin. Chem. (1975), 21, 1344-1345.
107. Bishop, C.; Assay of glucose-6-phosphate dehydrogenase
and 6-phosphogluconate dehydrogenase in red cell. J.
Lab. Clin. Med. (1966), 68, 149-155.
108. Yoshida, A.; and Lin, M.; Regulation of glucose-6-
phosphate dehydrogenase activity in red blood cells from
hemolytic and non hemolytic variant subjects, Blood
(1973), 41, 877-891.
109. Dror, Y.; Sasson, H. F.; Watson, J. J.; and Johnson, B. C.;
Glucose-6-phosphate dehydrogenase assay in liver and blood.
Clin. Chim. Acta (1970), 28, 291-298.
110. Nicholson, John F.; Bodourian, Selma, H.; and Pesce, M. A.;
Measurement of glucose-6-phosphate dehydrogenase and
6-phosphogluconate dehydrogenase activities in erythrocytes
by use of a centrifugal analyzer. Clin. Chem. (1974),
20, 1349-1352.
111. Catalano, Edward W.; Johnson, George F.; and Solomon,
Harvey, M.; Measurement of erythrocytes glucose-6-
phosphate dehydrogenase activity with a centrifugal
analyzer. Clin. Chem. (1975), 21, 134-138.
112. Yoshida, A.; Hemolytic anemia and G6PD deficiency.
Science (1973), 179, 532-537.

8

Modern Liquid Chromatography in Clinical Chemistry

BARRY L. KARGER

Institute of Chemical Analysis, Applications and Forensic Science,
Northeastern University, Boston, Mass. 02115

Over the past few years one of the most rapid growing fields
of chemical analysis has been high performance column liquid
chromatography (HPLC). Whereas classical LC was characterized
as a relatively slow and inefficient process, HPLC approaches
the separation speeds obtained in gas chromatography. Accompanying the developments in design of high performance columns
has been the introduction of modern instrumentation (e.g. pumps,
detectors). Today, one can purchase from instrument companies
complete HPLC packages or modular components. HPLC is rapidly
becoming a standard tool in a variety of applications, including pharmaceutical analysis, biochemical research and natural
products research. Complete texts on HPLC, as well as extensive reviews, are available (e.g. 1-6).

With notable exceptions, the application of HPLC to clinical chemistry has not as yet been extensive. This is somewhat
surprising in view of the potential the method has for this
area. This potential arises, in part, from the fact that HPLC
is well suited to the types of substances that must be analyzed
in the biomedical field. Ionic, relatively polar species can
be directly chromatographed, without the need to make volatile
derivatives as in gas chromatography. Typically, columns are
operated at room temperature so that thermally labile substances
can be separated. Finally, certain modes of HPLC allow fractionation of high molecular weight species, such as biopolymers.

The purpose of this article is to present HPLC and to summarize some typical applications in the clinical laboratory.
The directions which HPLC will take in the future will also be
suggested. It is hoped that this review will develop interest
in HPLC by clinical chemists.

Overview of HPLC

General Description. Liquid chromatography encompasses
any chromatographic method in which the mobile phase is a
liquid (c.f. gas chromatography). A variety of stationary
phases and retention mechanisms are available such that a broad
range of modes of separation are possible. It is worthwhile to
briefly describe the important modes that find use in clinical
chemistry.

Adsorption and ion exchange chromatography are well-known
methods of LC. In adsorption, one frequently selects either
silica or alumina as stationary phase for separation of non-
ionic, moderately polar substances (e.g. alcohols, aromatic
heterocycles, etc.). This mode works best in the fractionation
of classes of compounds and the resolution of isomeric substances (7). Ion exchange, on the other hand, is applicable
to the separation of ionic substances. As to be discussed later,
this mode has been well developed as a tool for analysis of
urine constituents (8).

Other modes of LC operation include liquid-liquid partition
chromatography (LLC) and bonded phase chromatography. In the
former, a stationary liquid phase which is immiscible with the
mobile phase is coated on a porous support, with separation
based on partition equilibrium differences of components between the two liquid phases. This mode offers an alternative
to ion exchange in the fractionation of polar, water soluble
substances. While quite useful, the danger exists in LLC that
the stationary phase can be stripped from the column, if proper
precautions are not taken. Hence, it is typical to pre-equil-
ibrate carefully the mobile and stationary phases and to use a
forecolumn, heavily loaded with stationary phase (9).

Recently, the use of chemically bonded phases has become
of great interest. In the typical case an organochlorosilane
is reacted with dry porous silica to produce a surface that
consists of an organic matrix (10).

$$\text{Si-OH} + \text{Cl-Si-R}_3 \longrightarrow \text{Si-O-Si-R}_3 + \text{HCl}\uparrow$$

By far the most popular phase system at the present time is the
one in which R = n-octadecyl. Since the stationary phase is
hydrophobic and nonpolar, while the mobile phase is relatively
polar, this mode of operation is frequently called reverse phase

chromatography. This mode finds use in the separation of
substances of weak to moderate polarity. Moreover, since the
phase is covalently bonded to the surface, there is no need
for a forecolumn. Another feature of this phase system
is the rapid equilibration of the column with solvent changeover. Other bonded phases employ functional groups such
as amino, hydroxyl and ether. In addition, chemically bonded
ion exchangers are now commercially available. We shall
discuss the usefulness of these phase systems later in this
paper.

Finally, two other column LC modes should be mentioned —
exclusion chromatography and affinity chromatography. Exclusion chromatography (i.e. gel filtration or gel permeation)
(11) is a high molecular weight separation method based on
size differences of molecules. One uses a porous support
of a well controlled pore structure (e.g. dextran gel or
porous glass) for the fractionation of biopolymers. Very
large species are unable to penetrate the porous matrix and
hence elute first. Small substances travel fully through
the pore structure and elute last. Those species of intermediate size elute between the two extremes. Gel filtration
finds some use in the analysis and especially the preparative separation of biopolymers.

Affinity chromatography (12) has become an important tool
in the isolation of purified fractions of such substances as
enzymes. Advantage is taken of specific interactions such as
antigen-antibody interactions. One substance of the pair (e.g.
antigen) is bonded to a support. When a mixture is passed
through the column, the specific interaction retains the corresponding antibody relative to other substances. A change
of mobile phase conditions then elutes the pure antibody. This
method has a real potential for analysis of specific proteins
in body fluids.

Classical vs. High Performance LC. Most workers are
familiar with classical LC, a tool that has been predominantly
used for preparative scale clean-up of samples. In order to
appreciate more fully HPLC, Table I compares some of the column
characteristics of classical vs. HPLC.

We first note the very large differences in column performance for the two methods. Effective plates per second represents the speed characteristics of a column (e.g., the number
of plates that can be generated in a given time interval) (13).
As can be seen, HPLC is 100 to 1000 times faster than classical
LC. (We shall discuss the differences between PLB and PB in
the next section.) This improved performance arises mainly
from the use of significantly smaller particle sizes in HPLC.
Moreover, in classical LC, the mobile phase is delivered to
the column by gravity feed, hence, the very low mobile phase
velocities. In HPLC, it is desireable to improve performance

by operating at velocities 10 to 100 times larger. The use of
smaller particle sizes and higher velocities in HPLC requires
high pressure pumping systems to deliver the mobile phase
through the column. In a sense, pressure is the price that
one must pay for the high performance. On the other hand, it
is worth pointing out that in the pressure ranges used in HPLC,
liquids are not very compressible so that there is no danger
from explosions (as would be the case in gas chromatography
at these pressures).

Below the dotted line in Table I we list less fundamental
differences between the two methods. Column lengths tend to
be somewhat shorter in HPLC using small particle PB as a consequence of the high efficiencies that can be generated with the
smaller particle sizes. For analytical scale HPLC, tube diameters of 3-4 mm are selected; however, for preparative scale,
tube diameters of 1 cm or above are not uncommon.

Besides differences in column design, we need to note that
instrumentation is quite different for HPLC relative to the
classical mode. Pumps, injectors and detectors are all important components in the achievement of high performance. In
addition, automated injection is available which could be important in the clinical chemistry field.

Column Packings in HPLC

We have seen that particle sizes of 100-150 μ in classical
LC lead to slow and inefficient columns. The reason for this
is related to the slow diffusion of molecules in the liquid
state (e.g., gaseous diffusion coefficient $\approx 10^5$ liquid diffusion coefficients).

Figure 1A illustrates a porous particle with the flow
stream of mobile phase indicated by the arrows. If we consider,
for simplicity, the particle as an adsorbent, then the pores
will be filled with "stagnant" mobile phase. Molecules that
enter the pores must diffuse through this liquid in order to
be released again into the flow stream. (Adsorption-desorption
rates are assumed to be rapid.). The time it takes to travel
through the particle will be a function of the diffusion coefficient and the square of the pore depth. Slow mass transfer
rates through the particles will mean that there will be excessive losses in efficiency (i.e., broad bands) at reasonable
mobile phase velocities in the flowing stream, as solute molecules inside the pores will be unable to keep up with molecules
in the flowing system. The obvious solution to improved separation speeds is to decrease pore depths, so that the distance
over which diffusion in the stagnant mobile phase must occur
is reduced.

Two approaches have been taken to achieve faster analysis

TABLE I

CLASSICAL vs. HIGH PERFORMANCE LIQUID CHROMATOGRAPHY

Parameter	Classical	HPLC
effective plates per second	.01	2-5 PLB* ~ 25 PB**
particle diameter	100-150 µ	30-40 µ PLB* 5-15 µ PB**
mobile phase velocity	.01 cm/sec	.1-1 cm/sec
pressure drop	15 psi	~ 500-3000 psi
column length	1 meter	1 meter PLB 25 cm PB
column diameter	1 cm	4 mm

*   PLB = porous layer bead
** PB = porous bead

A. STAGNANT MOBILE PHASE MASS TRANSFER

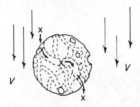

B. POROUS LAYER BEAD

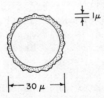

Figure 1. A, porous particle used to illustrate slow mass transfer due to diffusion in the stagnant mobile phase within the particle. B, illustration of a porous layer bead.

times -- porous layer beads (PLB) and small particle porous
beads (PB). Porous layer beads, as illustrated in Figure 1B,
consists of spherical beads of∼ 40 μ diameter upon which is
deposited a thin (∼ 1 μ) porous layer. The small porous
layers allow fast mass transfer in and out of the pores, in
comparison to the fully porous 150 μ . A variety of PLB are
commercially available (2) both as packing itself and in the
form of prepacked columns. Many porous surfaces can be used as
a stationary phases, including silica, alumina and chemically
bonded phases.

While PLB were introduced first (14,15) more recently small
PB (∼ 5-15 μ diameter) have become of major interest. This is
a result of the higher separation speeds found with such particles. Not only is the "stagnant" mobile phase mass transfer
problem reduced, as in PLB, but solute mixing in the flowing
stream is enhanced as a result of the smaller distance between
the particles. The performances achieved with the small particle columns are equivalent to those obtained with capillary
columns in gas chromatography (13). Examples illustrating the
separation speed of such columns will be presented in the applications section of this paper.

The question arises as to which column packing to use in
practice. Table II compares PLB and PB from this point of view.
Besides producing higher column performance PB also have high
sample capacities by virture of the larger stationary phase
content per column volume (recall that most of a PLB particle
is simply a spherical bead). Counterbalancing these advantages
is the fact that the small particle columns are much more difficult to pack reproducibly. While PLB can be dry packed into a
column, PB must use special slurry packing techniques (16), in
order to prevent particle agglomeration in the column. It is
recommended that commercially packed small particle PB columns
be used by anyone not well experienced in the field. In addition, the narrow bands produced with such columns require care
in terms of extra column effects (e.g., injections, connections,
detector). For a recent discussion on the practical handling
of such columns, the reader is referred to (17).

From Table II, we can reach the following important conclu-
sions. First, for simple separations of only a few components
and not great demands on analysis time (e.g., ∼ 15-30 minutes),
PLB are the logical choice. As the number of components increase, as their relative retentions become smaller, or as the
time demands increase, one ought to use small particle PB. With
respect to clinical chemistry, many problems can now be successfully solved with PLB. Ultimately because of the faster analysis potential, small particle PB will be column of choice. However extra care must be excerised in using such columns. As
experience grows with small particle PB, it is clear that they
will become simpler to work with.

EQUIPMENT

Major advances have occurred over the past few years in
equipment for HPLC. Figure 2 presents a block diagram of a
basic LC instrument. We shall now discuss individual components.
    The solvent reservoir provides a source of mobile phase
for the column. For the most part, this component is separate
from the pump; however, in a few cases, it is part of the pumping system (e.g., gas displacement pump). Depending on the flow
rate or the time of operation, the reservoir may consist of a
few hundred mls or several liters. Obviously care must be
exercised that solvent evaporation is minimized, so that the
composition of mixed solvents does not vary with time. Moreover, since the water content of the mobile phase can greatly
affect retention in adsorption chromatography (7), control of
the water vapor above the solvent can be important. A further
precaution is degassing of solvents (1). If sufficient quantities of gases are dissolved in the mobile phase, it is possible that gas bubbles will be released in the detector cell and
thus cause excessive noise and loss of signal. Generally,
solvents are first heated or ultrasonically treated prior to
use. This is especially necessary when aqueous solutions are
employed.
    The flow stream then typically travels through a filter
(preferably less than 2 μ pore size) which may or may not be
part of the pumping system. This component is necessary to
remove particles that could damage the check valves of most
pumps. Since microorganisms can grow in water, it is required
that aqueous solutions be filtered before use.
    A central component of the LC instrument is the pump, for
its characteristics can strongly influence an analysis (e.g.,
flow reproducibility). The three principal types of systems--
pneumatic, syringe type and reciprocating piston--have been
reviewed in the literature (18-20).
    In the pneumatic pumping system, the pressure (and not
the flow rate) is maintained constant as variations in chromatographic conditions occur. Thus, a change in mobile phase
viscosity (e.g. gradient elution) or column back pressure will
result in a change in flow rate for these types of pumps. The
gas displacement pump in which a solvent is delivered to the
column by gas pressure is an example of such a pneumatic pump.
The gas displacement system is among the least expensive pumps
available and is found in several low cost instruments. While
the pump is nonpulsating and hence, produces low noise levels
with the detectors in current use, its flow stability and reproducibility are only adequate. In addition, its upper pressure
limit is only ∿ 2000 psi which may be too low in certain applications.
    The second type of constant pressure pumping system is the

TABLE II

COMPARISON OF PLB AND PB COLUMNS

Characteristic	PLB	PB
speed	fast	faster
capacity	low	good
packing procedure	easy	difficult
instrument demands	moderate	high
applicability	simple separations	demanding separations

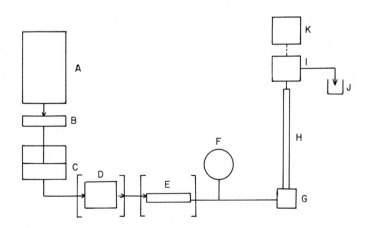

Figure 2. Block diagram of a liquid chromatograph. A, solvent reservoir; B, filter; C, pump; D, pulse dampener (optional); E, pre-column (used only in liquid–liquid chromatography); F, pressure gauge; G, injector; H, column; I, detector; J, fraction collector; K, recorder or other readout device.

pneumatic amplifier pump, in which gas pressure is amplified to
higher liquid pressures by the use of pistons of different
areas. This pump is nonpulsating and is capable of reasonably
high flow rates which can be important in preparative scale LC.
     The syringe type pump consists of mechanically driven
piston emptying a large volume chamber ($\sim$ 250 ml). In some
variations, two large piston chambers are used so that as one
empties the other fills. These pumps tend to maintain fairly
constant flow rate and are pulseless. However, solvent changeover is not rapid and can be wasteful of solvent. While quite
satisfactory, these pumps tend to be expensive.
     Finally, the dual reciporcating piston pumps consist of
two small volume chambers ($\sim$ 0.1-0.4 ml) that alternately
empty and fill. The two pistons travel in a phase and variable
speed relationship such that pulsations are minimized. Moreover, pressure or flow detection downstream is part of a feed-
back loop to maintain flow constant by variation in the speed
of the piston movements. These pumps allow easy changeover of
solvents and simple variation in mobile phase flow rate. Other
pumping systems can be found in the articles that have been
referenced.
     The next device is a pulsation dampener which is placed in
brackets in Figure 2 to indicate that its inclusion will be a
function of whether the pump produces pulsations and whether
the detector senses these pulsations as noise. The pulsation
dampener could simply consist of a coil of tubing or a pressure
gauge Bourdon tube. Following this device is a forecolumn which
is again placed in brackets since it is only used in the case of
liquid-liquid chromatography. The forecolumn consists of a
short column of large particle packing heavily loaded with the
stationary liquid phase. The forecolumn thus provides pro-
tection that the mobile phase is preequilibrated with the stationary phase before entering the column. If not, then bleeding
of stationary phase from the column can take place with the
ensuing change in retention. The next component, a pressure
gauge, is typically inserted into the system in order to determine the pressure drop in the column.
     The injection device is also an important component in the
LC system and has been discussed elsewhere (2,18). One type
of injector is analogous to sample delivery in gas chromatography, namely syringe injection through a self-sealing
septum. While this injection procedure can lead to good
column efficiency, it generally is pressure limited, and the
septum material can be attacked by the mobile phase solvent.
For higher pressures, stopped flow injection has been used in
which a valve releases the pressure in the column to atmosphere,
at which point syringe injection at the top of the column (without septum) takes place. There has, however, been a trend in
recent years to use valve injectors because of their generally
high pressure capabilities and their ability to deliver large

volumes of sample (in excess of 100 μl) rapidly to the column.
In clinical chemistry, the selection of valve-loop injectors
makes further sense, since the reproducibility of sample volume
is higher than can be obtained with a syringe, and automatic
injection is possible.

The final component to be discussed is the detection device of which much has already been written (2,21,22). Table
3 lists the most popular detectors at the present time with
an indication of the detection limits obtainable for favorable
substances.

By far, the most frequently used device is the ultraviolet
detector. Three types are employed (23) -- single wavelength
with low pressure mercury source, multiwavelength filter photomer
with medium pressure mercury source, and spectrophotometer.
In all cases, low volume detector cells (~ 8 μl) are employed
in order to limit extra band broadening.

In the single wavelength detector, 254 nm and 280 nm are
strong lines from the mercury source and hence, are selected
in most commercial instruments. Of the three types of U.V.
detectors, this one gives the lowest noise level (down to
0.00002 O.D.), but, of course, some flexibility is lost in not
being able to work at other wavelengths. Nevertheless, when
one purchases an instrument, this is the first detector selected.

The filter photometer provides the ability to detect at
wavelengths above 280 nm and, indeed into the visible region.
However its noise level in 2-5 times higher than the single
wavelength low pressure mercury source. Finally, the major
advantage that the spectrophotometer provides is the capability to detect in the 200-250 nm region. Substances that are
not ordinarily considered to be U.V. active (e.g., alkyl
bromides) can be analyzed with this detector. The noise level
with this detector is 5-20 times larger than with the single
wavelength device. Examples of the usefulness of the three
detectors can be found in the references (21,22).

The second most widely used detector in HPLC is the differential refractometer (RI). Being a bulk property detector,
the RI responds to all substances. As noted in Table 3 the
detection limits are several orders of magnitude higher than
obtained with the UV detector. Thus, one turns to the RI detector in those cases in which substances are non-UV active,
e.g. lipids, prostaglandins. In addition, the RI detector
finds use in preparative scale operation. Finally, relative
to the UV detector, the RI is significantly more temperature
and flow sensitive and cannot be used in gradient elution.

In some respects, the detector comparable to the RI is the
moving wire system. Here, the solution eluting from the column
drips on to a wire, with roughly 3% remaining on the wire.
The wire transports the deposited material to an oven where
the mobile phase is removed by evaporation. Further transport

brings the deposited sample to a combustion chamber where the substance is brought into the vapor state and reduced to methane. The methane is finally swept into a flame ionization detector for final analysis. As can be seen in Table III, the detection levels are roughly equivalent to the RI detector, both detectors responding to concentration. The moving wire detector finds value in the analysis of non-UV active substances in which gradient elution must be employed. However, the moving wire detector has not found great acceptance in the U.S., undoubtedly because of its sophisticated operation and high price.

Fluorescence detection is becoming more popular, especially in the analysis of biochemical substances. In favorable cases, detection levels as low if not lower than the UV detector can be achieved. Of course, it must be recognized that some solvents can strongly influence the detection limits through such processes as quenching. The key advantage of fluorescence, however, is in its high selectivity. Another aspect of fluorescence detection is the use of fluorescent derivatives to enhance selectivity and detection levels. A good example of this is the use of fluorescamine with primary amines such as amino acids, peptides, catecholamines, etc. (24).

The final detector to be discussed is based on electrochemical processes. The use of a polarographic detector has been well documented in the literature (25). More recently, advanced electrochemical systems have been selected for detection at trace levels (26). In essence, the redox reaction is performed in thin layers between the electrodes, and thus, essentially all material is electrolyzed to produce high current efficiencies. In the right set of circumstances the detector is outstanding; for example, it can be used to analyze picogram levels of catecholamines. The detector, however, is not a general one as the potential at which, for example, oxidation occurs must be relatively low in order that many other substances will not be oxidized. In addition, electrode surfaces can be altered during operation which can markedly affect reproducibility. Nevertheless, much interest exists with this detector and its future is certainly bright.

Analytical Capability

Successful use of modern liquid chromatography in the clinical laboratory requires an appreciation of the method's analytical characteristics. The quantitative reproducibility with respect to peak height or peak area is quite good. With a sample loop injector relative standard deviations better than 1% are to be expected. The variability of syringe injection (3-4% relative standard deviation) requires the use of an internal standard to reach the 1% level (2,27).

TABLE III

Detectors for HPLC

Detector	Lowest Detection Levels*, gm/ml
UV	5×10^{-10}
RI	5×10^{-7}
Moving Wire	5×10^{-7}
Fluorescence	5×10^{-10}
Electrochemical	$\sim 10^{-10}$

*A function of sample type in most cases

The precision in retention from injection to injection
will often be better than 1%. Over longer periods of time
such precision requires the following (a) good flow control
from the pump (b) constant mobile and stationary phases and
(c) temperature control of the column. The critical question
of reproducibility from column to column is still a matter of
concern, especially when dealing with the more sophisticated
packing materials, e.g. small porous particles, bonded phases.
While frequently this reproducibility is quite good, workers
should recognize that care must be exercised to achieve and/or
maintain reproducible columns. Undoubtedly, with experience,
this need not be a severe problem.

Finally, some comments on trace analysis are in order
(28,29). It needs to be recognized that large volumes of liquid
samples can be injected into the column. This is contrary to
gas chromatography in which a phase change (i.e. vaporization)
must occur upon injection. The large sample volumes mean that
column dilution in liquid chromatography can be significantly
lower than gas chromatography. In the right set of circumstances subnanogram detection levels can be achieved. Of
course, the type of detector also plays an important role, as
well as the use of specific derivatives to enhance detection
(30).

Applications

A number of applications of modern LC of relevance to
clinical chemistry have appeared in the literature. It is
obviously not possible to mention all examples; rather, we
shall try to select applications which illustrate the efforts
to date.

One area of extensive development has been the use of
small particle ion exchange resins for the separation of complex biological mixtures. Originally studied by Paul Hamilton
(31), C.D. Scott and colleagues at Oak Ridge National Laboratory have extensively applied this methodology to the analysis
of constituents of urine (8). Using gradient elution in con-
junction with anion and cation exchange columns in series, a
large number of components can be detected from direct urine
injection. Most analyses involve U.V. detection; however, post
column reactions are sometimes employed, e.g. fluorescence detection of organic acids and other oxidizable substances from
Ce(IV) to Ce(III) (fluorescent) (32). At present over 120 U.V.
active substances and 18 carbohydrates (33) have been identified. Diseased states can be correlated with elevated levels
of certain components. A typical complex urine chromatogram
is shown in Figure 3. Note that this chromatogram is essentially obtained with no clean-up of the urine.

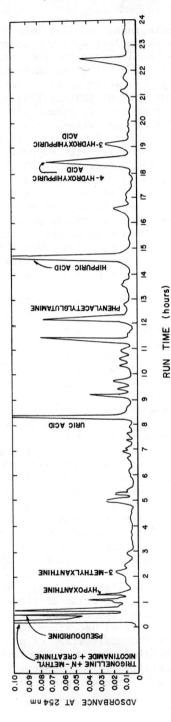

Figure 3. Typical chromatogram of UV-absorbing constituents of a 0.15-ml sample of urine. Conditions: 150-cm anion exchange column (12-15 μ, Aminex A-27); buffer concentration from 0.015M to 6M; gradient, buffer, acetate at pH 4.4; flow rate, 10.5 ml/hr, column temperature, 25°C for first 5 hr and 60°C thereafter (34).

Analytical Chemistry

Ion exchange chromatography has also been extensively applied to the analysis of nucleic acid components (3,14,35). A wide variety of bases, nucleosides and nucleotides have been separated using porous layer bead ion exchangers. A representative chromatogram of the separation of ribonucleoside monophosphoric acids from the work of Smukler (36) is shown in Figure 4. Recently, ion exchangers chemically bonded to small particle diameter (~10 µm) silica have been successfully applied to the separation of nucleic acid constitutents (37). The rapid separations using such supports undoubtedly mean that they will find increasing use in the future.

Adsorption chromatography using small particle silica or alumina has also been employed in the separation of biologically meaningful substances. Phospholipids, for example, have been separated on silica (38). One of the big problems for such substances is detection, since many of the compounds are not U.V. active. Generally, the refractive index detector is employed for isocratic operation, and the moving wire detector for gradient operation. Formation of U.V.-active derivatives is also possible (39).

Another example of the use of small particle silica is in the analysis of theophylline in plasma, as shown in Figure 5 (40). The clean-up procedure is simply a single extraction of the plasma with an organic solvent. This analysis has also been achieved by reverse phase chromatography (41), and this points out the fact that in some separations (e.g. with components of moderate polarity) either the adsorption or reverse phase mode can be used.

Reverse phase chromatography is finding increasing use in modern LC. For example, steroids (42) and fat soluble vitamins (43) are appropriately separated by this mode. Reverse phase with a chemically bonded stationary phase is popular because mobile phase conditions can be quickly found which produce reasonable retention. (In reverse phase LC the mobile phase is typically a water-organic solvent mixture.) Rapid solvent changeover also allows easy operation in gradient elution. Many examples of reverse phase separations can be found in the literature of the various instrument companies.

While most of the high speed-high pressure LC work to date has been with small molecules, i.e. MW < 1000, it is clear that the high performance techniques will play a role in the chromatographic separation of higher molecular weight species, e.g. proteins. While the LC separation of biopolymers is well established (11), many of the supports currently in use are unable to withstand the pressures necessary for high performance. We can anticipate the application of porous layer bead and especially small particle supports, capable of withstanding pressure, to the separation of biopolymers in the near future. Such materials will have an impact on clinical analysis.

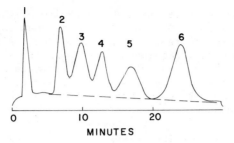

Journal of Chromatographic Science

Figure 4. Separation of ribonucleoside monophosphoric acids. Conditions: 250-cm anion exchange column; gradient, 0.01M KH_2PO_4 containing H_3PO_4 (pH 2.6) to 0.15M KH_2PO_4 in 30 min; column temperature, 70°C; detector, UV at 254 nm. 1, cytidine-5'-monophosphoric acid; 2, uridine-5'-monophosphoric acid; 3, adenosine-5'-monophosphoric acid; 4, inosine-5'-monophosphoric acid; 5, 3',5'-cyclic adenosine monophosphoric acid; 6, guanosine-5'-monophosphoric acid (36).

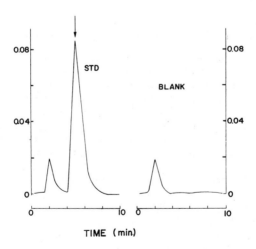

Clinical Chemistry

Figure 5. Chromatograms for theophylline in plasma extracts. Arrow indicates theophylline peak. Conditions: 50 cm × 3 mm (i.d.) column with 10 μm silica gel (Micropak Si 10; Varian); mobile phase, 84/15/1 chloroform/isopropanol/acetic acid; flow rate, 40 ml/hr; detector, UV, 273 nm (40).

As an example, consider the separation of the creatine
kinase isoenzymes, MM, MB, and BB. Mercer has used classical
ion-exchange chromatography (DEAE - Sephadex - A50) for the
resolution of these three isoenzymes (44). To speed up the
separation and ultimately to allow an automated analysis,
Toren has used porous layer bead ion exchangers (45). Separation of the MM and BB isoenzymes was achieved in less than
10 min, as seen in Figure 6. Interestingly, the MB isoenzyme
was strongly retained on the support (presumably through adsorption on exposed silanol groups). Through better chemical
bonding technology, however, it is possible to substantially
reduce the activity of the silica surface (46). Such chemically bonded phase systems for exclusion and ion exchange
chromatography will prove to be quite useful.

It is useful to conclude with several examples from our
laboratory. We have applied the procedure of ion pair partition chromatography to the separation of biochemically important mixtures (47,48). In this method of liquid-liquid partition, the basic distribution process can be written as

$$(A,B)_o \rightleftharpoons A^+_{aq} + B^-_{aq}$$

where $(A,B)_o$ is the ion pair in the organic phase and A^+_{aq} and
B^-_{aq} are oppositely charged ions in the aqueous phase. In a
typical experiment, e.g. the separation of amines, the stationary phase would consist of an acidified aqueous solution containing a high concentration ($\sim$ 0.1M - 1M) of counterion,
e.g. ClO_4^-. This phase would be coated on small particle
($\sim$ 5 - 10 μ) porous silica. The mobile phase would consist
of an immiscible organic solvent mixture, e.g. butanol/heptane.

Because a chemical step is imposed on top of the physical
distribution process of partition, there is a great potential
for selectivity, as noted by Schill et al. (49,50). Such
factors as pH, type and composition of the organic phase, and
ionic strength of the aqueous phase can be used to control
relative retention. The concentration and type of counterion
mainly control the absolute retention.

Taking advantage of the high performance conditions of the
silica columns, we have separated a variety of mixtures including thyroid hormones, sulfa drugs and catecholamines. Figure
7 shows the rapid separation of eight catecholamines using
perchlorate as counterion and the organic phase listed in the
figure. It is to be noted that reverse phase ion pair partition using C_{18} chemically bonded phases and an aqueous mobile
mobile phase can also be successfully employed (51). The ion

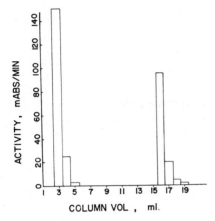

ACTIVITY, mABS/MIN

COLUMN VOL , ml.

Clinical Chemistry

Figure 6. High pressure liquid chromatogram of creatine kinase isoenzymes. First peak, MM; second peak, BB. Conditions: 50 cm × 4.6 mm (i.d.) column with "Vydac" porous layer bead anion exchange; mobile phase, step gradient; Solvent A, 10 mmol/liter Tris buffer, pH 8.3; solvent B, 10 mmol/liter Tris buffer, pH 7.0, 0.5 mol KCl; flow rate, 2 ml/min; detection, collected fractions assayed (45).

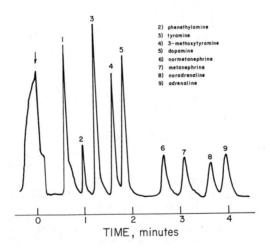

2) phenethylamine
3) tyramine
4) 3-methoxytyramine
5) dopamine
6) normetanephrine
7) metanephrine
8) noradrenaline
9) adrenaline

TIME, minutes

Journal of Chromatographic Science

Figure 7. Separation of eight biogenic amines using ion pair partition liquid chromatography. Conditions: 30 cm column with 4 μm silica; stationary phase, 0.1M $HClO_4$/0.9M $NaClO_4$; mobile phase, ethylacetate/tributyl phosphate/hexane (72.5/10/17.5); velocity, 0.8 cm/sec (47).

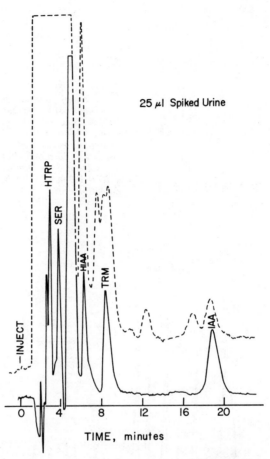

Figure 8. Chromatograms of ultraviolet (····) and fluorescence (——) response of deproteinized urine doped with 0.4 μmoles of standard indoles. Conditions: 30-cm column; stationary phase, μ Bondapak C_{18}; mobile phase, 10/90 methanol in 0.01M NaAc, pH = 4.6; flow rate, 2.5 ml/min. HTRP,5-hydroxytryptophan; SER, serine; HIAA, 5-hydroxyindole acetic acid; TRM, tryptamine; IAA, indoleacetic acid (52).

pair method should prove of value in the clinical laboratory.
A second example from our work involves the analysis of
indole compounds in urine using high performance reverse phase
liquid chromatography with fluorescence detection (52). By
control of pH and methanol composition the separation of a
series of standard indole derivatives was achieved. The selective detection afforded by fluorescence permitted a very simple
clean-up of the urine sample. The urinary proteins are first
precipitated from a 10 ml urine sample. Using a spiked sample
of ∿ 1 nanomole each, 25 µl of urine after precipitation is
injected directly into the liquid chromatograph and the resulting chromatogram is shown in Figure 8. The dotted line represents the UV detection which, as can be seen, contains a large
number of components that prevent analysis of the components
of interest. On the other hand, five indoles can be easily
detected and the three chemically important 5-hydroxindoles
can be analyzed in less than eight minutes. Detection limits
are ∿ 5 nanogram using a filter fluorimeter, a level more
than adequate for diseased states.

Conclusion

This introduction to modern liquid chromatography should
suggest some of the roles LC might play in clinical analysis.
An area worthy of study is the development of systems of increasing sample throughput beyond the single column operation.
Scott has introduced a prototype multicolumn system based on
the centrifugal analyzer principle (53). In this set-up a
series of LC columns is rotated on a disc, with sample delivery
at the center of the disc and elution and spectrophotometric
analysis on the outside. He has suggested using affinity columns for rapid serum protein analysis by this approach. Of
course, other principles, such as segmented flow, could be
envisioned in an automated LC system as well. Undoubtedly, we
can expect to see the availability of such systems in the next
few years.

Literature Cited

1. Kirkland, J. J., ed.; "Modern Practice of Liquid Chromatography", John Wiley & Sons, New York, 1971.
2. Snyder, L.R.; and Kirkland, J.J.; "Introduction to Modern
Liquid Chromatography", Interscience, New York, 1974.
3. Brown, P.R.; "High Pressure Liquid Chromatography,
Biochemical and Biomedical Applications", Academic Press,
New York, 1973.
4. Hadden, N., et al.; "Basic Liquid Chromatography", Varian
Aerograph, Walnut Creek, California, 1972.

5. Done, J. N.; Knox, J. H.; and Loheac, J.; "Applications
    of High-Speed Liquid Chromatography", John Wiley and
    Sons, New York, 1974.
6. Michaelis, A. F.; Cornish, D. W.; and Vivilecchia, R;
    J. Pharm. Sci. (1973), 62, 1399.
7. Snyder, L. R.; "Principles of Adsorption Chromatography",
    Marcel Dekker, New York, 1968.
8. Scott, C. D.; Science (1974), 186, 226.
9. Snyder, L. R.; and Kirkland, J. J.; Chapter 7, op cit.
10. Pryde, A.; J. Chromatog. Sci. (1974), 12, 486.
11. Determann, H.; "Gel Chromatography", Springer-Verlag,
    New York, 1968.
12. Lowe, C.R.; and Dean, P. D. G.; "Affinity Chromatography",
    John Wiley and Sons, New York, 1974.
13. Karger, B. L.; "Modern Practice of Liquid Chromatography",
    Kirkland, J. J., ed.; John Wiley and Sons, New York, 1971.
14. Horvath, C.; Preiss, B.; and Lipsky, S. R.; Anal. Chem.
    (1967), 39, 1422.
15. Kirkland, J. J.; J. Chromatog. Sci. (1969), 7, 7.
16. Majors, R. E.; Anal. Chem. (1972), 44, 1822.
17. Rabel, F. M.; American Laboratory (May, 1974), 7, 53.
18. Berry, L. V.; and Karger, B. L.; Anal. Chem. (1973),
    45, 819A.
19. Bombaugh, K. J.; Amer. Lab. (1973), 5, 69.
20. Jackson, M. T.; and Henry, R. A.; Amer. Lab. (1974),
    October.
21. Veening, H.; J. Chem. Ed. (1970), 47, A-675.
22. Schomberg, G.; Z. Anal. Chem. (1975), 277, 275.
23. Baker, P. R.; Williams, R. C.; and Steichen, Y. C.;
    J. Chromatog. Sci. (1974), 12, 499.
24. Udenfriend, S.; Stein, S.; Bohlen, P.; Dairman, W.;
    Leimgruber, W.; and Weigele, M.; Science (1972), 178,
    871.
25. Koen, J. G.; Huber, J. F. K.; Poppe, H.; and
    du Boef, G.; J. Chromatog. Sci. (1970), 8, 192.
26. Kissinger, P. T.; Felice, L. J.; Riggin, R. M.;
    Pachla, L. A.; and Wenke, D. C.; Clin. Chem. (1974),
    20, 992.
27. Barth, H.; Dallmeier, E.; Courtois, G.; Keller, H. E.;
    and Karger, B. L.; J. Chromatog. (1973), 83, 289.
28. Kirkland, J. J.; Analyst (1974), 99, 859.
29. Karger, B. L.; Martin, M.; and Guiochon, G.; Anal. Chem.
    (1974), 46, 1640.
30. Frei, R. W.; and Santi, W.; Z. Anal. Chem. (1975),
    277, 303.
31. Hamilton, P.B.; "Handbook of Biochemistry, Selected Data
    for Molecular Biology", Sober, H. A. Ed.; Chemical Rubber
    Co., Cleveland, 1968, p.B43.
32. Katz, S.; and Pitt, W.W.; Anal. Lett. (1972), 5, 177.
33. Pitt, W. W.; Scott, C. D.; Johnson, W. F.; and Jones, G.;

Clin. Chem. (1970), 16, 657.
34. Scott, C. D.; Chilcote, D. D.; and Lee, N.E.; Anal. Chem. (1972), 44, 85.
35. Burtis, C. A.; and Gere, D. R.; "Nucleic Acid Constituents by Liquid Chromatography", Varian Aerograph, California, 1970.
36. Shmukler, H. W.; J. Chromatog. Sci. (1972), 10, 137.
37. Hartwick. R. A.; and Brown, P. R.; J. Chromatog. (1975), 112, 651.
38. Aitzetmuller, K.; Chromatog. Rev. (1975), 113, 231.
39. Jungalwala, F. B.; Turel, R. J.; Evans, J. E.; and McCluer, R.H.; Biochem. J. (1975), 145, 517.
40. Sitar, D. S.; Piafoky, K. M.; Rangno, R.E.; and Ogilvie, R.I.; Clin, Chem. (1974), 99, 35.
41. Manion, C. V.; Shoeman, D. W.; and Azarnoff, D. L.; J. Chromatog. (1974), 101, 169.
42. Fitzpatrick, F. A.; Siggia, S.; and Dingman, J. Sr.; Anal. Chem. (1972), 44, 2211.
43. Williams, R. C.; Schmidt, J. A.; and Henry, R. A.; J. Chromatog. Sci. (1972), 10, 494.
44. Mercer, D.W.; Clin. Chem. (1974), 20, 36.
45. Kudirka, P. J.; Busby, M. G.; Carey, R. N.; and Toren, E. C. Jr.; Clin. Chem. (1975), 21, 250.
46. Regnier, F.; Purdue University, unpublished results.
47. Persson, B. A.; and Karger, B. L.; J. Chromatog. Sci. (1974), 12, 521.
48. Karger, B. L.; Su, S.; Marchese, S.; and Persson, B. A.; J. Chromatog. Sci. (1974), 12, 678.
49. Eksborg, S.; and Schill, G.; Anal. Chem. (1973), 45, 2092.
50. Schill, G.; "Advances in Ion Exchange and Solvent Extraction, Vol. 6", Marinsky, J. A.; and Marcus, Y., eds.; Marcel Dekker, 1974.
51. Knox, J.; and Jurand, J.; J. Chromatog. (1975), 110, 103.
52. Graffeo, A.P.; and Karger, B.L.; Clin Chem. (1976), 22, 184.
53. Scott, C. D.; Pitt, W. W.; and Johnson, W. F.; J. Chromatog. (1974), 99, 35.

The author greatly acknowledges NIH for support of this work. Contribution #7 from the Institute of Chemical Analysis, Applications and Forensic Science.

9

Electrothermal Atomic Absorption Spectrometry of Trace Metals in Biological Fluids

F. WILLIAM SUNDERMAN, JR.

Department of Laboratory Medicine, University of Connecticut School of Medicine, Farmington, Conn. 06032

As a consequence of the recent increase of scientific knowledge regarding the metabolism, biochemical pathology and toxicology of trace metals, there has arisen widespread clinical interest in measurements of trace metals in body fluids, tissues and excreta (33,41,65,77). Laboratories in many university medical centers and governmental institutions have become involved in determinations of copper, zinc, lithium, gold, lead, cadmium, mercury, manganese, nickel and other metals in biological materials. Increasing attention has been focused upon clinical applications of electrothermal atomic absorption spectrometry, since this relatively new technique has appeared to provide the requisite analytical sensitivity, specificity and convenience (33,41,65,77). Regrettably, this technique is subject to pitfalls, interferences, and sources of imprecision that have hindered its clinical use. As will be discussed in this review, progressive refinements of electrothermal atomizers and of optical systems for background compensation have largely overcome these obstacles. It now appears probable that electrothermal atomic absorption spectrometry will be adopted by clinical chemistry laboratories as a routine method for measurements of trace metals in body fluids.

The scope of this review is limited to electrothermal atomic absorption spectrometry, with emphasis upon its clinical applications. This article is intended to supplement the recent treatises on the basic technique which have been written by Aggett and Sprott (1), Ingle (29), Kirkbright (34), Price (63), and Woodriff (83). This resume does not consider various related topics, such as (a) atomic fluorescence or emission spectrometry; (b) non-flame atomization devices which employ direct current

*Supported by Grant #AT(11-1)-3140 from the U.S. Energy Research & Development Agency and by Public Health Service Contract #HSM 99-72-24 from the National Institute of Occupational Safety & Health.

arcs, radio-frequency plasma jets, microwave excitation fields,
or demountable hollow-cathode sputtering cells; (c) relatively
low-temperature atomic absorption spectrometry of Hg vapor; or (d)
atomic absorption spectrometry of As and Se following volatiza-
tion by chemical reduction to their respective gaseous hydrides.

Electrothermal Atomizers

In 1961, L'vov (44) described the first electrothermal atomizer for atomic absorption analysis of trace metals. L'vov's
atomizer consisted of a graphite plug which fitted into a socket
in an electrically heated graphite tube. A liquid sample was
dried on the plug, which was then inserted into the tube. An
alternating current arc was used to discharge the sample into an
argon atmosphere within the graphite tube. Atomic recombination
was retarded by the high temperature and the inert gas, and
atomic absorption spectrometry of the atom cloud was performed by
an optical beam along the axis of the tube (44). Numerous ingenious variations of the electrothermal atomizer have been developed, including use of graphite tubes, rods and braided filaments
(2,3,8,12,22,42,50,51,52,54,55,56,81,83,84), as well as metallic
ribbons, cups and filaments constructed of tungsten, tantalum,
molybdenum or platinum (12,26,27,28,48,82). In this discussion,
attention is focused primarily upon the three designs of electrothermal atomizers that have been most widely used for analyses
of trace metals in biological materials.

Massmann (51,52) devised the graphite tube furnace which
has served as the prototype of commercial graphite furnaces that
have been manufactured by Perkin-Elmer Co. (50), Beckman Instruments Gmbh. (Germany), and Jarrell-Ash Division of Fisher
Scientific Co. A liquid sample with a volume from 5 to 50 µl is
introduced into a hollow graphite tube by means of a micropipet.
The graphite tube is heated electrically by electrode connections at both ends of the tube. The graphite tube assembly is
encased within a water-cooled jacket, and the cavity of the tube
is slowly flushed with an inert gas such as argon or nitrogen.
During each analysis, the temperature of the graphite tube is
increased in a stepwise fashion so that (a) the sample is dried
at 100-125°C, (b) the sample is pyrolyzed at 500-1200°C, so that
organic constituents are destroyed, and (c) the metals in the
sample are vaporized and atomized at 1500-3000°C. During this
programmed sequence, the slow stream of inert gas flows through
the cavity of the graphite tube, successively sweeping away (a)
the water or solvent vapors that are released during drying, (b)
the smoke and fumes that are generated during pyrolysis, and (c)
the atom cloud that is liberated during atomization. The light
path of the atomic absorption spectrometer traverses the length
of the graphite tube. During the atomization phase, atomic
absorption of the analyte in the atom cloud is measured by the
spectrometer and is recorded with a strip-chart recorder. The

peak atomic concentration, "N", (atoms/ml) in the cavity of the
graphite furnace is related to the analyte concentration, "C",
(mol/liter of solution injected into the graphite tube by a
micropipet) by the following equation: $N = 6 \times 10^{20}$ $VCeB/V_c$,
where V = volume of analyte (ml), e = vaporization efficiency,
B = atomization efficiency, and V_c = volume of the cavity of the
graphite tube (ml), provided that the analyte diffuses slowly
out of the cavity (26).

West and Williams (81) and Amos *et al* (2) have employed an
alternative design for an electrothermal atomizer, which has
served as the prototype of the graphite rod atomizers manufactured by Varian-Techtron Pty, Ltd. (53). The sample (0.5 to
5 µl) is dried within a small cavity located at the mid-length
of a thin graphite rod, which is supported between two electrodes. The graphite rod is unenclosed, but is protected by a
laminar stream of an inert gas such as argon or nitrogen.
Optionally, the upward current of inert gas may be encircled by
a concentric laminar stream of hydrogen. The elevated temperature of the heated graphite rod ignites the hydrogen, which
forms a barrier that (a) entrains atmospheric oxygen, hindering
oxidation of the atom cloud, and (b) assists in the reduction of
metallic oxides to free metal atoms (64). During a brief atomization phase, the sample is suddenly vaporized, and the atom
cloud is measured by its attenuation of a transverse optical
beam that passes through an aperture at right angles to the
length of the graphite rod. This simple, economical design has
the apparent disadvantages of relatively limited sample volume
and relatively short path-length of light in the atom cloud.
However, Amos *et al* (2) have found that this atomizer provides
analytical sensitivity that rivals that obtained with Massmann's
graphite tube furnace.

A third design concept for an electrothermal atomizer uses
a metallic or graphite boat, as described by Donega and Burgess
(12). This configuration has been adapted by Hwang *et al* (26,
27,28) in the form of the tantalum ribbon atomizers which are
manufactured by Instrumentation Laboratories, Inc. and by
Jarrell-Ash Division of Fisher Scientific Co. The apparatus (26)
consists of a thin tantalum strip that is shaped to serve as a
combination sample boat and heating element. The ends of the
tantalum strip are clamped onto the tops of two electrodes, and
the assembly is enclosed within an argon-purged chamber. The
optical beam traverses quartz windows at the sides of the argon-
purged chamber, and passes immediately over the sample cavity in
the tantalum strip. A hinged door at the front of the chamber
permits access for introduction of the sample. By use of different tantalum strips with sample cavities of various sizes,
the atomizer can accomodate sample volumes from 1 to 100 µl.
When it is necessary to use atomization temperatures in the range
from 2500 to 3000°C, a graphite cuvet can be substituted for the
tantalum strip.

Torsi and Tessari (78) studied the influence of heating rate upon analytical sensitivities in electrothermal atomic absorption. They observed that in the graphite tube furnace the residence time of the atom cloud in the optical path is relatively long (5 to 20 sec), compared to the transitory burst of atoms (*ca* 0.5 sec) which occurs during the sudden heating of the graphite rod atomizer. The residence time of the atom cloud in the lightpath of the tantalum ribbon atomizer is presumably intermediate between that achieved with the other two basic designs.

Inert Atmospheres for Electrothermal Atomization
==

According to Reeves *et al* (64), the inert atmosphere of the electrothermal atomizer serves the dual purposes of (a) protecting the graphite tube or rod against oxidation, and (b) retarding the degradation of analyte atoms in the atom cloud by recombination (*e.g.* with O_2). From theoretical viewpoints, argon is the most suitable inert gas for these purposes. Thus, Maessen and Posma (46) showed that the diffusion coefficients of gold atoms in nitrogen and argon atmospheres are, respectively, one-fourth and one-fifth of that observed in a helium atmosphere. Hwang *et al* (26) reported that the specific heat of argon is lower than that of nitrogen and helium. Moreover, with use of nitrogen as the atmosphere, there is a possibility of forming a toxic gas, cyanogen, which has an absorption band in the ultraviolet spectrum. Despite these theoretical advantages of argon, many analysts prefer to employ nitrogen, which is less expensive than argon. Cruz and van Loon (10) discounted the possibility of generating cyanogen from nitrogen at 3000°C, and stated that cyanogen formation requires a higher temperature (*ca* 5000°C). From a practical viewpoint, there appears to be little difference between the use of argon and nitrogen atmospheres for most biological applications of electrothermal atomic absorption spectrometry. For greatest analytical sensitivity, the flow-rate of the inert gas should be adjusted to the minimum that is necessary to sweep away smoke and other interfering vapors, in order that the atom cloud be subjected to the least possible dilution (3). With some graphite tube atomizers, the flow of inert gas can be interrupted during the atomization cycle of the programmed sequence of changes in furnace temperature.

Characteristics of Graphite Tubes
==

After a brief period of use, the graphite tubes and rods that are commonly employed in electrothermal atomizers begin to deteriorate, and their electrical characteristics become subject to drift (7,9,47). This is one of the most troublesome sources of analytical variability. Maessen *et al* (47) demonstrated that the properties of graphite (*e.g.* porosity and conductivity)

change appreciably during heating. Alteration of the electrical
conductivity brings about changes in the rate of heating as well
as in the ultimate temperature. Changes of porosity of graphite
affect the deposition of liquid samples and also influence the
diffusion rate of sample vapors into the graphite. Substitution
of pyrolytic graphite for standard graphite has been an important
innovation in electrothermal atomic absorption spectrometry.
According to Aspila *et al* (3), pyrolytic graphite has the following advantages over standard graphite: (a) lower permeability
to liquids and gases; (b) higher thermal conductivity; (c) higher
resistance to oxidation; and (d) higher sublimation point (*ca*
3700°C). Clyburn *et al* (9) has introduced a simple technique
for depositing a layer of pyrolytic graphite upon the surfaces
of graphite heating elements. A mixture of methane and inert
gas (argon or nitrogen) is introduced into the graphite atomizer
system during operation at a temperature in excess of 2000°C.
The layer of pyrolytic graphite which is thus generated is
extremely dense, non-porous and resistant to oxidation. According to Clyburn *et al* (9) this treatment extends the effective
lifetime of the graphite elements and improves analytical precision.

Temperature Calibration and Regulation

Electrothermal apparatuses for atomic absorption spectrometry
are currently sold by most instrument manufacturers with "factory
calibrations" of temperature scales. These temperature calibrations may be grossly inaccurate under the conditions which
actually exist in analytical laboratories, owing to (a) local
variations in electrical current, (b) fluctuations in pressure
and temperature of coolant water, (c) variations in electrical
resistance of batches of graphite tubes and rods or metallic
ribbons or boats, and (d) changes in thermal response which
occur during repeated heating of atomization devices. Findlay
et al (18) observed that temperatures within a graphite furnace
were substantially lower than were indicated by the manufacturer's calibration, and that large temperature variations
occurred within the furnace, both axially and radially. Lundgren
et al (43) reported similar findings, and concluded that factory
calibrations cannot be relied upon for estimation of atomization
temperatures. Based upon the findings of Findlay *et al* (18) and
Lundgren *et al* (43), temperature calibrations should be verified
in each laboratory by use of a thermocouple, an optical pyro-
meter, and/or by observations of the melting and boiling points
of reference materials.

Inadequate regulation of atomizer temperature is a major
source of imprecision in electrothermal atomic absorption spectrometry. The programmed heating of electrothermal atomizers
can be achieved by five different methods, depending upon the
electrical or physical parameters which are monitoried during

the heating steps (55). The first and most common method is (a)
to utilize a two- or three-stage electrical current program for
heating the atomizer. Montaser and Crouch (55) noted that programmed heating can also be accomplished by monitoring and controlling (b) the voltage across the atomizer, (c) the power
dissipated by the atomizer, (d) the infrared radiation emitted
by the atomizer, and (e) the actual atomizer temperature, as
measured by a thermocouple. Montaser and Crouch (55) found that
thermal control by the radiation monitoring method is the most
satisfactory means of achieving stable plateaus of temperature.
They showed that the infrared radiation which is emitted by the
atomizer is directly related to the atomizer temperature, and
that a radiation feed-back control system can effectively compensate for changes in atomizer properties and other fluctuations
which influence the temperature produced by electrothermal systems. Similarly, Lundgren and Johansson (42) described a graphite tube furnace in which a photodiode detector for infrared
radiation is used as feed-back input for the temperature control-
ler. They demonstrated that it is feasible to keep the atomizer
temperature constant within $\pm$ 10°C (42,43). Such improved
methods for temperature regulation should soon be adopted by
instrument manufacturers, and will undoubtedly improve the
accuracy of trace metal analyses.

During analyses of protein-containing biological materials,
steadily progressive increases of temperature may be essential
during the drying and ashing steps, in order to avoid foaming of
the sample or sudden discharge of particles of ash, with attendant loss of analyte. Such gradual increments in temperature
(*i.e.* a "ramp-mode") have been recommended by Fuchs *et al* (20)
for analysis of serum aluminum, by Grafflage *et al* (23) for
analyses of serum chromium and manganese, and by Pekarek *et al*
(61) for analysis of serum chromium. The "ramp-mode" for drying
and ashing has also proven to be necessary for measurements of
serum nickel, using a direct electrothermal technique which has
recently been developed in the author's laboratory. The "ramp-
mode" can be achieved by careful manual adjustments of the
atomizer controls, but this procedure is tedious and imprecise.
Therefore, instruments which provide a "ramp-mode" for programmed increase of temperature during the drying and ashing cycles
are advantageous for biological applications. The Perkin-Elmer
Co. has recently introduced a "ramp-mode" accessory for their
Model HGA 2100 graphite tube furnace. It is desirable that a
sudden increase in temperature occur at the end of the ashing
cycle, in order to reach the high-temperature plateau of the
atomization cycle. This abrupt increase in temperature is
necessary in order to achieve optimal analytical sensitivity (78).
A brief (5 to 10 sec) "after-burn" cycle at the upper thermal
limit of the atomizer is oftimes necessary during analyses of
biological materials, in order (a) to minimize the accumulation
of ash, and (b) to prevent the "memory" effects which are

discussed later in this review. Unfortunately, the "after-burn" cycle shortens the lifetime of the heating elements.

Sampling and Contamination Problems

Micro-pipetting instruments such as the "Eppendorf" or "Oxford" pipettors with disposable plastic cone tips are customarily employed to dispense the liquid samples into electrothermal atomizers. Sampling problems which are associated with the use of these pipettors are among the troublesome aspects of electrothermal atomic absorption spectrometry (67,75). The plastic cone-tips are frequently contaminated with metals, and they should invariably be cleaned before use by soaking in dilute "ultra pure" nitric acid, followed by multiple rinses with demineralized water which has been distilled in a quartz still. Each cone-tip should be then prepared by repeatedly pipetting and discarding the specimen which is to be analyzed. Particular care must be exercised to avoid contamination of the cone-tip by allowing it to touch any portion of the graphite tube or rod or of the metallic boat. The delivery of the sample into the atomizer must be done meticulously in order to avoid irregular splattering of droplets within the sample cavity (67). After repeated use, the porosity of graphite tubes becomes variable at different locations within the sample cavity. Hence, failure to deposit successive samples at the identical site can be a source of variability in analytical results. Measurements of trace metals in body fluids should invariably be performed in duplicate or triplicate, in order to minimize imprecision and to detect sporadic contamination. The tedious attention that must be directed to manual sampling makes electrothermal analysis unacceptable to some technologists in clinical chemistry laboratories. For this reason it would be desirable to employ automatic sampling devices such as are used in automated systems for gas chromatography. An automatic sampler for electrothermal atomic absorption spectrometry has recently been designed by Maessen *et al* (47), and may be a harbinger of commercial developments in this field. Techniques for sampling of solid materials for electrothermal atomic absorption spectrometry have been described by Barnett and Kahn (4) and by Lundgren and Johansson (42), and a method for continuous sample introduction into an electrothermal atomizer has been introduced by Kantor *et al* (38). Perhaps the most promising device for automation of electrothermal atomic absorption is the "graphite yarn thermal atomizer" that has been developed by Applied Research Laboratories Division of Bausch and Lomb Co. Graphite yarn is dispensed from a spool and is automatically unreeled through (a) a sampling chamber where the sample is pipetted onto the yarn, and (b) an electric furnace for desolvation and vaporization.

Sweat from the fingers and palms of the hands is rich in trace metals (25) and is a common source of contamination in trace metal analysis. The graphite tubes, tantalum ribbons, plastic cone-tips and other components of electrothermal atomization systems should not be handled without use of plastic forceps or disposable plastic gloves. In electrothermal analyses of biological materials, it is necessary to remove the carbon ash from the sample cavity after almost every analysis. The lens paper which is customarily used for this purpose should be handled only with forceps or gloves in order to minimize contamination from sweat. In the design of electrothermal atomizers, it would be desirable to include an automatic system for ash removal, (such as vigorous flushing of the sample cavity with a jet of inert gas).

Methods for Standardization and Computation

Aqueous standard solutions are a source of certain difficulties in electrothermal atomic absorption spectrometry of trace metals in biological fluids. The viscosities and surface tensions of aqueous standard solutions are substantially less than the viscosities and surface tensions of serum, blood and other protein-containing fluids. These factors introduce volumetric disparities in pipetting of standard solutions and body fluids, and also cause differences in penetration of these liquids into porous graphite tubes or rods. Preliminary treatment of porous graphite with xylene may help to minimize the differences of liquid penetration (53,67). A more satisfactory solution of this problem is preparation of standards in aqueous solutions of metal-free dextran (50-60 g/liter), as first proposed by Pekarek *et al* (61) for the standardization of serum chromium analyses. This practice has been used successfully by the present author for standardization of analyses of serum nickel. The standard solutions which are prepared in aqueous dextran resemble serum in regard to viscosity and surface tension. Introduction of dextran-containing standard solutions is an important contribution to electrothermal atomic absorption analysis of trace metals in body fluids.

The "method of standard additions" has been employed as a technique for standardization of atomic absorption analyses of metals in biological fluids (13,21). In this procedure, several concentrations of standard analyte are added to samples of the biological fluid to be analyzed. The calibration curve which is obtained after additions of the standard analyte to the biological fluid should parallel that obtained when aqueous standards are analyzed. Extrapolation of the standard additions curve back to a negative intercept on the abscissa furnishes an estimate of the concentration of the analyte in the original sample (21). This technique is helpful in assessing the validity of methods of trace metal analysis (11,13,58). However, in the author's opinion, the "method of standard additions" is neither practical nor reliable as a routine method for standardization

of trace metal analyses in body fluids. Cruz and van Loon (10)
and Fuller (21) noted that non-linearity of the calibration
curves obtained by electrothermal atomic absorption spectrometry
limits the reliability of the "method of standard additions".
Moreover, the dilution of the sample which this technique entails
may mask matrix interferences.

Atomic absorption spectrometers with dual monochromators
are commercially available from Jarrell-Ash Division of Fisher
Scientific Co., and from Instrumentation Laboratories, Inc.
These instruments with dual wavelength monitoring capability
permit the use of "internal standards". In this technique, the
atomic absorption of the analyte is measured as a proportion of
the atomic absorption at a reference wavelength of a known
amount of another metal that has been added to the sample. This
arrangement can be very useful in compensating (a) for volumetric
differences in sampling, (b) for variations in atomizer temperature, and (c) to some extent for background compensation, as
discussed subsequently. However, care must be exercised in
selecting as the internal standard a metal with melting point,
vapor pressure, free energy of oxide dissociation, and resonance
wavelength which closely resemble those of the analyte (1).

Computations of the results of electrothermal atomic absorption analyses are usually based upon measurements of the peak
heights of the recorder tracings. This technique has the advantages of simplicity and convenience, but it may be responsible
for analytical errors. Maessen and Posma (46) showed that the
time-constant for response of the measurement system has a
critical influence upon the analytical signals. When they
employed a measurement and recording system with a time-constant
of 0.01 sec, undistorted signals were obtained by the strip-chart
recorder. In contrast, when the time-constant was 0.3 sec (such
as provided by common strip-chart recorders), highly distorted
signals were obtained, and the peak heights were reduced to
one-half or less of the undistorted peaks (46). Schramel (73)
concluded from a careful study of matrix effects upon the curve-
form of recorded absorption signals that the peak-height method
of computation is inaccurate and inadequate. Integration of the
output signal during the atomization phase furnishes a measure
of peak area, which leads to more accurate and more precise
analytical results. Schramel (73) emphasized that peak area
(not peak height) is the correct index of analyte atoms released
into the atomic cloud during electrothermal atomization. Sarbeck
and Landgraf (70) employed a mini-computer system for automated
integration of absorption signals which are detected during
electrothermal atomization of trace metals. Such a system is
marketed by Jarrell-Ash Division of Fisher Scientific Co.

Sources of Interference

In order to understand matrix interferences in electrother-

mal atomization, it is necessary to examine the mechanisms of
thermal vaporization of metals. Aggett and Sprott (1) showed
that some metals, such as silver, gold and copper vaporize at
temperatures that are considerably below their boiling points,
while other metals, such as calcium and magnesium, require temperatures in excess of their boiling points for vaporization.
From a penetrating study of the mechanisms of atomization, Aggett
and Sprott (1) inferred that the higher the temperature of vaporization of a metal relative to its boiling point, the greater is
the influence of the metallic oxide upon the atomization process.
The free energy levels that are required for the dissociation of
oxides of silver, gold and copper are negligible or very low, and
these oxides do not play a significant role in the atomization
process. On the other hand, the free energy levels that are
required for dissociation of calcium and magnesium are relatively
very high. Hence, the thermal dissociation of salts of calcium
and magnesium (and various other metals) involves intermediate
formation of metallic oxides prior to vaporization of the metal
atoms. When graphite is used as the electrothermal atomizer,
the graphite may reduce metallic oxides to the metals, with
attendant liberation of carbon monoxide. Aggett and Sprott (1)
found that the minimum temperatures for vaporization of Co, Fe,
Ni and Zn from a graphite rod were significantly lower than from
a tantalum filament, suggesting that these free metal atoms can
be liberated by chemical reduction of their respective oxides,
rather than by direct thermal dissociation. Findlay *et al* (19)
emphasized the hazards of preatomization losses of trace metals
in electrothermal atomic absorption spectrometry, when the ashing
temperature is permitted to exceed the minimum temperature for
vaporization of the analyte.

Interferences by matrix components in electrothermal atomic
absorption spectrometry have been categorized by Aggett and
Sprott (1) as either (a) "vapor phase", or (b) "surface phase".
Vapor-phase interference is usually attributed to condensation
of gaseous atoms in a manner so that analyte atoms are occluded
in clusters of condensing interferant atoms. Interfering metal
atoms tend to combine with traces of oxygen and to condense as
the oxides. Vapor phase interference can be identified by the
fact that the suppressive effect of the interferant upon the
atomic absorbance of the analyte increases as a function of
distance from the graphite or tantalum surface (1). Machata and
Binder (45) have shown that addition of lanthanum salts to biological fluids effectively suppresses certain vapor phase interferences in trace metal analysis. Surface-phase interference is
independent of the distance from the graphite or tantalum surface, and is attributed to changes in the thermal conductivity
of the graphite or tantalum which are induced by the matrix (1).
Surface phase interference results in broadening of the absorbance signal, and can be reduced by measurements of peak areas
rather than by peak heights (73). Moreover, surface-phase

interference can be minimized by use of the infrared radiation-monitoring technique of temperature regulation, as previously discussed.

Spectral overlap of emission and absorption wavelengths is a potential cause of interference in atomic absorption spectrometry (57). Thus, (a) the emission line of Fe at 352.424 nm is close to the resonance line of Ni at 352.454, (b) the emission line of Sb at 217.023 nm is close to the resonance line of Pb at 216.999 nm, and (c) the emission line of As at 228.812 nm is close to the resonance line of Cd at 228.802 (57). To date, these practically coincident spectral lines have not been reported to be of practical importance as sources of analytical interference in atomic absorption analyses of biological materials.

Interference owing to sample "carry-over" or "memory effect" can be a serious problem in electrothermal atomic absorption spectrometry (77). The memory effect may be caused by condensation of analyte in a cooler region of the atomizer, and subsequent revaporization of analyte during the next atomization cycle (3). Another cause of memory effect is occlusion of the analyte within porous graphite, owing to the presence of other metals and carbon ash. Memory effect can be minimized by (a) increasing the flow-rate of inert gas, (b) increasing the temperature and duration of the atomization cycle, (c) using an "after-burn" cycle, as previously mentioned, and (d) substituting pyrolytic graphite for common graphite.

Interference from molecular absorption bands may be troublesome in analyses of relatively volatile metals such as cadmium and bismuth, which vaporize within the temperature ranges that are necessary for destruction of organic constituents of biological materials (80). Another cause of interference in electrothermal atomic absorption spectrometry of body fluids is nonspecific light-scattering owing to smoke and combustion vapors. Interferences from molecular absorption bands and light scattering can usually be ameliorated by the use of optical systems for background compensation, as will be described subsequently. In order to understand the various background correction systems, it is necessary to appreciate the optical maneuvers which are used to prevent interference by light that is emitted by electrothermal atomizers during the atomization phase.

In electrothermal atomic absorption spectrometry, the vaporized metal atoms within the atom cloud are predominently in the ground state and are capable of absorbing discreet wavelengths of incident light. These specific resonance wavelengths are provided as monochromatic emission lines by a lamp with a hollow cathode containing the metal to be analyzed. The beam of light is passed through the atom cloud and is focused upon the entrance slit of a monochromator. Light at the selected wavelength is detected by a photomultiplier tube. In order to avoid interference by the intense light which is emitted from the

electrothermal atomizer, it is customary to modulate the incident
light beam with a mechanical or electronic chopper, and to tune
the photomultiplier detector to the same frequency of modulation.
Under these conditions, the photomultiplier detector circuit
should respond only to the pulsed signal from the light beam, and
should not respond to the continuous signal produced by light
emission from the electrothermal atomizer. The alternating
current from the photomultiplier detector circuit is amplified
and recorded. Owing to idiosyncrasies in the design of optical
systems, light from the electrothermal atomizer can sometimes be
reflected from the surfaces of a mechanical chopper, resulting
in a pulsed wide-band signal which is registered by the photodetector and recorded as a shift of base-line absorption during
the atomization cycle. A system of optical baffles and apertures
can be installed in recent models of the atomic absorption
spectrometers which are manufactured by the Perkin-Elmer Co. The
baffle and aperture system minimizes interference by pulsed
reflection of light which is emitted from the graphite tube furnace (31). Accurate installation of this baffle and aperture
system is necessary in order to achieve reliable measurements of
trace metals at concentrations near the detection limits.

Background Correction Systems

When biological materials are vaporized in an electrothermal
atomizer, there is atomic absorption at the specific resonance
wavelength of the analyte, and there is also nonspecific continuum absorption owing to molecular absorption bands and light-
scattering by smoke and combustion vapors. In order to measure
the specific absorption of the analyte, it is essential to correct or compensate for the nonspecific background absorption.
Several ingenious optical systems have been developed for this
purpose (8,27,49,85). For example, Hwang *et al* (27) described a
hydrogen background correction system for use with Instrumentation Laboratories' Model 353 atomic absorption spectrometer.
This system incorporates two hollow cathode lamps. One of the
lamps, which contains a hollow cathode constructed of an alloy
of the analyte, is electronically pulsed at a frequency of 0.5
kilohertz. The reference lamp is a hydrogen discharge tube
which is pulsed at 1 kilohertz. Coincident beams from the two
lamps are passed through the electrothermal atomizer, and a
specific resonance wavelength of light is selected by the monochromator. The absorbance at this wavelength that emanates from
the hydrogen lamp is electronically subtracted from that which
emanates from the analyte lamp, in order to generate an automatically compensated readout.

As an alternative approach, Koirtyohann *et al* (35) employed
a mechanical chopper system for deuterium-background correction
similar to the one that is marketed by Perkin-Elmer Co. (49).
One-half of the rotating chopper is transparent and the second-

TABLE I

Electrothermal Atomic Absorption Spectrometry of Trace Metals

in Body Fluids, Tissues and Excreta

Trace Metal	Boiling Point(1) °C	Minimum Vaporization Temp. from Graphite Rod(1) °C	Suitable Wavelengths for Atomic Absorption(63) nm	Suitable Wavelengths for Background Compensation(13,63) nm	References to Biological Applications		
					Whole Blood, Serum, or Plasma	Urine or Sweat	Tissues, Feces, or Hair
Al	2467	1550	309.3		20 / 46,47		72
Au	2966	1080	242.8		6	6	
Bi	1560	860	223.1				
Cd	765	270	228.8	226.8	6,45,62,74	6,36, / 45,62	14,72
Co	2900	1300	240.7	239.3	47		
Cr	2482	1380	357.9		11,23,60,61	11,69, 72 / 71	
Cu	2595	1160	324.8	296.1	6,16,22,53, / 79	6	4,14,72, / 76
Fe	3000	1230	248.3		53,59,86 / 47		72
Li			670.8				

TABLE I – Continued

Trace Metal	Boiling Point(1) °C	Minimum Vaporization Temp. from Graphite Rod(1) °C	Suitable Wavelengths for Atomic Absorption(63) nm	Suitable Wavelengths for Background Compensation(13,63) nm	References to Biological Applications		
					Whole Blood, Serum, or Plasma	Urine or Sweat	Tissues, Feces, or Hair
Mn	2097	1210	279.5		5,6,23,68	6	72
Ni	2732	1420	232.0	231.6	60,77,87	87	
Pb	1744	860	217.0,283.3	220.4,282.3	6,10,13,15,17,24,27,28,32,37,38,39,45,53,58,67	6,36	24,66,72
Sr			460.7		5		
Tl			276.8		24,45	24,45	24,36
Zn	907	800	213.9	210.4	7,24,40,45,53	34,40,45	14,24

half is mirrored. During one phase of the rotation of the chopper, light from the hollow cathode lamp passes through the transparent sector of the chopper and is passed through the electrothermal atomizer. During the second phase of rotation of the chopper, light from a deuterium continuum source is reflected from the mirrored sector of the chopper and is passed through the electrothermal atomizer. Both beams of light are focused on the spectrometer slit, and the signal from the photomultiplier tube is amplified by a phase-sensitive lock-in amplifier. When the two light beams are balanced, the amplifier output is zero. Continuum absorption owing to light-scattering or molecular bands reduces the intensity from both beams equally, causing no change in amplifier output. On the other hand, free atoms of the analyte absorb the narrow spectral band from the hollow cathode lamp much more efficiently than the broad spectral band from the continuum source. The two half-cycles are then of unequal energy, and the unbalance appears as the amplifier output signal.

Cruz and van Loon (10) pointed out the limitations of background correction systems that employ hydrogen or deuterium continuum sources. Such systems are limited to relatively low background absorption levels and to wavelengths where the H_2 or D_2 emissions are intense. Cruz and van Loon (10) recommend background correction by measuring the attenuation of a nearby non-resonance line of the analyte. This technique was employed by Ealy *et al* (13) for electrothermal atomic absorption of blood lead with the Jarrell-Ash Model 810 dualmonochromator spectrometer. Ealy *et al* (13) performed simultaneous measurements of lead at the 283.3 nm resonance line and at the nearby 282.3 nm non-resonance line. The specific absorbance owing to lead was automatically computed as the difference between the two absorbance measurements. Similarly, Kilroe-Smith (32) performed background compensation in electrothermal analyses of blood lead by measurements of the absorbance at 283.3 nm (resonance wavelength) and at 287.3 (non-resonance wavelength). Suitable pairs of resonance and non-resonance lines of several trace metals which are of clinical interest are listed in Table I.

Two additional optical systems for background correction deserve mention: Woodriff and Shrader (85) devised a system in which a light beam from a hollow cathode lamp is polarized horizontally, while a reference light beam from a hydrogen lamp is polarized vertically. After passing through the electrothermal atomizer and monochromator, the two perpendicularly polarized beams are separated by a polarizing prism and are measured by two photomultiplier tubes. In the system described by Church *et al* (8), a hollow cathode discharge lamp is placed in a uniform magnetic field (20 to 30 gauss) which splits the resonance line into three Zeeman components. One of the Zeeman lines lies within the absorption profile of the analyte atoms, and the other two Zeeman lines are symmetrically displaced on

either side of the absorption profile. The attenuation of the
lines which lie outside the absorption profile of the analyte
represents non-specific absorption, whereas the attenuation of
the central line which lies within the absorption profile represents specific plus non-specific absorption. By difference,
the specific absorption of the analyte can be measured. According to studies cited by Church *et al* (8), this method of background correction is applicable to every element that can be
measured by atomic absorption spectrometry. A Zeeman-effect
background correction system is sold by Arthur H. Thomas Co.

Applications to Biological Materials

In Table I are listed comprehensive citations of published
methods for analyses of trace metals in body fluids and other
clinical specimens by means of electrothermal atomic absorption
spectrometry. Readers are cautioned that many of the early
methods that are cited in Table I have become outmoded, owing to
improvements in instrumentation for electrothermal atomic absorption spectrometry. All of the published methods need to be
critically evaluated in the prospective analyst's laboratory
before they can be confidently employed for diagnostic measurements of trace metals in body fluids. Despite these caveats,
the author believes that Table I should be helpful as a guide to
the growing literature on clinical and biological applications
of electrothermal atomic absorption spectrometry.

Abstract

Electrothermal atomic absorption spectrometry has five major
advantages for measurements of trace metals in biological
materials, in comparison to measurements by conventional flame
atomic absorption analysis: (1) Trace metal contamination is
minimized by avoidance of preliminary chemical extractions and
additions of reagents. (2) Sample volumes are small (1 to 50 μl).
The entire sample is vaporized in electrothermal atomization,
whereas in most flame nebulization systems only a small fraction
of the sample enters the flame. (3) Atoms are released in
higher concentrations. In electrothermal atomization, the atom
cloud is released into a relatively small volume of gas. In
contrast, in flame atomization, the atom cloud is diluted by the
high flow rate of gases and by expansion of gases during combustion. (4) Molecular recombination of atoms is retarded by the
atmosphere of inert gas which restricts chemical reactions
(*e.g.* oxidation). In contrast, in flame atomization, oxidation
occurs very rapidly. (5) By programmed increments in temperature, electrothermal atomization permits organic constituents to
be pyrolyzed prior to vaporization and atomization of metals.
Despite these advantages, electrothermal atomic absorption is
particularly subject to interferences and sources of imprecision

264   CLINICAL CHEMISTRY

which necessitate critical evaluations in the prospective
analyst's laboratory before an electrothermal method can be confidently employed for diagnostic measurements of a specific trace
metal in body fluids.

Literature Cited

1. Aggett, J. and Sprott, A. J.; "Non-Flame Atomization in
    Atomic Absorption Spectrometry". Anal. Chim. Acta (1974),
    72, 49-56.
2. Amos, M.D., Bennett, P.A., Brodie, K. G., Lung, P. W. Y.,
    and Matousek, J. P.; "Carbon Rod Atomizer in Atomic Absorp-
    tion and Fluorescence Spectrometry and its Clinical Appli-
    cation". Anal. Chem. (1971), 43, 211-215.
3. Aspila, K. I., Chakrabarti, C. L., and Bratzel, M. P., Jr.;
    "Pyrolytic Graphite-Tube Micro-Furnace for Trace Analysis
    by Atomic Absorption Spectrometry". Anal. Chem. (1972),
    44, 1718-1720.
4. Barnett, W. B. and Kahn, H. L.; "Determination of Copper in
    Fingernails by Atomic Absorption with the Graphite Furnace".
    Clin. Chem. (1972), 18, 923-927.
5. Bek, F., Janouskova, J., and Moldan, B.; "Direct Determina-
    tion of Manganese and Strontium in Human Blood Serum by
    Means of the Graphite Furnace, Perkin-Elmer HGA-70". Chem.
    Listy (1972), 66, 867-875.
6. Bourdon, R., Galliot, M., and Prouillet, F.; "Dosage du
    cuivre, du plomb, du manganèse, du bismuth, du cadmium et
    de l'or dans les liquides biologiques par spectrométrie
    d'absorption atomique sans flamme". Ann. Biol. Clin. (1974),
    32, 413-422.
7. Chooi, M. K., Todd, J. K., and Boyd, N. D.; "Effect of
    Carbon Cup Aging on Plasma Zinc Determination by Flameless
    Atomic Absorption Spectrometry". Clin. Chem. (1975), 21,
    632-634.
8. Church, D. A., Hadeishi, T., Leong, L., McLaughlin, R. D.,
    and Zak, B. D.; "Two-Chamber Furnace for Flameless Atomic
    Absorption Spectrometry". Anal. Chem. (1974), 46, 1352-
    1355.
9. Clyburn, S. A., Kantor, T., and Veillon, C.; "Pyrolysis
    Treatment for Graphite Atomization Systems". Anal. Chem.
    (1974), 46, 2213-2215.
10. Cruz, R. B. and Loon, J. C. van; "A Critical Study of the
    Application of Graphite-Furnace Non-Flame Atomic Absorption
    Spectrometry to the Determination of Trace Base Metals in
    Complex Heavy-Matrix Sample Solutions". Anal. Chim. Acta
    (1974), 72, 231-243.
11. Davidson, I. W. F. and Secrest, W. L.; "Determination of
    Chromium in Biological Materials by Atomic Absorption
    Spectrometry Using a Graphite Furnace Atomizer". Anal.
    Chem. (1972), 44, 1808-1813.

12. Donega, H. M. and Burgess, T. E.; "Atomic Absorption Analysis by Flameless Atomization in a Controlled Atmosphere". Anal. Chem. (1970), 42, 1521-1524.
13. Ealy, J. A., Bolton, N. E., McElheny, R. J., and Morrow, R. W.; "Determination of Lead in Whole Blood by Graphite Furnace Atomic Absorption Spectrophotometry". Amer. Ind. Hyg. Assoc. J. (1974), 35, 566-570.
14. Evenson, M. A. and Anderson, C. T., Jr.; "Ultramicro Analysis for Copper, Cadmium and Zinc in Human Liver Tissue by Use of Atomic Absorption Spectrophotometry and the Heated Graphite Tube Atomizer". Clin. Chem. (1975), 21, 537-543.
15. Evenson, M. A. and Pendergast, D. D.; "Rapid Ultramicro Direct Determination of Erythrocyte Lead Concentration by Atomic Absorption Spectrophotometry with Use of a Graphite Tube Furnace". Clin. Chem. (1974), 20, 163-171.
16. Evenson, M. A. and Warren, B. L.; "Determination of Serum Copper by Atomic Absorption, With Use of the Graphite Cuvette". Clin. Chem. (1975), 21, 619-625.
17. Fernandez, F. J.; "Micromethod for Lead Determination in Whole Blood by Atomic Absorption, With Use of the Graphite Furnace". Clin. Chem. (1975), 21, 558-561.
18. Findlay, W. J., Zdrojewski, A., and Quickert, N.; "Temperature Measurements of a Graphite Furnace Used in Flameless Atomic Absorption". Spectrosc. Lett. (1974), 7, 63-72.
19. Findlay, W. J., Zdrojewski, A., and Quickert, N.; "Preatomization Losses in Flameless Atomic Absorption Spectroscopy". Spectrosc. Lett. (1974), 7, 355-364.
20. Fuchs, C., Brasche, M., Paschen, K., Norbeck, H., and Quellhorst, E.; "Aluminium-Bestimmung im Serum mit Flammenloser Atomabsorption". Clin. Chim Acta (1974), 52, 71-80.
21. Fuller, C. W.; "A Simple Standards Additions Technique Using the Model 306 Atomic Absorption Spectrophotometer". At. Absorp. Newsl. (1972), 11, 65-66.
22. Glenn, M., Savory, J., Hart, L., Glenn, T., and Winefordner, J.; "Determination of Copper in Serum With a Graphite Rod Atomizer for Atomic Absorption Spectrophotometry". Anal. Chim. Acta (1971), 57, 263-269.
23. Grafflage, B., Buttgereit, G., Kubler, W., and Mertens, H. M.; "Die Messung der Spurenelemente Chrom und Mangan im Serum mittels flammenloser Atomabsorption". Z. Klin. Chem. Klin. Biochem. (1974), 12, 287-293.
24. Hauck, G.; "Erfahrungen mit der flammenlosen Atomabsorption bei der Untersuchung biologischen Materials auf Spuren von Schwermetallen". Z. Anal. Chem. (1973), 267, 337-341.
25. Hohnadel, D. C., Sunderman, F. W., Jr., Nechay, M. W., and McNeely, M. D.; "Atomic Absorption Spectrometry of Nickel, Copper, Zinc, and Lead in Sweat from Healthy Subjects during Sauna Bathing". Clin. Chem. (1973), 19, 1288-1292.
26. Hwang, J. Y., Mokeler, C. J., and Ullucci, P. A.; "Maximization of Sensitivities in Tantalum Ribbon Flameless Atomic

10. Boué, J.; Boué, A.; and Lazar, P.; "The Epidemiology of Human Spontaneous Abortions With Chromosomal Abnormalities". Aging Gametes, Int. Symp. Seattle, (1975), 330-348.
11. Fuchs, F.; and Riis, P.; "Antenatal Sex Determination". Nature (Lond.), (1956), 177, 330.
12. Steele, M. W.; and Breg, W. T.; "Chromosome Analysis of Human Amniotic Fluid Cells". Lancet, (1966), 1, 383-385.
13. Jacobson, C. B.; and Barter, R. H.; "Intrauterine Diagnosis and Management of Genetic Defects". Am. J. Obstet. Gynecol. (1967), 99, 796-807.
14. Nadler, H. L.; "Antenatal Detection of Hereditary Disorders". Pediatrics, (1968), 42, 912.
15. Levine, M. D.; McNeil, D. E.; Kaback, M. M.; Frazer, R. E.; Okada, D. M.; and Hobel, C. J.; "Second-Trimester Fetoscopy and Fetal Blood Sampling: Current Limitations and Problems." Amer. J. Obstet. Gynecol., (1974), 120, 937-943.
16. Valenti, C.; "Antenatal Detection of Hemoglobinopathies". Am. J. Obstet. Gynecol., (1973), 115, 851-853.
17. Hobbins, J. C.; and Mohoney, M. J.; "Fetal Blood Drawing". Lancet, (1975), 2, 107-109.
18. Omenn, G. S.; Figley, M. M.; Graham, C. B.; and Heinrichs, W. L.; "Prospects for Radiographic Intrauterine Diagnosis - The Syndrome of Thrombocytopenia With Absent Radii". N. Engl. J. Med., (1973), 288, 777-778.
19. Campbell, S.; Johnston, F. D.; Holt, E. M.; and May, P.; "Anencephaly: Early Ultrasonic Diagnosis and Active Management". Lancet, (1972), 2, 1226-1227.
20. Campbell, S.; "The Prenatal Detection of Fetal Abnormality by Ultrasonic Diagnosis". Birth Defects, Proc. 4th Int. Conf., Motulsky, A. G. and Lenz, W., ed., Excerpta Medica, Amsterdam, 1974, 234-239.
21. Kan, Y. W.; Valenti, C.; Guidotti, R.; Carnazza, V.; and Rieder, R. F.; "Fetal Blood Sampling in Utero". Lancet, (1974), 1, 79-80.
22. Kan, Y. W.; Golbus, M. S.; Klein, P.; and Dozy, M.; "Successful Application of Prenatal Diagnosis in a Pregnancy at Risk for Homozygous β-thalassemia". New Engl. J. Med., (1975), 292, 1096-1099.
23. Hollenberg, M. D.; Kaback, M. M.; and Kazazian, H. H., Jr.; "Adult Hemoglobin Synthesis by Reticulocytes From the Human Fetus at Mid-Trimester". Science, (1971), 174, 698-702.
24. Kadotani, T.; Sato, H.; Ohama, K.; and Takahara, H.; "A Technical Note on the Antenatal Chromosome Analysis by Transabdominal Fetal Skin Biopsy". Jap. Jour. Human Genet., (1972), 16, 42-47.
25. Hahnemann, N.; "Early Prenatal Diagnosis; A Study of Biopsy Techniques and Cell Culturing From Extraembryonic Membranes". Clin. Genet., (1974), 6, 294-306.
26. Lind, T.; and Hytten, F. E.; "Relation of Amniotic Fluid Volume to Fetal Weight in the First Half of Pregnancy".

Absorption Spectrometry". Anal. Chem. (1972), <u>44</u>, 2018-2121.

27. Hwang, J. Y., Ullucci, P. A., and Mokeler, C. J.; "Direct Flameless Atomic Absorption Determination of Lead in Blood". Anal. Chem. (1973), <u>45</u>, 795-798.

28. Hwang, J. Y., Ullucci, P. A., Smith, S. B., Jr., and Malenfant, A. L.; "Microdetermination of Lead in Blood by Flameless Atomic Absorption Spectrometry". Anal. Chem. (1971), <u>43</u>, 1319-1321.

29. Ingle, J. D., Jr.; "Precision of Atomic Absorption Spectrometric Measurements". Anal. Chem. (1974), <u>46</u>, 2161-2171.

30. Kantor, T., Clyburn, S. A., and Veillon, C.; "Continuous Sample Introduction with Graphite Atomization Systems for Atomic Absorption Spectrometry". Anal. Chem. (1974), <u>46</u>, 2205-2213.

31. Kerber, J. D., Russo, A. J., Peterson, G. E., and Ediger, R. D.; "Performance Improvements with the Graphite Furnace". At. Absorp. Newsl. (1973), <u>12</u>, 106-108.

32. Kilroe-Smith, T. A.; "Linear Working Graphs in Blood Lead Determinations with the Beckman Flameless Atomic Absorption Cuvet". Clin. Chem. (1975), <u>21</u>, 630-632.

33. King, J. S.; "Editorial: A Burgeoning Branch of Clinical Analysis". Clin. Chem. (1975), <u>21</u>, 467.

34. Kirkbright, G. F.; "The Application of Non-Flame Atom Cells in Atomic Absorption and Atomic Fluorescence Spectroscopy. A Review". Analyst (London) (1971), <u>96</u>, 609-623.

35. Koirtyohann, S. R., Sievers, H., and Pickett, E. E.; "The Electrically Heated Furnace in Atomic Absorption" In "Trace Substances in Environmental Health - V". (D. D. Hemphill, Ed.), University of Missouri Press, Columbia, Mo., 1972, pp. 463-471.

36. Kubasik, N. P. and Volosin, M. T.; "A Simplified Determination of Urinary Cadmium, Lead, and Thallium, with Use of Carbon Rod Atomization and Atomic Absorption Spectrophotometry". Clin. Chem. (1973), <u>19</u>, 954-958.

37. Kubasik, N. P. and Volosin, M. T.; "Use of the Carbon Rod Atomizer for Direct Analysis of Lead in Blood". Clin. Chem. (1974), <u>20</u>, 300-301.

38. Kubasik, N. P., Volosin, M. T., and Murray, M. H.; "A Quantitative Micro Technique for the Analysis of Lead in Blood by Carbon Rod Atomization and Atomic Absorption Spectrophotometry". Clin. Biochem. (1972), <u>5</u>, 266-270.

39. Kubasik, N. P., Volosin, M. T., and Murray, M. H.; "Carbon Rod Atomizer Applied to Measurement of Lead in Whole Blood by Atomic Absorption Spectrophotometry". Clin. Chem. (1972), <u>18</u>, 410-412.

40. Kurz, D., Roach, J., and Eyring, E. J.; "Determination of Zinc by Flameless Atomic Absorption Spectrophotometry". Anal. Biochem. (1973), <u>53</u>, 586-593.

41. Lisk, D. J.; "Recent Developments in the Analysis of Toxic

Elements". Science (1974), 184, 1137-1141.

42. Lundgren, G. and Johansson, G.; "A Temperature-Controlled Graphite Tube Furnace for the Determination of Trace Metals in Solid Biological Tissue". Talanta (1974), 21, 257-264.

43. Lundgren, G., Lundmark, L., and Johansson, G.; "Temperature Controlled Heating of the Graphite Tube Atomizer in Flameless Atomic Absorption Spectrometry". Anal. Chem. (1974), 46, 1028-1031.

44. L'vov, B. V.; "The Analytical Use of Atomic Absorption Spectra". Spectrochim. Acta (1961), 17, 761-770.

45. Machata, G. and Binder, R.; "The Determination of Lead, Thallium, Zinc and Cadmium Traces in Biological Material with Flameless Atomic Absorption". Z. Rechtsmed. (1973), 73, 29-34.

46. Maessen, F. J. M. J., and Posma, F. D.; "Fundamental Aspects of Flameless Atomic Absorption Using the Mini-Massmann Carbon Rod Atomizer". Anal. Chem. (1974), 46, 1439-1444.

47. Maessen, F. J. M. J., Posma, F. D., and Balke, J.; "Direct Determination of Gold, Cobalt, and Lithium in Blood Plasma Using the Mini-Massmann Carbon Rod Atomizer". Anal. Chem. (1974), 46, 1445-1449.

48. McIntyre, N. S., Cook M. G., and Boase, D. G.; "Flameless Atomic Absorption Determination of Cobalt, Nickel, and Copper - A Comparison of Tantalum and Molybdenum Evaporation Surfaces". Anal. Chem. (1974), 46, 1983-1987.

49. Manning, D. C.; "Using the Perkin-Elmer Deuterium Background Correction System". At. Absorp. Newsl. (1972), 11, 112-113.

50. Manning, D. C. and Fernandez, F.; "Atomization for Atomic Absorption Using a Heated Graphite Tube". At. Absorp. Newsl. (1970), 9, 65-70.

51. Massmann, H.; "Heutiger Stand der Atomabsorptionsspektrometrie". Chimia (1967), 21, 217-226.

52. Massmann, H.; "Vergleich von Atomabsorption und Atomfluoreszenz in der Graphitküvette". Spectrochim. Acta (Part B) (1968), 23B, 215-226.

53. Matousek, J. P. and Stevens, B. J.; "Biological Applications of the Carbon Rod Atomizer in Atomic Absorption Spectroscopy". Clin. Chem. (1971), 17, 363-368.

54. Montaser, A. and Crouch, S. R.; "Analytical Applications of the Graphite Braid Nonflame Atomizer". Anal. Chem. (1974), 46, 1817-1820.

55. Montaser, A. and Crouch, S. R.; "New Methods for Programmed Heating of Electrically Heated Nonflame Atomic Vapor Cells". Anal. Chem. (1975), 47, 38-45.

56. Montaser, A., Goode, S. R., and Crouch, S. R.; "Graphite Braid Atomizer for Atomic Absorption and Atomic Fluorescence Spectrometry". Anal. Chem. (1974), 46, 599-601.

57. Norris, J. D. and West, T. S.; "Some Applications of Spectral Overlap in Atomic Absorption Spectrometry". Anal. Chem. (1974), 46, 1423-1425.

58. Norval, E. and Butler, L. R. P.; "The Determination of Lead
     in Blood by Atomic Absorption with the High-Temperature
     Graphite Tube". Anal. Chim. Acta (1972), 58, 47-56.
59. Olsen, E. D., Jatlow, P. I., Fernandez, F. J., and Kahn,
     H. L.; "Ultramicro Method for Determination of Iron in Serum
     with the Graphite Furnace". Clin. Chem. (1973), 19, 326-329.
60. Pekarek, R. S. and Hauer, E. C.; "Direct Determination of
     Serum Chromium and Nickel by an Atomic Absorption Spectro-
     photometer with a Heated Graphite Furnace". Fed. Proc.
     (1972), 31, 700 Abs.
61. Pekarek, R. S., Hauer, E. C., Wannemacher, R. W., Jr., and
     Beisel, W. R.; "The Direct Determination of Serum Chromium
     by an Atomic Absorption Spectrophotometer with a Heated
     Graphite Atomizer". Anal. Biochem. (1974), 59, 283-292.
62. Perry, E. F., Koirtyohann, S. R., and Perry, H. M., Jr.;
     "Determination of Cadmium in Blood and Urine by Graphite
     Furnace Atomic Absorption Spectrophotometry". Clin. Chem.
     (1975), 21, 626-629.
63. Price, W. J.; "Analytical Atomic Absorption Spectrometry".
     Heyden and Son, Ltd., London, 1972, pp. 1-239.
64. Reeves, R. D., Patel, B. M., Molnar, C. J., and Winefordner,
     J. D.; "Decay of Atom Populations Following Graphite Rod
     Atomization in Atomic Absorption Spectrometry". Anal. Chem.
     (1973), 45, 246-249.
65. Reinhold, J. G.; "Trace Elements - A Selective Survey".
     Clin. Chem. (1975), 21, 476-500.
66. Renshaw, G. D., Pounds, C. A., and Pearson, E. F.;
     "Variation in Lead Concentration Along Single Hairs as
     Measured by Non-Flame Atomic Absorption Spectrophotometry".
     Nature (1972), 238, 162-163.
67. Rosen, J. F. and Trinidad, E. E.; "The Microdetermination
     of Blood Lead in Children by Flameless Atomic Absorption:
     The Carbon Rod Atomizer". J. Lab. Clin. Med. (1972), 80,
     567-576.
68. Ross, R. T. and Gonzalez, J. G.; "Direct Determination of
     Trace Quantities of Manganese in Blood and Serum Samples
     Using Selective Volatilization and Graphite Tube Reservoir
     Atomic Absorption Spectrophotometry". Bull. Environ.
     Contam. Toxicol. (1974), 12, 470-474.
69. Ross, R. T., Gonzalez, J. G., and Segar, D. A.; "The Direct
     Determination of Chromium in Urine by Selective Volatiliza-
     tion with Atom Reservoir Atomic Absorption". Anal. Chim.
     Acta (1973), 63, 205-209.
70. Sarbeck, J. R. and Landgraf, W. C.; "Automated Peak Dis-
     crimination and Integration for Nonflame Atomic Absorption
     Analysis at Nanogram Levels". J. Pharm. Sci (1974), 63,
     929-930.
71. Schaller, K. H., Essing, H. G., Valentin, H., and Schäcke,
     G.; "Quantitative Chrombestimmung im Harn mit flammenloser
     Atomabsorptions-Spektrometrie". Z. Klin. Chem. Klin. Biochem.

(1972), 10, 434–437.

72. Schramel, P.; "Determination of Eight Metals in the International Biological Standard by Flameless Atomic Absorption Spectrometry". Anal. Chim. Acta (1973), 67, 69–77.

73. Schramel, P.; "The Application of Peak Integration in Flameless Atomic Absorption Spectrometry". Anal. Chim. Acta (1974), 72, 414–418.

74. Schumacher, E. and Umland, F.; "Verbesserte, schnelle Aufschlussmethode zur Cadmiumbestimmung in Körperflüssigkeiten mit Hilfe der Graphitrohrküvette". Z. Anal. Chem. (1974), 270, 285–286.

75. Sommerfeld, M. R., Love, T. D., and Olsen, R. D.; "Trace Metal Contamination of Disposable Pipet Tips". At. Absorp. Newsl. (1975), 14, 31–32.

76. Stevens, B. J.; "Biological Applications of the Carbon Rod Atomizer in Atomic Absorption Spectroscopy. 2. Determination of Copper in Small Samples of Tissue". Clin. Chem. (1972), 18, 1379–1384.

77. Sunderman, F. W., Jr.; "Atomic Absorption Spectrometry of Trace Metals in Clinical Pathology". Hum. Pathol. (1973), 4, 549–582.

78. Torsi, G. and Tessari, G.; "Influence of Heating Rate on Analytical Response in Flameless Atomic Absorption Spectrometry". Anal. Chem. (1973), 45, 1812–1816.

79. Welz, B. and Wiedeking, E.; "Bestimmung von Spurenelementen im Serum und Urin mit flammenloser Atomisierung". Z. Anal. Chem. (1970), 252, 111–117.

80. West, C. D.; "Relative Effect of Molecular Absorption on Atomic Absorption and Atomic Fluorescence". Anal. Chem. (1974), 46, 797–799.

81. West, T. S. and Williams, X. K.; "Atomic Absorption and Fluorescence Spectroscopy with a Carbon Filament Atom Reservoir". Anal. Chim. Acta (1969), 45, 27–41.

82. Williams, M. and Piepmeier, E. H.; "Commercial Tungsten Filament Atomizer for Analytical Atomic Spectrometry". Anal. Chem. (1972), 44, 1342–1344.

83. Woodriff, R.; "Atomization Chambers for Atomic Absorption Spectrochemical Analysis: A Review". Appl. Spectrosc. (1974), 28, 413–416.

84. Woodriff, R. and Ramelow, G.; "Atomic Absorption Spectroscopy with a High-Temperature Furnace". Spectrochim. Acta (Part B) (1968), 23B, 665–671.

85. Woodriff, R. and Shrader, D.; "Furnace Atomic Absorption with Reference Channel". Anal. Chem. (1971), 43, 1918–1920.

86. Yeh, Y-Y., and Zee, P.; "Micromethod for Determining Total Iron-Binding Capacity by Flameless Atomic Absorption Spectrophotometry". Clin. Chem. (1974), 20, 360–364.

87. Zachariasen, H., Andersen, I., Kostol, C., and Barton, R.; "Technique for Determining Nickel in Blood by Flameless Atomic Absorption Spectrophotometry". Clin. Chem. (1975), 21, 562–567.

Drug Interference in Laboratory Testing

DONALD T. FORMAN
Department of Pathology and Laboratory Medicine, Evanston Hospital,
Evanston, Ill. 60201

DONALD S. YOUNG
Clinical Center, National Institutes of Health, Bethesda, Md. 20014

Over the past decades, the practice of medicine has undergone
considerable sophistication. Potent new drugs in practically
every therapeutic category are available. Whenever a patient
receives a drug, there is a possibility of drug-test interferences. When more than one drug is administered there may also
be drug-drug interactions. These developments have created new
problems for the laboratory scientist. A characteristic problem
is the interpretation of laboratory data when a drug or its
metabolite may interfere with a laboratory procedure. One
drug may affect the action of another given at the same time, thus
changing the value of a test result. Numerous attempts have
been made by a number of compilations and articles to document
these effects. In 1962, Caraway (2) published a comprehensive
article on the chemical and diagnostic specificity of laboratory
tests. In 1964, Borushek and Gold (1) published an article containing a list of drugs interfering with routine endocrine procedures. Wirth and Thompson (19) in 1965 published a list of
substances and conditions which affect the results of laboratory
procedures. They included such factors as temperature, light
and drugs. Other review articles (8,11,14,17) have been of great
value in helping to define this problem. One of the most
ambitious approaches to this problem has been the development of
a 9000-entry computerfile based on a compilation of 1030 literature references (20). This computerized compilation of effects
of drugs on laboratory tests has been used to assist in the
interpretation of unusual test results in the clinical chemistry
laboratories of the National Institutes of Health and the
Evanston Hospital of Northwestern University Medical Center, as
well as in some other centers.
    A major problem facing users of the various collations of
laboratory test interferences is the relationship between drug
dosage and diagnostic test interference and the possible syner-
gistic effect of several drugs. The metabolic and clinical states

of the patient also affect the degree of laboratory interference.
If an individual has normal kidney and liver function, he will
respond differently to a drug dosage than the patient who is
unable to detoxify or excrete the compound.

In order to cope with the problem of drug induced modifications of laboratory test values, laboratory scientists should
possess an understanding of the mechanisms involved in these
interferences. The purpose of this article is to consider these
mechanisms and discuss the role of the computerized drug-test
interference file in assisting in the prediction as well as
interpretation of apparent test results.

Mechanisms of Interference

There are four distinct mechanisms of interference in
laboratory testing. Physical, chemical, pharmacological and
drug-drug interactions are of special interest to the laboratory
scientist. The mechanisms of the interferences will be briefly
reviewed and wherever possible, solutions suggested.

Physical Effects

Drugs may interfere with colorimetric, photometric or
fluorometric analyses by imparting a characteristic color to the
specimen. Table I describes some unusually colored urines and
their relationship to drug administration or metabolic disorders.
This type of interference can be detected visually by laboratory
personnel and drug interferences may be circumvented by collecting the specimen after an appropriate length of time during
which the drug in question has been discontinued. There are
many varieties of drugs and foods that can cause this type of
interference. These should be considered first as possible
causes of any unusually colored urine.

Some drugs act as indicators (e.g. phenolphthalein,
vegetable laxatives) and affect tests carried out at a particular
pH. The presence of sulfobromophthalein dye (BSP) in serum will
interfere with serum protein determined by the biuret method.
The dye is colorless at the pH of blood, but purple when made
alkaline during the assay.

Chemical Effects

Drugs may be measured as analytes, either because of their
similarity in chemical structure or because they contain a component that is an analyte. Patients who have received radiographic contrast media containing iodine will have an altered
protein-bound iodine, although thyroxine is not affected when
determined by protein binding methods. The most serious and
long-lasting interferences are those caused by intravenously
administered iodinated radiopaque agents (e.g. acetrizoate and

TABLE I

COLORED URINES DUE TO DRUGS OR METABOLIC DISORDERS

Color of Urine	Cause	Disorder
Orange-Red	Phenazopyridine Phenindione Phensuximide	Drug Related
Red	Porphyrins	Congenital Porphyria Acute Intermittant Porphyria
Red-Brown	Hemoglobin and Derivatives	Crush Syndrome
Red-Brown	Urobilin	Hemolytic Anemia
Yellow	Chloroquine	Drug Related
Green-Yellow	Bile Pigments	Regurgitative Janudice
Blue	Methylene Blue Triamterene	Drug Related
Blue	Indigo Compounds	Intestinal Disease (Indicanemia)
Blue-Green	Amitriptylene	Drug Related
Brown-Black	Melanin Homogentisic Acid	Malignant Melanoma Alkaptonuria

adipiodone). The drugs orabilex and dionsil have a negligible effect on the analysis of protein bound iodine at a concentration no greater than 100 μg/dl, but seriously affect the procedure at 1000 μg/dl.

Serum potassium concentration is increased by the concurrent administration of intravenous potassium penicillin G. The penicillin preparation contains 1.7 mmol of potassium per million units. Thus, a patient receiving 10 million units of the anti-biotic receives 17 mmol (mEq.) of potassium.

A chemical interference may also result when the substance being determined reacts in vivo with a drug administered prior to the collection of blood for analysis. For example, serum calcium determinations may be affected by the administration of the chelating agent ethylenediaminetetracetate (EDTA) (3). In certain conditions such as lead poisoning and collagen disease, EDTA has been used therapeutically to reduce the lead and calcium concentrations, respectively. Less well recognized is the fact that various chelating agents are also used as preservatives to prevent oxidation reactions in drug preparations. In patients on EDTA therapy, calcium cannot be determined by the indirect colorimetric or fluorometric methods based on the chelation of a calcium - EDTA complex. However, in calcium determinations by atomic-absorption spectroscopy, the complexing agent is destroyed in the flame and the direct concentration of calcium can be determined.

Drugs can also interfere with laboratory results by negating certain nonspecific oxidation and reduction reactions essential for the chemical assay. Penicillin, streptomycin and ascorbic acid are known to react with cupric ion; thus, false positive results for glucose may occur if a copper reduction method is used. If the specific enzymatic glucose-oxidase method is employed, ascorbic acid can cause a false negative result by preventing the oxidation of a specific chromogen in the reaction.

Increased transaminase activity has been observed when the diazocolorimetric method is used. Unusually increased activity has been reported in patients with ketosis and also in patients receiving erythromycin (13) or p-aminosalicylic acid (9). These test interferences can be obviated by employing ultraviolet kinetic procedures.

Colorimetric procedures used in steroid assays are often subject to drug interference. In the determination of 17-Ketosteroids by the Zimmerman reaction, drugs with the 17-Keto basic structure such as ascorbic acid, morphine and reserpine will cause increased values. In the determination of 17,21 - dihydroxysteroids by the Porter-Silber reaction the dihydroxy-acetone chain is the reactive unit. Drugs like meprobamate, chloral hydrate, chloropromazine and potassium iodide will inter-fere with this reaction and cause elevated values. In the colorimetric determination of vanillylmandelic acid (VMA) by a diazo reaction, drugs like methocarbamol and methyl dopa cause falsely elevated results.

Where specific drugs have been demonstrated to interfere with chemical reactions, patients should be maintained free of these drugs for at least 72 hours before collecting the specimen. Other analytical techniques, e.g. column chromatography and radioimmunoassay procedures, can also be substituted for an affected method.

Pharmacological Effects

This type of interference usually results from the pharmacological or toxic activity of drugs but may also arise from therapeutic quantities of drugs. An example of this type is the increase in prothrombin time which results from the administration of a therapeutic amount of sodium warfarin. However, unexpected interferences resulting from side effects or adverse reactions may create problems in the interpretation of laboratory data. Disturbances in fluid and electrolyte balance and hypopotassemia are common. Thiazide diuretics and large doses of glucocorticosteroids may severely reduce the concentration of plasma potassium. Acetazolamide and ethoxazolamide may cause metabolic acidosis, a raised serum uric acid, and a lowered urinary excretion of uric acid. A rise in serum uric acid has also been reported following the administration of levodopa (4). The thiazides can also have a hyperglycemic activity and diabetics may require more insulin or oral antidiabetic drugs. Patients with latent diabetes occasionally develop an abnormal glucose tolerance curve. Salicylates have also been reported to reduce hyperglycemia in diabetics and produce hypoglycemia in normal children. Tables II and III list various drugs capable of increasing or decreasing blood glucose in non-diabetic subjects.

Hydantoin anticonvulsants may cause the appearance of positive L.E. cells and methemoglobinemia. Chloropromazine has been implicated in causing a syndrome like systemic lupus erythematosus with accompanying positive tests for L.E. cells and antinuclear antibodies (6).

In many instances administered drugs alter a metabolic pathway and directly produce changes in biochemical values. Insulin administration results in changes in blood glucose, potassium, phosphorus and fatty acids. Allopurinol reduces uric acid by inhibiting the enzyme, xanthine oxidase; other drugs e.g. azoserine and methotrexate do so by preventing its biosynthesis. Hydrochlorothiazide increases uric acid retention by decreasing its tubular excretion. Oral contraceptives have a marked effect on plasma glucose, fatty acids and growth hormone levels (16). Estrogen-progestin oral contraceptives produce increases in serum iron, iron-binding capacity, transferrin, ceruloplasmin and copper (18). These effects on endocrine functions are quite marked as evidenced by measurement of the related biochemical constituents (Table IV) (12).

TABLE II

DRUGS CAPABLE OF INCREASING BLOOD GLUCOSE

Dextrothyroxine	Nicotinic Acid
Diazoxide	Phenothiazines
Diphenylhydantoin	Steroids
	Adrenocorticosteroids
Diuretics	Estrogens
	Sympathomimetic Amines

TABLE III

DRUGS CAPABLE OF DECREASING BLOOD GLUCOSE

Alcohol	Propoxyphene
Asparaginase	Propranolol
Caffeine	Anabolic Agents
Haloperidol	
Monoamine Oxidase Inhibitors	

Some drugs induce unexpected side effects unrelated to their therapeutic actions. Inheritance of hemoglobins differing in structure from normal hemoglobin A is well described. All types of hemoglobin are oxidized to methemoglobin by a wide range of agents and about 1% of hemoglobin present in the blood of normal people is in this form. Many drugs slightly increase the amount of methemoglobin, even in normal people, but induce a striking and sometimes fatal methemoglobinemia in susceptible patients. These drugs include chlorates, sulfonamides, nitrites, quinones, acetanilid and acetophenetidin. A similar phenomenon occurs with primaquine sensitivity. Susceptible patients have an inherited defect in red cell glucose 6-phosphate dehydrogenase (G6PD) and develop a severe hemolytic anemia when exposed to primaquine. Another abnormal drug response is porphyria. Acute porphyria on exposure to drugs can be caused by sudden massive induction of deltaamino levulinic acid synthetase in hepatic mitochondria; which results in uncontrolled formation of porphobilinogen and its metabolites. Susceptibility is inherited as an autosomal dominant trait and occurs even in heterozygotes. The nature of the molecular defect is unclear and presumably lies in the repression mechanism for the gene controlling formation of the enzyme protein. Exposure to any of the drugs listed in Table V results in further marked de-repression of enzyme synthesis and severe porphyria.

Table VI lists several drugs inducing hepatic microsomal enzymes (5). These enzymes can metabolize the drug as well as other substrates. Barbiturates, griseofulvin, and glutethimide induce enzymes which metabolize coumarin and phenindione derivatives and thus reduce their anticoagulant activity. Diphenylhydantoin and phenylbutazone stimulate cortisol hydroxylase activity and increase the urinary excretion of B-hydroxy cortisol and decrease the concentration of cortisol in the plasma.

Adverse side reactions may also occur with pharmacologically active drugs. Many drugs have been associated with inducing abnormal liver, renal and pulmonary function (10). These drug-test effects are unexpected and should be recognized. Drugs in this group include methyltestosterone, reserpine, phenacemide, oxyphenylbutazone, anesthetics and a variety of cancer chemotherapeutic agents.

Drug-Drug Interactions

Drugs which independently have little effect on laboratory tests may interact to produce a significant alteration of test values. Table VII presents several drug interactions in diabetic human subjects which can affect an apparent test result (15).

The administration of clofibrate to a patient taking warfarin will potentiate the anticoagulant effect of warfarin by displacing it from its protein binding site (7). This interaction will cause

TABLE IV

HORMONE LEVELS IN WOMEN ON ORAL CONTRACEPTIVES*

Hormone	Level in Menstruating Women	Level in Women on Oral Contraceptives
Plasma Cortisol (8 AM)	15.0 ± 4.0 µg/dl	40.0 ± 11 µg/dl
Serum Thyroxine	6.6 ± 1.4 µg/dl	9.4 ± 1.7 µg/dl
Urinary 17-OH Corticosteroids	4.6 ± 1.1 mg/d	2.6 ± 0.9 mg/d
Estrogens, Total (Urine)	40.0 ± 18 µg/d	26.0 ± 7.4 µg/d
Vanilylmandelic Acid (Urine)	3.5 ± 1.6 mg/d	3.3 ± 1.6 mg/d

*   from Lucis, O.J. and Lucis, R.;   Bull. W.H.O. (1972), 46, 443-450.

TABLE V

DRUGS INDUCING MARKED
DE-REPRESSION OF ENZYME SYNTHESIS

Chloroquine

Aminopyrine

Sulfonamides

Diallylbarbiturate

Allylisopropylacetylurea

Hexachlorobenzene

TABLE VI

DRUGS INDUCING HEPATIC MICROSOMAL ENZYMES

Phenylbutazone	Barbiturates
Cortisone	Glutethimide
Aminopyrine	Chlordiazepoxide
Diphenylhydantoin	Testosterone
Carbutamide	Norethynodrel

TABLE VII

DRUG INTERACTIONS REPORTED IN DIABETIC SUBJECTS

Drug Interaction	Hypoglycemic Drug	Reaction
Alcohol	Insulin Sulfonylurea	Inhibition of Gluconeogenesis
	Phenformin	Lactic Acidosis
Bishydroxycoumarin	Chlorpropamide	Decrease in Excretion or Metabolism of Hypoglycemic Agent
Guanethidine	Insulin	Decrease in Insulin Dosage Needed to Control Patient
Oxytetracycline	Insulin	Decrease in Insulin Dosage Needed to Control Patient
Phenothiazine	Insulin	Increase in Insulin Dosage Needed to Control Subject
Propranolol	Insulin	Decrease in Insulin Dosage Needed to Control Subject

a significant increase in the prothrombin time test used to regulate warfarin administration. Displacement of drugs from their binding sites is a common mechanism by which drug–drug interactions result in unexpected laboratory data. After absorption, about 50 to 80 percent of salicylate is bound to serum albumin, from which it displaces other substances such as bilirubin and thyroxine. Other drugs such as coumarin may also be displaced with a sudden change in prothrombin time.

Drug-drug interactions may also cause enzyme induction. Ethchlorvynol, glutethimide and haloperidol are known to inhibit the effectiveness of warfarin therapy by this mechanism (7). These drug–drug interactions may result in a reduced prothrombin time. Enzyme inhibition is another result of drug–drug interaction and the impairment of the hepatic glucuronyl transferase system by phenothiazine derivatives is a good example. Whenever several drugs are administered concurrently to a patient, their combined effect on laboratory results should be carefully considered.

Effectiveness of Computerized Drug Interference File

The computerized drug interference file has been used in two modes. In one, possible interactions are listed in response to direct queries (the role for which it was originally designed). In the other, the file has been used to provide automatic interpretation of effects of drugs on tests. In this mode, the file is used to provide a report alerting a physician to a possible interaction between a drug and a test (Figure 1). Without a computerized hospital information system, which could be accessed to provide information about a patient's clinical state and non therapeutic-drug procedures, the drug file cannot be completely effective in providing explanations for changes in laboratory data. Its role must be that of a warning system to highlight possible causes of changes in test values which can be accepted or rejected by the patient's physician on the basis of his clinical judgement.

Our experience in a University teaching hospital, in which over 10,000 patient days were monitoried, indicated that the drug file provided the correct explanation for changes in laboratory data in approximately 21 percent of all the occasions in which a report was produced (21). A report, similar in content and format to an entry in the master file (20), was generated when an abnormal test result was produced and one of the administered drugs had been described as causing this effect. The yield of correct explanations would undoubtedly be increased by elimination of effects that were unlikely to arise in hospital practice, e.g. effects due to overdoses or toxic effects of drugs. To make it appropriate for on-line use in any particular hospital, the file should be modified to eliminate these effects. The only methodological interferences that should be included are those involving the procedures in use in the hospital laboratory. The file is

```
DRUG:  HEPARIN
-----

CLOTTING TIME INC               BLOOD (WHOLE)           PHYSIOLOGICAL EFFECT
CONCENTRATION RELATED EFFECT                            REF: 0704

FACTOR IX DEC                   BLOOD (WHOLE)           PHYSIOLOGICAL EFFECT
REPORTED EFFECT                                         REF: 0384

FACTOR V DEC                    BLOOD (WHOLE)           PHYSIOLOGICAL EFFECT
CONCENTRATION RELATED EFFECT                            REF: 0384

FACTOR XI DEC                   BLOOD (WHOLE)           PHYSIOLOGICAL EFFECT
CONCENTRATION RELATED EFFECT                            REF: 0384

PLATELET COUNT DEC              BLOOD (WHOLE)           PHYSIOLOGICAL EFFECT
REPORTED EFFECT FOLLOWING I.V. INFUSIONS                REF: 0656

PTT INC                         BLOOD (WHOLE)           PHYSIOLOGICAL EFFECT
CONCENTRATION RELATED EFFECT                            REF: 0704

THROMBIN TIME INC               BLOOD (WHOLE)           PHYSIOLOGICAL EFFECT
RELATED TO CONC OF CIRCULATING HEPARIN                  REF: 0704

THROMBOPLASTIN GEN DEC          BLOOD (WHOLE)           PHYSIOLOGICAL EFFECT
ABNORMAL RESPONSE (INHIBITION)                          REF: 0384

AMMONIA INC                     PLASMA                  ANALYTICAL EFFECT
CONTAINS VARIABLE AMOUNTS OF AMMONIUM SALTS             REF: 0181

CORTICOSTEROIDS INC             PLASMA                  ANALYTICAL EFFECT
IF CONTAMINATED BY IMPURITIES                           REF: 0524

INSULIN DEC                     PLASMA                  ANALYTICAL EFFECT
EFFECT IN HEPARINIZED PLASMA AND SERUM                  REF: 0709

INSULIN INC                     PLASMA                  ANALYTICAL EFFECT
SPURIOUSLY HIGH VALUES REPORTED FOR IMMUNOASSAY         REF: 0064

PROTHROMBIN TIME INC            PLASMA                  PHYSIOLOGICAL EFFECT
CONCENTRATION RELATED EFFECT                            REF: 0704

TSH DEC                         PLASMA                  PHYSIOLOGICAL EFFECT
INTERFERES WITH THYROXINE BINDING TO PROTEIN            REF: 0502
```

Figure 1. Report alerting physician to drug interference in laboratory testing

being modified for use in the automatic warning role in a community hospital to determine if it can provide a useful service for physicians with a different orientation from those in a University hospital.

In the off-line mode of use of the drug file the data-base, stored in a time-shared computer, is interrogated through a remote device such as a cathode ray terminal. The questions that may be asked include all the affects of a drug, all the drugs that affect a test, or more specifically does a particular drug affect a particular test procedure by a particular mechanism. In each of these situations it is possible to list the appropriate literature reference. The search procedure has been designed in an interactive mode so that even an individual who has never used it may obtain an explanation for a particular problem, but the experienced searcher can by-pass the longer interactive search routine. This mode of operation is in use only at the National Institutes of Health and a simpler procedure is used in Evanston Hospital.

The most important use of a computer in setting up the CLAUDE (computer listing of abnormal and usual drug effects) concept may be that of a text editor and sorter. Scanning a printout is much more efficient than searching the file in the computer except for any information that is not yet available on a printout. It is our intention to reproduce printouts of the file in a journal with a wide circulation to the appropriate audience when a significant amount of new information has been added to the master-file. The second edition has recently been published (22). It includes some information on the probabilities of certain effects occurring as well as an indication of the concentration of drug at which the effects occur, at least for the methodological effects.

The file is used routinely in the laboratory at the National Institutes of Health in an attempt to explain abnormal test results. The resident physicians affiliated with the Clinical Chemistry Service discuss the results with the patient-care physicians and determine if the results were due to the patient's clinical state or to a drug effect. This close monitoring of test results has led to recognition of deficiencies in what is believed are specific enzymatic procedures for the measurement of glucose and uric acid. Likewise, the guaiac procedure for occult blood in feces was found to yield false negative results under certain circumstances. This has prompted the development of a more specific procedure (Jaffe et al. unpublished).

The file may be queried in response to questions from clinical staff at the National Institutes of Health and physicians and laboratory scientists throughout the country who submit their problems by letter or telephone. The file has been used to provide information for a pharmaceutical manufacturing company preparing a new drug application to the Food and Drug Administration. For the latter organization the file has been used as a background resource for product class standards.

On many occasions the file has provided information about effects of drugs of which the user was previously unaware. Undoubtedly this has helped the care of some patients. We are aware of several cases in which prolonged workups of unusual test values were avoided because of the simple explanations provided by the file. We expect to expand the application of the file by introducing it in a revised form into several hospitals for on-line interpretation of data. Also, discussions have been held with several different institutions overseas to set up national centers for dissemination of information and to provide a better monitoring of foreign language publications to augment the content of the file.

Literature Cited

1. Borushek, S. and Gold, J.; "Commonly Used Medications That Interfere With Routine Endocrine Laboratory Procedures". Clin. Chem. (1964), 10, 41-52.
2. Caraway, W.T.; "Chemical and Diagnostic Specificity of Laboratory Tests". Amer. J. Clin. Pathol. (1962), 37, 445-464.
3. Carr, M.H. and Frank, H.A.; "Calcium Analysis in Patients Being Treated With EDTA". Clin. Chem. (1957), 3, 20-21.
4. Cohon, M.S.; "Drug Interactions Involving Levodopa". Rev. Drug Interactions (1974), 1, 45-62.
5. Connery, A.H.; "Pharmacological Implications of Microsomal Enzyme Induction". Pharm. Rev. (1967), 19, 317-366.
6. Dubois, E.L.; Tallman, E. and Wonka, R.A.; "Chloropromazine-Induced Systemic Lupus Erythematosis". J.A.M.A. (1972), 221, 595-596.
7. Ebert, R.; "Oral Anticoagulants and Drug Interactions". Arch. Intern. Med. (1968), 121, 373-374.
8. Elkins, M.P. and Kabat, H.F.; "Drug Induced Modifications of Laboratory Test Values". Amer. J. Hosp. Pharm. (1968), 25, 484-519.
9. Glynn, K.P.; Carfaro, A.F.; Fowler, C.W. and Stead, W.W.; "False Elevations of Serum Glutamic Oxaloacetic Transaminase Due to Paraaminosalicylic Acid". Ann. Intern. Med. (1970), 72, 525-527.
10. Little, D.M. and Eststone, H.J.; "Anaesthesia and the Liver". Anaesthesiology (1964), 25, 815-853.
11. Lubran, M.; "The Effects of Drugs on Laboratory Values". Med. Clin. N. Amer. (1969), 53, 211-222.
12. Lucis, O.J. and Lucis, R.; "Oral Contraceptives and Endocrine Changes". Bull. W. H. O. (1972), 46, 443-450.
13. Sabath, L.D.; Gerstein, D.A. and Finland, M.; "Serum Glutamic-Oxalacetic Transaminase. False Elevations During Administration of Erythromycin". New Engl. J. Med. (1968), 279, 1137-1139.

14. Schwartz, M.K.; "Interferences in Diagnostic Biochemical Procedures". Advances in Clinical Chemistry, pp. 1-45, Vol. 16, Bodansky, O. and Latner, A.L., Editors, Academic Press, New York, 1973.

15. Solomon, H.M. and Schrogie, J.J.; "Effect of Phenyramidol and Bishydroxycoumarin on the Metabolism of Tolbutamide in Human Subjects". Metabolism (1967), 16, 1029-1033.

16. Spellacy, W.N.; Buhl, W.C.; Spellacy, C.E.; Moses, L.E. and Golzieher, J.W.; "Glucose, Insulin and Growth Hormone Studies in Long Term Uses of Oral Contraceptives". Amer. J. Obstet. Gynecol. (1970), 106, 173-176.

17. Sunderman, F.W., Jr.; "Drug Interference in Clinical Biochemistry". Crit. Rev. Clin. Lab. Sci. (1970), 1, 427-449.

18. Sunderman, F.W., Jr.; "Effects of Drugs Upon Hematological Tests". Ann. Clin. Lab. Sci. (1972), 2, 2-11.

19. Wirth, W.A. and Thompson, R.L.; "The Effect of Various Conditions and Substances on the Results of Laboratory Procedures". Amer. J. Clin. Path. (1965), 43, 579-590.

20. Young, D.S.; Thomas, D.W.; Friedman, R.B..and Pestaner, L.C.; "Effects of Drugs on Clinical Laboratory Tests". Clin. Chem. (1972), 18, 1041-1301.

21. Young, D.S.; Friedman, R.B. and Pestaner, L.C.; "Automatic Monitoring of Drug-Laboratory Test Interactions." Drug Interactions, pp. 393-401, Morselli, P.L., Garattini, S., and Cohen, S.N., Editors, Raven Press, New York, 1974.

22. Young, D.S.; Pestaner, L.C. and Gibberman, V.; "Effects of Drugs on Clinical Laboratory Tests". Clin. Chem (1975), 21, 1D-432D.

INDEX

INDEX

287